James Leighton is a professi... [barcode obscures text]
Alligator Blood is his fifth book. While James is an avid ... s
local football team, Cardiff City, he also enjoys playing poker,
watching Quentin Tarantino films, and anything to do with the
Beatles. To keep up to date with his forthcoming projects, you can
find him on twitter at @jamesL1927.

ALLIGATOR BLOOD

THE SPECTACULAR RISE AND FALL OF THE HIGH-ROLLING WHIZ-KID WHO CONTROLLED ONLINE POKER'S BILLIONS

JAMES LEIGHTON

**SIMON &
SCHUSTER**

London · New York · Sydney · Toronto · New Delhi

A CBS COMPANY

First published in Great Britain by Simon & Schuster UK Ltd, 2013
This paperback edition published by Simon & Schuster UK Ltd, 2014
A CBS COMPANY

1 3 5 7 9 10 8 6 4 2

Simon & Schuster UK Ltd
1st Floor
222 Gray's Inn Road
London WC1X 8HB

www.simonandschuster.co.uk

Simon & Schuster Australia, Sydney
Simon & Schuster India, New Delhi

A CIP catalogue record for this book
is available from the British Library

ISBN 978-1-47111-330-7
ebook ISBN 978-1-47111-331-4

Typeset in UK by M Rules
Printed and bound by CPI Group (UK) Ltd, Croydon CR0 4YY

*For two wonderful women: my beautiful girlfriend Charlotte Watkins
and my ever patient, caring mother, Jacqueline Leighton*

Acknowledgements

So many people have helped in so many different ways when researching and writing this book. Without them the task would have been far more difficult than it already was. The list is lengthy but every single person in it was a real help or support and for that I cannot thank them enough.

First and foremost my girlfriend Charlotte Watkins has been an incredible rock throughout. She has helped in every way imaginable, all the while putting a smile on my face. As I often tell her, she's a champion! The same goes for my amazing family, from Mum, Dad, Slim, Anita and Roy. I count myself lucky to have you all in my life. I couldn't have done it without you.

My friends have also been a great source of comfort when writing this book, either by listening to me witter on for hours about the challenges I faced or helping me unwind by taking me out of the writing cocoon. For helping to keep me sane I must thank Giles Watkins, Rachel Watkins, Alice Watkins, Ben Syder, Ed Aris, Tariq Aris, James Gundy, Nikki Rees and Daniel Mason. I must also thank film maker extraordinaire, Chris Griffiths, Neil Major of website design company Cimplicity, genius photographer Bartosz Nowicki (www.bartosznowicki.co.uk) and Degsy Williamson, the lead singer of the best tribute act in the world, The Oasis Experience.

The many people who willingly agreed to be interviewed for this book, all without expecting anything in return, also deserve my upmost gratitude. My thanks therefore go to Nolan Dalla, Professor

JAMES LEIGHTON

I Nelson Rose, Haley Hintze, Brian Hastings, Greg Merson and John Pappas. Many others only agreed to speak to me under condition of anonymity; I therefore must generally thank friends and family of Daniel Tzvetkoff, former employees of Intabill/Trendsact, as well as former employees of some of the top poker companies, banks and payment processors. The names of a few minor characters have been changed in the book.

Indeed, many in the poker community were also of monumental assistance, from the superb Marco Valerio of www.quadjacks.com, to Kristin Wilson of Poker Refugees, Seth Palansky of the World Series of Poker and the members of poker forum Two Plus Two.

Every writer needs a strong team around them and I therefore count myself lucky that I have the very best in the business. Not a single word of this story would have touched the page were it not for the help of my agent, Darley Anderson and his incredible 'Darley's Angels'. Furthermore, once again Simon & Schuster have been a pleasure to work with. In particular I must thank Rhea Halford for firstly commissioning this book, the staff of Simon & Schuster Australia who greeted me warmly when I visited them in Sydney, and of course my brilliant and patient editor, Ian Marshall.

In true poker parlance, thanks to all of the above, I truly flopped the nuts!

Alligator Blood

'Describes a player whose play is bold and aggressive'

(The Poker Encyclopaedia)

Prologue

Las Vegas, USA, April 2010

Just one year after losing close to $500 million Daniel Tzvetkoff was back at the scene of the crime. Las Vegas. Sin City. And this time he was feeling lucky.

In the shadow of the glowing amber tombstone that was the Encore Hotel, the baby-faced twenty-six-year-old sat in a private outdoor cabana in the luxurious XS nightclub. Above him a fan whirred relentlessly, engaged in a fruitless battle against the arid desert heat. On the glass table to his left was a flute of chilled Cristal. His favourite. In his mouth hung a Cuban cigar. And on his wrist, a gold Rolex, whose diamond-encrusted dial told him that it was coming up to midnight. The night was still young.

Picking up his glass of champagne, the stocky Australian briefly left the sanctuary of the cabana to make his way to the edge of the first-floor balcony. By now his friend, Michael Kollosche, Gold Coast real estate agent to the super rich, had been gone for well over half an hour. It was typical Kollosche. The sociable millionaire couldn't help but talk to anyone who crossed his path, especially when he'd had a few drinks.

Peering below, hoping to catch a glimpse of his party-loving friend, Daniel saw several nubile young girls liberally casting aside their short skirts, high heels and boob tubes to dive into the azure pool. Their boyfriends cast a blind eye. Otherwise indisposed, they were either drunkenly playing Blackjack on the outdoor tables or eyeing up the scantily clad dancers who gyrated to R'n'B music on poles adjacent to the pool.

Casting his eyes around the chaotic scene, Daniel noticed several king-sized beds dotted around the venue, all occupied by frisky 'couples'. Skirts were being hitched up, zips pulled down. Strangers fully acquainted. These weren't the last days of Rome. This was slap bang in the middle of the Las Vegas boom. Debauchery was every-where. From the bar in the middle of the pool, where patrons downed shots until they puked, to the sweaty, indoor dancefloor, where packs of guys and girls went hunting for prey. But among the spiralling depravity Daniel failed to spot Kollosche. He was M.I.A.

Returning to the privacy of his lavish VIP cabana, Daniel stood under the fan, trying in vain to cool down. As he did so a soft voice suddenly purred behind him, 'Got room for one more in here?'

Turning around, Daniel was confronted by Las Vegas perfection. Long, blonde hair extensions, which flowed to the bottom of an impossibly tiny waist. Fake tits, with nipples protruding through a short white dress which was hitched so high it revealed a tantalising glimpse of pert tanned bum cheeks. Lean long legs, which arched from black high heels all the way to the bow tattoo that wrapped itself around thick toned thighs. And inviting pneumatically enhanced lips that looked ripe, soft and moist. But Daniel had been in Vegas too many times not to know one thing: the vision before him was a hooker. And he looked like a lonely young kid with money to burn. In other words, easy pickings.

By the time Daniel had gathered his thoughts, the blonde had already invited herself inside. Sat on the mauve sofa she slowly crossed her legs and introduced herself. 'I'm Whitney,' she said, hold-ing out her manicured hand for Daniel to shake. As Daniel reciprocated, Whitney's eyes darted to the ice bucket on the table next to her, where a half-drunk bottle of Cristal protruded from the top. 'It's hot tonight,' she smiled, lifting the bottle from the ice. 'Mind if I have a glass to cool off?'

'Be my guest,' Daniel replied, wrapping his lips around his Cuban cigar and then blowing a plume of smoke skywards.

Watching on as Whitney poured herself a drink, he remembered the promise he had made to his heavily pregnant fiancée, Nicole, before he had boarded the plane: no girls would be involved, not under any circumstances. This trip was strictly business. That was all. But those words were now in danger of being washed away by a tidal wave of cheap perfume, fake tan and bright cherry-red lipstick.

'So where are you from sweetheart?' Whitney enquired, the champagne glass lingering in front of her lips.

Entranced, Daniel leant back against the bar, trying to play it cool. 'Australia. Brisbane, actually.'

'And what do you do with yourself in Brisbane?'

'I own a high-risk payment processing company,' Daniel proudly announced, not expecting her to have a clue what he was talking about. To be fair, not many people did.

But Whitney was a professional. It didn't matter to her what Daniel did. What mattered was whether or not it was a lucrative profession. 'Is there a lot of money in that game?' she enquired in her sultry voice, leaning forward, her breasts in danger of falling out of her dress.

'Sure,' Daniel smiled. 'If you know what you're doing.'

'And do you know what you're doing?' she asked, her eyes shimmering with a naughty glint.

'Sure,' Daniel replied. A turnover of close to $1 billion in just eighteen months had been proof of that. As had been the purchase of one of Australia's most expensive homes, a yacht, private jet, a night-club and countless luxury cars. If only it wasn't all gone . . .

Whitney flashed a smile and broke Daniel's trailing thoughts. 'So what are you doing tonight?'

Sipping some of his champagne, Daniel placed the glass down next to him before saying, 'I've been to the ETA conference at the Mandalay Bay.'

'And what do you want to do for the rest of the night?' she asked, cutting right to the chase, softly biting her lower lip seductively as she did so.

Ninety-nine per cent of the time, Whitney's targets would have expressed an interest in spending it with her, whatever the price. Daniel Tzvetkoff's answer, however, fell in the one per cent bracket.

Snapping out of the sexually charged moment, he replied, 'I'm going to go straight to bed to call my fiancée and my three-year-old son.'

To Whitney's shock, Daniel strolled out of the cabana and left her where she was sitting without another word being spoken. He had had enough. It was time to cash in. In another life, he had bled Vegas dry: nightclubs, strippers, parties with Mike Tyson. The lot. That was then, this was now. The last twelve months had certainly matured him. He now had no desire to spend the night talking to a hooker when he could just return to his room and speak to the most important people in his world: Nicole, and his son, Hugo.

He had argued fiercely with Nicole before coming to Vegas. She thought there was too much to risk. He thought there was everything to gain. This was the trip that was going to signal his triumphant comeback after a year of unadulterated shit. He couldn't wait to tell her the evening had gone better than he would have hoped.

Meandering through the pulsating poolside area, Daniel entered the opulent indoor club to try to find the exit. Trying his best to avoid bumping into the drunkenly swaying partygoers on the dance floor, he looked up at the VIP area where girls danced in their high heels on the marble tables. Sat below them, wannabe playboys drank champagne straight from the bottle. For a night they were the centre of attention, but by Monday they would all be back at work trying to figure out how they were going to pay off their Visa bill.

Having been there and done it, Daniel shook his head and grinned. They had been great days, there was no doubting that. But now he realised that nothing beat the feeling of walking along the beach with his fiancée and son. This time tomorrow he would be back home with them on the Gold Coast, telling them of his new plans for the future. It seemed everything was going to be all right after all.

Slipping the doorman twenty bucks as he lifted the red velvet rope for Daniel to leave the venue, he walked up the extravagantly decorated, cream marble, corridor towards the lobby. From all directions he could hear the cacophony of slot machines chiming, dealers shuffling, chips clicking and punters shouting in despair or victory. It was just another regular night in Las Vegas, where fortunes were won or lost in seconds.

Looking towards the action he noticed a pot-bellied redneck curse his luck at the low-limit Blackjack table; Daniel remembered that feeling all too well. That punch in the gut when you lose more than you can afford: nausea, frustration, regret. However, he hadn't lost his fortune at the tables. No. While he had also lost his fortune in Las Vegas, his had been lost in circumstances more painful than he would care to remember.

Trying to shake that depressing thought from his head, he instead focused on the joy he was going to feel when he spoke to his young son once he had returned to his room. That was who he worked for now. Not for Gulfstream jets, yachts, luxury cars or VIP nightclubs, but to see the smile on the face of little Hugo, his pride and joy.

Clicking the button for the lift, Daniel put his hands in his pockets as he waited impatiently for it to arrive in the lobby. Soon he would be back in his suite on the 53rd floor, overlooking the neon-splattered mayhem of The Strip, enjoying a quiet drink from the minibar while everyone else succumbed to the charms of Sin City down below. However, as he day-dreamed away, he failed to spot the murky reflection in the gold elevator door of a large, dark-suited man appearing behind him. Suddenly there was a click next to his ear. A feeling of cold metal being placed against his head.

'Don't fucking move,' the New Jersey accent ordered. 'Stay right where you are.'

Daniel stood frozen to the spot: a gun was being pointed to his head. By whom he didn't know. But in that moment he knew there were only two organisations it could possibly be – the FBI or The Mob. Either way, as the barrel of the gun continued to bore into his temple, he knew one thing: the comeback was over. A jail cell or a hole in the desert awaited him. And at that moment he wasn't sure what was worse.

1

Las Vegas, USA, July 2012

What do a National Hockey League strike, the inventor of Transformers, a struggling accountant and 'Jesus' all have to do with kickstarting the poker boom? And how did Daniel Tzvetkoff tie in with all of this? These are questions that my host, Nolan Dalla, Media Director of the World Series of Poker, had promised to answer upon my arrival in Las Vegas.

Despite suffering from jet lag, and general weariness following three weeks of travelling, it was hard not to feel excited when I awoke in my hotel room at The Flamingo. It was the first day of the Main Event of the World Series of Poker. Vegas was buzzing. It seemed everyone was in town either to play in the tournament or to watch. And the great thing was, for the sum of $10,000, anyone could enter. It's the only tournament in the world where an abject amateur can go head-to-head with legends of the game and have a shot, no matter how small, of being crowned a world champion. It's the equivalent of a fan paying to take part in the Super Bowl.

Waking bright and early, I wolfed down a hearty stack of blueberry pancakes at the Paradise Garden Buffet, before hailing a cab.

'Where you wanna go?' the surly driver asked.

'The Rio,' I answered.

'Oh, the Rio,' he replied, this time more cheerfully, looking at me enviously in his mirror. 'You playing at the World Series?'

Having told him I was there just to observe, he proceeded to spend the ten minutes it took to travel to the Rio, which is located half a mile off The Strip, telling me about the time he made a run at the World Series himself, but he just didn't get any cards. It was a familiar Las Vegas story. Bad beats. It's weird but everyone, apart from the very best players, seems to consistently get them.

Finally, after waiting behind a snaking queue of taxis, all shepherding players and the world's media into the towering purple Rio, which overlooks the desert on one side, and Interstate 15 on the other, I made my way through the bustling casino. It was only 9.30am yet the place was jumping: the tables were full, the bar was packed and the air was crackling with excitement.

I didn't have a clue where I was going, but I reckoned that following the crowd was probably my best bet. Blending in with the eclectic mix of players, who all seemed to be leaving the casino area, I followed them down a long corridor which had 'World Series of Poker 2012' banners emblazoned across the walls. Either side of me were a number of stalls selling assorted World Series merchandise, from hoodies, caps, cards and poker strategy books to sunglasses. I certainly seemed to be in the right place. Poker central.

Such is the sheer size of the Rio that it took me almost ten minutes to navigate my way to my destination, the media room. Once inside, I joined a queue of fellow journalists in order to pick up my press pass. With the pass hanging from my neck, I then joined the mad rush to the Brasilia Room, where the tournament's oldest competitor, ninety-two-year-old Ellen Deeb, officially got the tournament started by saying: 'I just want you all to know you're playing for second place. Shuffle up and deal.' And as soon as she said those words, the race to be crowned 2012 World Series of Poker Main Event champion was underway.

Since the event first started in 1970, at Binion's Horseshoe (now known simply as Binion's Hotel and Casino), where only seven players entered, the tournament's growth has been astonishing. So much so that in 2005 it finally had to leave its spiritual home, and relocate to the much larger Rio in order to accommodate the thousands of players wanting to take part. Unlike other American sporting events that call themselves the 'World Series', such as baseball, this truly is an international competition. Over 6,500 competitors, male and female, old and young, professional and amateur, had travelled across the globe to take part.

But despite being one of the world's most popular tournaments, it wasn't until 2003 when things really went into overdrive. I found the man who I was hoping would explain why, waiting for me when I returned to the media room.

Nolan Dalla is one of poker's true aficionados. He has probably forgotten more about poker than most people know. Not only has he worked as the Media Director for the World Series since 2002 but he has also co-authored a terrific book, *One of a Kind*, the riveting biography of poker legend, Stu 'The Kid' Ungar, as well as having written thousands of articles on the game for countless poker publications. Whenever I asked who would be the most appropriate person I should speak to about the background to the poker boom, it was Nolan's name that kept cropping up.

With a well-trimmed grey beard, short, blondish-grey hair, and dressed in a black double-breasted Italian suit, the dapper Nolan greeted me warmly. He was genial, bubbly and unfailingly polite. And for the next three days he had agreed to be my guide, to give me the inside track into how and why poker became one of the world's most popular games at the turn of the millennium.

Our first port of call on my journey of discovery was the Amazon

Room. Not quite as vast as the other tournament rooms, the Brasilia or the Pavilion Room, the Amazon was dimly lit, with lights hanging over the hundred or so green felt tables where the players were hard at work, each one grinding away for dear life. As we entered the darkened room, all I could hear was the constant clicking of chips, something which resembled the buzzing of thousands of crickets. Occasionally the buzzing was interrupted by a loud roar – a sign of victory, or of defeat. More bad beats for someone, usually.

Leading me to the back of the room, Nolan pointed to ESPN's high-tech poker table, which would serve as the centrepiece for all of the TV highlights of the tournament. Surrounded by tiered spectator seating, with sponsors' logos all around it, such as Jack Link's Beef Jerky, Southern Comfort, Bicycle Playing Cards and Miller Light, the raised table was illuminated by spotlights from every angle. For now it was empty, but later in the day this would be the epicentre of the poker world. Poker's version of the Roman Coliseum.

'What you are looking at was revolutionary just a few years ago. It's one of the major reasons for poker's popularity,' Nolan told me, as we walked towards the table, and he pointed to the small cameras, barely visible, tucked inside the rail. 'Do you remember Transformers?'

'Sure,' I replied, wondering what the success of poker had to do with my love for Optimus Prime.

'Henry Orenstein, the visionary who invented Transformers, also patented these small cameras, which are known as hole-cams,' Nolan explained, tapping his fingers under the table. 'You see, before these cameras were introduced to the poker scene, you hardly ever saw poker on television. Why not? Because viewers didn't know what in hell was going on. They couldn't see the players' hole cards. But when Orenstein created the hole-cam concept, viewers could see everything for the first time. It introduced a much-needed moment of drama to the game.'

Nolan went on to tell me that when the Travel Channel aired the

World Poker Tour in 2003, using hole-cams for the very first time, they were shocked when overnight it became their highest rated programme. ESPN, the self-described 'Leader in Sports Television', picked up on this apparent new-found appetite for televised poker and subsequently used the hole-cam for their coverage of the 2003 World Series of Poker. A year earlier, their viewing figures for the 2002 tournament had been a modest 408,000. Now, with the use of the hole-cam, those figures rocketed to an impressive 1,248,000.

Yet while the hole-cam led to increased viewing figures it was also fortunate that this revolution met headfirst with one of the most romantic and dramatic poker stories of all time. Something which Nolan told me about on day two of the tournament, when he led me into the cavernous Pavilion Room to see a player appropriately named Chris Moneymaker.

Plump, slightly dishevelled, and wearing shorts and T-shirt, it was hard to imagine that this was the guy who Nolan, and many others, credited with really igniting the poker boom. He looked like an 'everyman', a regular Joe Bloggs. And that was no doubt part of his appeal. As we watched him play, Nolan told me that back in 2003 Moneymaker was a run-of-the-mill accountant struggling to get by. Yet, after winning a satellite tournament on PokerStars, an online poker card room, he won a seat at the World Series of Poker Main Event. However, he actually cursed his luck, wishing he had instead finished in second place, as at least then he would have won a much-needed cash prize rather than entry into a tournament he thought he had no chance of winning.

A complete unknown, Moneymaker rocked up to the tournament and had just one goal: not to humiliate himself. Yet, to his dismay, he found that he could not just fade into obscurity, as his table was chosen to be featured on ESPN. What's more, one of his competitors would also be two-time former World Series champion, Johnny Chan. Humiliation beckoned.

Despite being up against overwhelming odds, the completely unheralded Moneymaker went on the rampage as he played the best cards of his life. Eliminating Chan in a shocking course of events, he proceeded to knock out more of the game's legends, such as Phil Ivey, before winding up in the final where he faced off against eight grizzled veterans of the green felt. With TV cameras capturing his every move, aided by the hole-cam, the audience became immersed in this rags-to-riches, underdog story. And a legend was born when Moneymaker emerged victorious, hitting a full house, seeing him crowned 2003 world champion, as well as receiving $2.5 million in prize money.

'You know,' Nolan said, as we sat on the rail, watching Moneymaker engage his opponents in some light-hearted banter. 'Chris may very well be the most important person in poker history. I know that's a big statement, but Chris helped the game go mainstream like no other. He was on prime-time TV shows like David Letterman and everyone loved him. Plus he had the perfect name as well, "Moneymaker". Everyone just saw this completely normal guy come out of absolutely nowhere and become a millionaire overnight. Millions of Americans, and later people all over the world, suddenly thought, if he can do it so can I.'

While the hole-cam, and Moneymaker's epic win, led to increased publicity, an NHL lockout for the 2004–05 season would also contribute to poker's burgeoning popularity. 'Suddenly, major television networks were facing gaping voids in their programming schedules,' Nolan recalled, as we walked among the tables, passing movie star Kevin Pollak on one side and UFC fighter Georges St-Pierre, on the other. 'And due to the success of the hole-cam, and Moneymaker's storybook win the previous year, ESPN in particular decided to fill the void by devoting more coverage to the 2004 World Series of Poker, which now had more than two thousand five hundred entrants, more than three times the number of the previous year. Then lightning struck the same place twice. We had another winner who was an everyman figure who had also won his seat from a PokerStars satellite tournament, a patent attorney called Greg Raymer.'

As Nolan explained to me how the World Series benefited from such coverage, seeing it attract major sponsors such as Miller, Hershey's, Planter's, Hertz and Corum watches, he also pointed to a row of giant banners, which were hung on the wall. Each banner contained a picture of a former World Series champion. Hanging before us was the banner of the 2000 winner, Chris Ferguson, who was nicknamed 'Jesus' due to his long brown hair and goatee. And Ferguson was yet another person who had played his part in the poker boom.

Heading into the millennium, playing poker on the internet had largely been an anonymous and sometimes arduous task. While a number of poker sites, both free and real money, had emerged since the early nineties, such as Internet Relay Chat Poker, EA World Play Poker, Planet Poker and Paradise Poker, most suffered from software issues, slow internet bandwidth or had problems repaying their customers on time. Unsurprisingly, online play didn't really take off.

However, the new millennium heralded the dawn of a new age for online poker. Broadband internet was starting to get rolled out, which improved the experience dramatically. What's more, new sites, such as PartyPoker and PokerStars, arrived on the scene with slick software and reliable payout methods.

All of a sudden there was a perfect storm. There was increased coverage on TV, with at least nine poker shows on eight major networks, and an underdog icon in Chris Moneymaker. This was all coupled with a vast improvement in the experience of playing online, with players now being able to play 24/7, not having to leave the comfort of their home, as well as being able to play up to 300 hands an hour, compared to just fifty in a casino.

As a result of all of this, online poker took off. Revenues for sites surged from $82.7 million in 2001 to $2.4 billion in 2005, while some operators, such as PartyGaming, the parent company of PartyPoker, floated on the London Stock Exchange for £1 billion, with the company valued at £4.6 billion.

An ocean of money was now up for grabs. It was almost like the great gold rush at the end of the nineteenth century. Everyone wanted a piece of the action. Thanks to the rake, which saw poker sites make their money by taking a cut of every hand that was played on their site, they couldn't lose. They weren't playing against their customers, but simply providing a place to let them play. PokerStars was said to be making $1 million in profit a day, while PartyPoker experienced an annual growth rate of 206 per cent. Eager to stake a claim, other online poker sites, such as Absolute Poker and Ultimate Bet, entered the market, as did Chris Ferguson's Full Tilt Poker.

Chris Ferguson was not just a poker champion. He had also spent eighteen years at UCLA studying maths and computer science. Combining all of these skills, he set about designing the ultimate online poker experience. Putting his friend and trading company boss Ray Bitar in charge of his new site, he also recruited fellow poker professional Howard Lederer to the board. Together, they proceeded to sponsor a number of high-profile poker players, such as Phil Ivey, to help market their site, and advertised themselves as the site where players could 'Come And Play With The Pros'.

With an eye-catching marketing strategy, as well as state-of-the-art software, including clever niche ideas, such as players' avatars having emotions, Full Tilt soon became one of the big boys. Other poker sites started to follow Full Tilt's lead, particularly in sponsoring players. Soon live tournaments were full of players emblazoned in Full Tilt, PokerStars, PartyPoker, Absolute Poker or Ultimate Bet baseball caps and/or jerseys. It was as if they were sports stars playing for a team. And many of them were treated in just that manner. Now the top poker players in the world, such as Phil Ivey, Chris Moneymaker, Doyle Brunson, Phil Hellmuth and Johnny Chan, were treated like major celebrities. They were on TV shows, recognised in the street, and signed up for major endorsements.

'Most of the online companies were raking in huge amounts of money,' Nolan told me, while we sat comfortably at a bar in the Rio where many of the poker players hung out. 'PartyPoker was at one stage registering eighty-two thousand new players a month! Over $125 million a day was being wagered on that site, a remarkable sum. Not even land-based casinos were putting up those numbers. Americans really went for it. By 2005 the United States accounted for fifty-one per cent of global online revenue. It was just insane. Out of absolutely nowhere online poker became one of the fastest growing businesses in the world.'

Yet it wasn't just the online sites that benefited. In 2005 casinos in Nevada and New Jersey reported revenues up by thirty-seven per cent compared to the previous year. At the start of the 1990s the casinos had shunned poker, with most shutting down their poker rooms. Now they raced to make them bigger and better than ever to capitalise on the boom. Indeed, in 2003 just 839 players entered the World Series Main Event, but by 2006 that figure had jumped to 8,773.

'So what do you make of Daniel Tzvetkoff's role in all of this?' I asked.

'I would whisper that name quietly around here,' Nolan replied, raising his eyebrows, lowering the tone of his voice as he did so. 'He's the guy many think almost brought all of this to an end.'

And while that was certainly the perception of many who I spoke to at the World Series, I had already found that the truth was far more complicated, and far more dramatic, than most could have ever imagined.

2

Brisbane, Australia, June 2002

It had all started with porn ... and pizza.

Scrubbing his hands furiously together under the oversized kitchen sink, Daniel stared at the mirror on the white-tiled wall in front of him in a daze. He looked like shit. He had dark bags under his eyes, his face was unshaven, his skin was grey, and his short, black hair was sticking out at all angles – all evidence he had hardly slept or seen the sun in days. Vampires got more daylight than he did.

The clock on the wall to his right told him it was 11.35pm. He had been working since just before midday; no wonder he felt like death. Thankfully his shift was over, but the next one would begin in just a few hours. It was relentless. Making pizza for a living sucked. Saying his goodbyes to some of his colleagues, who had opted to stay behind to enjoy one of the few perks of working in Pizza Hut – free pizza – Daniel took off his hair net and walked towards the back entrance.

'Hey, Dan,' his manager, Robbie, shouted. 'Don't forget to take out the rubbish.'

Can I take you with it? Daniel felt like saying. Instead he bit his tongue: 'Sure thing, Rob.' Doubling back, he grabbed the bin bag, tossed it over his shoulder, and walked outside, towards the dumpsters at the back of the building. However, despite living in the so-called 'Sunshine State' of Queensland, the weather in Brisbane had taken a turn for the worse. It was pouring down. After tossing the rubbish into the dumpster, he quickly put his black hood up over his head to shelter himself from the downpour. He was thoroughly fed up. At least the bus was due in ten minutes. All being well he would soon be back home.

Sloshing through the puddles as he walked towards the bus stop, he kept to the far side of the pavement to avoid the steady stream of traffic splashing him. The Brisbane Lions AFL game at the nearby Gabba had finished over an hour ago, but it seemed the roads were still full of fans. Looking at the happy faces of those in the cars, it appeared that the Lions had won. Again. They were on a roll. Not that Daniel cared. Unless it was motor racing, sport wasn't really his thing.

These days even motor racing wasn't getting his blood pumping as it used to. Trivial things that had once occupied his young mind had been replaced by ambition, money and dreams. Plenty of them. Daniel's brain constantly hummed with ideas. The problem was he had too many. By the time he had devoted some of his time to one of them, another would pop up. Teachers, classmates, friends and work colleagues had all told him, at one time or another, he was a day-dreamer, a waste of time in some of their eyes, destined never to accomplish anything. But the last few months he had knuckled down. Things were about to change.

However, as these thoughts raced through his head, Daniel saw his bus pull up to the stop in the distance. It was early. Racing towards it, he was suddenly hit by an almighty wall of water. The onrushing traffic had crashed a huge puddle into him. Squinting his eyes together, holding out his dripping wet arms in exasperation, he saw the bus pull away. 'Ah c'mon!' he cried out loud to no one but himself. That was the last one. He'd have to walk home.

Thirty minutes later, sodden, cold, and thoroughly fed up, Daniel finally arrived at his family home in the middle-class district of Camp Hill. Quietly putting his key into the lock he tiptoed into the small house, conscious of the fact that his parents, Kim and Julie, and his younger sister, Jessie, would now be fast asleep. Meandering through the dark corridor, he turned left into the small kitchen and opened the fridge where an ice-cold bottle of beer was calling his name. That would take the edge off the day.

Biting off the cap with his teeth he went to his bedroom, shut the door behind him, and changed out of his soaking wet, pizza smelling, clothes into grey tracksuit bottoms and a hoodie. Finally at his desk, by a condensation-stained window, which reverberated with the sound of the beating rain, he got down to work. His shift at Pizza Hut may have been over, but his shift for his IT company, BT Projects, had only just begun.

The company had only been in existence for a few months. Having left school, Villanova College, as soon as he could, he had dreamed of making his mark in the world of business, yet he was too scatter-brained. Nothing had really paid off. In the end he had to make do working all hours making pizza. And despite seeming to be constantly working, he had nothing to show for it: no car, no house, no girlfriend. He knew there had to be more to life than this.

While he slaved away, some of his closest friends were doing very well for themselves. Dave, in particular, an old schoolmate, who had shared Daniel's enthusiasm for technology, had started some programming work for the so-called 'Porn Mafia', a media term used to describe a group of young guys from Brisbane who had set up some of the world's first porn websites in the early 1990s and were now making some serious coin. Some said as much as $3 million a month. Not really that surprising when you consider that at one stage their websites accounted for almost seventy-five per cent of the world's online porn.

Daniel Hicks, John Johnson and other young adult website entrepreneurs were now legends in Brisbane. They had the best cars, biggest houses and hottest girls – basically anything a young guy could want. Daniel looked up to them in awe. They were proof that with a good idea you could make it to the top, no matter your age. And that's exactly what he wanted for himself: to reach the top, the sooner the better. He had an overwhelming urge to prove to everyone, and to himself, that he wasn't a nobody. And a quote from the *Scarface* poster he had emblazoned above his bed told him exactly what he needed to do to make it, 'In this country, you gotta make the money first. Then when you get the money, you get the power. Then when you get the power, then you get the women.' Wise words.

So, with this in mind, Daniel had put an end to his day-dreaming. Every spare minute that he had, he scoured the internet for the latest technology news. He taught himself basic programming, search engine optimisation, website design as well as anything else connected to computers. In his eyes, this was the future. If he could grasp basic technology then an opportunity would soon present itself in this ever-evolving field which could make him his fortune. Until that day came, and it would eventually, he knew he could do very nicely offering various IT services.

Lately, things had been picking up. A prominent law firm had been so taken with his apparent expertise in search engine optimisation (the ability to engineer websites to the top of a specific Google search) that they had flown him to Sydney to give a presentation. Moreover, he had also helped to set up an eBay style website for the market stalls of Brisbane, where his father worked as a coordinator. This had been very popular, although to date not profitable. Yet slowly but surely he was putting his name on the map.

However, the real feather in his cap had been getting in with the porn boys. Now he was working with his idols, helping them to drive traffic to their sites. He was given a fifty per cent share of the proceeds from every new subscriber they picked up because of him. It was still early days, but Daniel estimated that by the end of the month he could be in for a payday of at least $20,000. Then he could finally kiss Pizza Hut goodbye and work on this full time. Hopefully he might also be able to move out and finally get his own place. Living at home was killing his chances of getting a girlfriend.

Daniel's fingers tapped furiously away as he busily installed meta-tags into one of his client's websites. In other words, writing invisible key search words, such as 'sex', into the fabric of the website so that Google's 'spiders' would pick them up. It wasn't exactly a thrilling task but it certainly worked. All he had to do was get in the zone, bombard the site with as many key words as he could think of, and then sit back and let the money roll in. That was the plan anyway.

After close to an hour of relentless typing, Daniel's hands started to cramp up. Shaking them vigorously, he arched his back and stretched. It was almost 2am. He still had at least another two hours of work left ahead of him before he would have to get up at eight to prepare for the early pizza shift. Banishing that depressing thought from his head, Daniel decided it was time to mix some work with pleasure.

Typing www.pinkbits.com into his web browser, the site he had just been working on, a picture of a naked young blonde slowly downloaded onto his computer. But just as the picture resolution was about to become completely clear, Daniel jumped as he heard a bang against his window. Leaning over, and peering between his blinds, he could make out a thick, curly mop of black hair and a pair of steamy square glasses below. It was Dave.

'I've been trying to ring you!' his friend shouted, trying to be heard above the crashing of the rain.

'Shhhhh . . .,' Daniel replied, placing his fingers to his lips. Dave was going to wake the whole neighbourhood, not to mention his own family if he carried on. 'I'm working. My phone is on silent.'

'Open the bloody door and let me in!' Dave yelled, holding his jacket above his head. 'It's pissing down.'

Turning off his monitor, Daniel quickly walked towards the front door and delicately undid the latch, letting Dave dive inside. 'For fuck's sake, mate,' he cursed, shaking his head like a wet dog. 'I've been trying to call you.'

Once again placing his fingers to his lips, Daniel gestured for Dave to follow him to his room if he wanted to speak. Yet before he did so, Dave took a diversion into the kitchen. Opening the refrigerator, he scoured away, looking for something to take his fancy. Finally he spotted a chicken drumstick hidden under some foil. Ripping chunks of flesh off the bone like a hungry barbarian, he made himself at home on Daniel's bed, disregarding the fact he was dripping wet.

Glancing around at the posters of *The Sopranos* and 'Playboy Playmates' that plastered the walls, Dave smiled as he chewed hungrily. 'Jesus mate. You need to move out.'

'What do you want?' Daniel snapped, finally losing his patience.

'Have you heard from John?'

'No. Why?'

'Some shit has gone down. One of the processors called and said the bank in St Kitts has frozen a big chunk of funds.'

Daniel shot upright in his chair. This was serious. It was an occupational hazard that he had heard about but had not yet experienced. Visa and MasterCard were not big fans of the porn industry. As such they did everything in their power to stop transactions linked to porn, as well as a host of other 'high risk' online industries, such as pharmaceuticals, gaming, travel and dating.

To get around this inconvenience, a number of middlemen had emerged in recent years. They had ways and means to get around these obstacles. Whenever a customer wanted to buy a product, or subscribe to something online, the middleman utilised whatever means necessary to take the payment from the customer's bank account/credit card on the merchant's behalf. More often than not they would then filter that money to offshore banks, in the likes of St Kitts or the Philippines, before eventually paying the clean money onto the merchant, taking a percentage for their troubles along the way. Usually these methods left the credit card companies and banks, none the wiser. These middlemen were known in the trade as high-risk payment processors. However, sometimes even their techniques failed. And when they did, the credit card companies froze the offending bank account and usually seized the monies held within it.

Trying to digest Dave's bombshell news, Daniel looked up at the ceiling and slowly closed his eyes. After a moment of silence he finally uttered: 'So what's the deal? How much is gone?'

'It's a big one,' came Dave's solemn reply. 'Four million dollars.'

'FUCK!'

Better get used to making pizza for a while yet. All of Daniel's hard work looked to be completely down the drain.

Caught up in his thoughts, his heart skipped a beat as the door suddenly opened. 'Daniel! It's two o'clock in the bloody morning. I've got to be in school for six,' his bleary-eyed mother scolded. 'What on earth are you doing?'

'Hi, Mrs Tzvetkoff,' Dave waved from the bed, his mouth half-full of chicken.

'David! What are you doing here?'

Dave shrugged. 'I was hungry.'

'Sorry, Mum,' Daniel apologised, stepping in. 'We'll keep it down.'

'Make sure that you do.'

As his mother shut the door behind her, Daniel knew more than ever that it was time to move out. His parents had been nothing but supportive. They didn't pretend to understand what he did, but they had still helped him to buy equipment and encouraged him at every turn. But trying to run a business while having your mother tell you off was not the professional image Daniel was trying to project. Once he had been paid for his work, he would rent an apartment some-where. But then a horrible thought struck him: if the bank had gone down would that mean the money he was owed was gone?

'We're still going to get paid, though?' Daniel hopefully asked Dave. 'Right? I mean it's not our fault.'

Sat on the side of the bed, Dave didn't need to answer. His laughter told its own story.

Daniel couldn't believe it. 'So that's it? We're not getting a penny?'

'Nothing, mate,' Dave answered unhelpfully. 'That's it. Everyone is fucked.'

'What the hell happened?'

'Chargebacks apparently,' Dave tried to explain. 'Either too many fuckwits using stolen credit cards to subscribe to porn or too many idiots not realising that the fake descriptor on their statement, like i-billing, was for their yearly subscription to teen gang bangs. These morons call up the credit card company and charge it back. If the processor has a certain amount of chargebacks then the bank pulls the plug. They take all the money in the account, slam you with a huge fine, and wash their hands of you. Game over. See ya later.'

'That's it?'

'Yup!'

Wow. When there was so much money at stake, it defied belief that no processor had thought to put procedures in place to double-check all purchases were legitimate before the information was passed on to the banks or to inform customers of the fake descriptor that would be used on their statement. It would hardly be rocket science. All of a sudden, Daniel felt a familiar feeling within his head. The gears were whirring together and a jolt of energy slowly pulsed through his body. He was onto something.

'The processors,' he began, as he tried to untangle his thoughts, 'those guys don't do any checks on the cards they process, you know, to see if they're stolen?'

'Doesn't look like it,' Dave sighed. 'If they do, they're not doing them properly. This happens all the time. Since I've been working with the boys I reckon they've lost at least twelve million dollars because of this. They just say it's the way it is. Suck it up.'

Maybe they didn't have to suck it up though, Daniel thought, with a smile creeping across his face. Maybe he had the idea he had been searching for. And maybe it could even be his ticket out of Pizza Hut ...

But while Daniel's mind exploded with possibilities, he forgot to consider one very important thing; there was a very good reason the industry was called 'high risk'. Soon he would find out why.

3

Brisbane, Australia, February 2006

Four years had passed in a flash. And things looked to have changed. Big time.

Stood at the end of the large, oak boardroom table, a suited and booted Daniel offered his guests from Japan a seat. He looked the business. This had been the dream when he had been working at Pizza Hut: big office, fancy suit, international clients. To all intents and purposes, it looked like he had made it. But things weren't quite as they seemed. He may have looked the epitome of an international jetsetter but the truth wasn't quite so glamorous.

For a start, the office wasn't his. Situated in downtown Brisbane, it was the property of Sciacca's, a law firm where his lawyer, Sam Sciacca, was a partner. Daniel's own offices, in the gritty Fortitude Valley, were nowhere near as prestigious. Thankfully, the bald and bespectacled Sam, who was sat next to him, had allowed him to use the office in order to impress his visitors from the Far East.

While he gave off the impression of a Silicon Valley whiz-kid, and seemed to have a revolutionary product, Daniel had found making real money a lot harder than he had first thought. Long since leaving the world of Pizza Hut behind, he had thrown himself into learning

everything there was to know about the high-risk payment processing world. He already had something unique he could add to the mix
and now he just needed to know the basics. As a result, despite being
just twenty-two years old, the young gun now knew better than most
how to go about getting credit card companies to process transactions on behalf of porn websites. But in the world of business that
wasn't enough. What use is there in having the best product if no one
knows about it? Consequently business was sluggish.

However, Daniel looked to have finally caught himself a whale.
Apparently the two Japanese men at the end of the table owned one
of the biggest online providers of geisha girls in Asia. It was big money,
but also the type of money that wasn't easy to get out of a customer's
credit card and then transfer into a merchant's bank account. The men
needed the services of a middleman who knew how to get around the
system. And Daniel had told them he was just that man. Now they
had travelled to Brisbane to see if he was as good as his word.

Feeling hot and flustered, with his white shirt sticking to his back,
Daniel took off his jacket and undid the top button on his collar, loos-
ening his grey tie as he did so. Through the boardroom window he
could see Sam's assistant, Nicole, sat at her desk. She was still hard at
work. Sam had told him that he had hired the pretty brunette on the
recommendation of a friend when she was just sixteen and, despite
her age, she had proven over the past few years that she was more
than capable. So capable in fact that she had quickly graduated from
the role of simple secretary to performing tasks that even some of
Sam's junior lawyers found beyond them.

While he was meant to be concentrating on the meeting, Daniel
just couldn't avert his gaze from her. He thought she always looked
hot, but today she appeared especially stunning in her black high
heels, black skirt and tight-fitting blouse. If only he could build up the
courage to ask her out. He knew she liked him, so why did he find it
so damn difficult to do it? Catching her glance towards him, as she

pretended to work, he flashed her a quick smile before he addressed the geisha girl kings.

'As I was saying, gentlemen,' he continued, while pointing to a graph that was being shown on the overhead projector screen, 'my company Merchant Solutions uses open-source coding for my gateway, which allows me to take payments from your customer's credit card before then filtering that money through to one of my offshore bank accounts.'

As Daniel continued with his spiel, Sam tapped his feet impatiently to the side of him. From an Italian–Sicilian background, thirty-six year old Sam had been Daniel's legal representative for the past year. During that time he had worked on a variety of things for him, from tidying up contracts to gaining an injunction against an adult entertainment forum for spreading malicious rumours that had connected Merchant Solutions to a scam. Sam liked Daniel. He saw some serious potential in the kid. And while he liked to help him in any way that he could, such as letting him use his office to impress clients, Sam had told him that on this occasion he needed to be quick. He had a dinner date with his ever patient wife, childhood sweetheart Jo-Anne, and friends he needed to keep.

Yet as Daniel continued to discuss his software, Sam grew increasingly restless. He had sat through this presentation many times before. At the end of the day, he knew it all came down to one thing: Merchant Solutions' unique selling point, fraud control. With Daniel dramatically failing to get this point across it seemed the two prospective clients, who spoke only limited English, were in danger of slipping into a coma. Satono, the younger of the two, who was dressed like a flash Yakuza gangster, was fiddling with an oversized gold Breitling watch on his wrist, while his middle-aged boss, who looked like a regular Japanese businessman, was just about keeping his eyes open.

'Daniel,' Sam interrupted, unable to bite his tongue any longer, as his client was going off on a tangent trying to explain the intricacies of his software. 'Perhaps I should outline to our guests just how you keep the chargebacks down?'

'Uh, yeah, sure,' Daniel answered, taking a seat, not quite sure where his lawyer was going with this, but trusting him nevertheless.

'Gentlemen,' Sam said, standing up from his chair and making sure he projected his voice loudly and clearly. 'Merchant Solutions does something that virtually no other processor in this industry does. It has a comprehensive fraud control system.'

Over the course of the next ten minutes, Sam explained simply why it was that fraud control was so vital. Daniel had grasped that if you did your due diligence you cut down on your chargebacks. And if you cut down on your chargebacks, then banks were less likely to blow up. Ultimately this meant one very important thing: if you could keep the banks happy then merchants were far more likely to get their money. As one of the few in the processing world who had grasped this, the self-taught technology prodigy had added a host of applications to his processing gateway. These included:

1. Carrying out due diligence on a client to ensure they weren't engaged in anything illegal, such as drugs or child porn, a sure-fire way to get your bank account frozen or seized.

2. Emailing a customer to confirm they had actually made the transaction and that it wasn't a stolen credit card.

3. Informing the customer of the descriptor that would be on their bank statement.

4. Using geotechnology which showed whether the computer terminal where the purchase was made was in close proximity to the customer's registered address for their credit card.

5. Taking a 'fingerprint' of a consumer's computer and limiting that computer to one purchase per day to cut down on someone using a load of stolen credit cards in one go.

It was all relatively simple stuff. Daniel certainly hadn't been the first to invent the technology. But he was one of the first in the high-risk payment processing industry to put it all together, and utilise it effectively. As Sam told the now enraptured prospective clients, this all meant one thing: Merchant Solutions could reduce the chances of banks freezing or seizing your money better than anyone else in the game.

Nodding their heads to Sam's every word, Daniel looked around the table in amazement. His lawyer was killing it. He knew you had to be a good public speaker to be a lawyer, but this was something else. Incredibly, within fifteen minutes of Sam speaking, Satono and his boss were signing on the dotted line. In fact, Sam had been so keen to get it all tied up he had virtually grabbed Satono's hand and scribbled his signature himself. Daniel was blown away.

Following the signing, Sam had foregone the pleasantries and made his excuses. Grabbing his suitcase he had virtually run out of the room, despite protestations that he should join the happy threesome for a celebratory drink. There was no chance of that. It was already 6.45pm. His wife Jo-Anne had already sent him two texts asking when he would be home, seeing as he had promised her 6.00pm, no later. The boys would just have to do without him.

Close to midnight in the Sciacca household, Sam was spread on the bed, next to his sleeping wife, trying desperately to get some sleep. It had been a long day and the alarm was already set for the crack of dawn so he could take his sons to play rugby. It was non-stop. But just as he finally drifted into a deep sleep the shrill sound of his mobile phone ringing woke him. Wearily reaching over in the darkness to the bedside table, he looked at the illuminated screen. It was Daniel.

'What is it, mate?' he murmured, annoyed to be woken and already mentally billing his client for the intrusion.

'Sam,' Daniel slurred, clearly intoxicated. 'Come down to Universal Girls and join us for some saki.'

'Saki. Saki. Saki,' came the voice of a highly inebriated Satono in the background. 'Come do saki, Sam. See girls with big titties also.' Sam could hear Daniel laughing loudly. He was in Brisbane's premier strip club – a standard place to take Japanese clients when celebrating a big deal.

'Sam. Get down here,' Daniel continued to urge, as Sam got out of bed and walked in the dark to his en-suite bathroom to avoid waking Jo-Anne. 'These guys are fucking crazy. Satono is trying to strip on stage with all the girls.'

Closing the door behind him, Sam sat on the edge of the bath and whispered, 'Maybe another time, mate. I'm in bed. Hope you enjoy yourselves.'

'Sam. Sam. Sam. Don't go. Listen right. You nailed it today! We could make a bundle together. How do you fancy partnering up?'

Partner? Was Daniel for real?

Sam had actually been contemplating exploring other options for a few months now, having tired of the relentless grind of life at a big law firm, but the world of high-risk payment processing hadn't really crossed his mind. There was no doubt, though, that Daniel had created a product that if marketed properly could be enormously successful. Sure, Daniel was still rough around the edges, but Sam recognised he was streets ahead of most others in the industry. Having worked with some very impressive figures in the world of IT, he had never before come across someone with so much knowledge for one so young. However, this was a big move. He had a young family to support. He was making good money as a lawyer. Could he really put all of that at risk taking a leap into the unknown?

Holding on to a brass rail, while a small Asian stripper squatted in a G-string, thrusting her groin towards Daniel's entranced face from just a few feet away, he did his best to stand upright. 'I'm serious, Sam. I'll deal with the processing and you deal with the business side of things. Together we would be unstoppable.'

'Just out of interest, mate. How much was that deal worth to you today?'

'One hundred and fifty thousand dollars,' Daniel quickly answered, suddenly feeling nauseous following the saki frenzy from a few minutes ago. It was big money, especially for a twenty-two-year-old. Sam was impressed.

'Not bad for a year,' Sam replied.

'A year?' Daniel laughed. 'A month!'

Sam couldn't believe his ears. That was serious cash – and all from just one client. If he could help Daniel sort out the business side of things then there was no telling just how far they could go. It was very, very tempting.

'Give me a call tomorrow when you've sobered up. Until then I'll give it some thought.'

With one important conversation down, Daniel had one more to go. Scrolling through the address book on his phone he found the name he was looking for and pressed the call button. Deep down he knew he would regret this in the morning, but that was the joy of drunken calling. In the moment you stopped analysing things and just did it. After a few rings a soft female voice on the other end finally answered, 'Hello ... Hello,' she mumbled, clearly half asleep.

'Nicole. It's Daniel. Look, I was just wondering, do you maybe want to go out together sometime?'

But before Nicole could answer, Daniel jumped backwards as a drunk Satono fell to his knees and puked all over his shoes. Wiping his mouth with the sleeve of his shirt, Satono happily looked up at Daniel with a glazed look on his face and announced, 'Saki and titties, man. I fucking love it.'

4

New York, USA, November 2006

New York City, the land of opportunity. If you can make it here you can make it anywhere. All sayings that Daniel and his new business partner, Sam, were hoping were true. Having changed his company's name from Merchant Solutions to Intabill, at Sam's request, Daniel had also listened when Sam had suggested they needed to be more pro-active in signing up clients. The old way of scouring adult entertainment forums wasn't going to cut it any more. What they needed was a more professional approach. As a result they had signed up for a booth at the Ad-Tech Exhibition in the main conference area of the Hilton Hotel, just a few blocks away from Times Square, hoping that this would be their gateway to the big time.

Ad-Tech was one of the world's top technology exhibitions. Anyone who was anyone in the online world was there. If you were looking to land the scalp of big business, then this was where you came. After a few days of relaxation in LA, where Sam, the consummate family man, had taken Jo-Anne and the kids to Disneyland, and Daniel had spared no expense entertaining his new girlfriend, Nicole, in Sunset Boulevard's Chateau Marmont Hotel, the duo had arrived ready for action. This was their moment, their time to announce the arrival of Intabill on the world stage. They were going to go in all guns blazing.

Yet, despite spending three, long agonising days, working all hours, speaking to anyone who came within ten yards of their booth, they had absolutely nothing to show for it: no clients, no concrete enquiries, no real leads. All they had was a bunch of business cards from people who had tried to sell services to them. It was a complete washout.

Slumped across the desk in front of the booth, Daniel struggled to raise the enthusiasm to carry on. He had bought a brand new Armani suit for this, got a short, sharp haircut, had a proper shave, and had even polished his shoes until he could see his face in them. Nothing had been left to chance. With Sam, the well-respected lawyer, pulling the strings on the business development side, and Daniel, the fresh-faced whiz-kid, focusing on explaining the company's unique fraud control system in detail, it was all meant to be perfect.

Looking on, as Sam stood out front, trying in vain to engage everyone and anyone in a conversation, Daniel's spirits lifted a little when he saw Nicole saunter across the busy floor towards them. They had been dating now for just over six months. Things were going great. For the first time in his life he actually thought he might be in love. He hadn't told her this yet, of course. In the back of his mind, he still felt she was too good for him, out of his league. If she didn't say it to him back, he would be devastated.

'Hey, babe,' Nicole smiled, leaning down to kiss Daniel, giving him a whiff of her Chanel perfume. 'How you doing?'

'We are dying,' Daniel explained down-heartedly. 'It's a disaster.'

Pulling a brown paper bag from behind her back, Nicole offered a sympathetic smile, 'Well I've brought some food for you and Sam to cheer you both up.'

Daniel grinned. This girl was just too good. 'What is it?'

'Shake Shack burgers and fries. Your favourite,' she answered, handing over the bulging bag to her ravenous and exhausted boyfriend.

Not wanting to interrupt Sam, who seemed to have cornered someone in conversation, Daniel opened the bag, took out a carton of fries and hungrily dug in. 'How are you feeling?' he asked between mouthfuls, alluding to the fact that since they had drunk the bar dry at The Sky Bar in LA a few days previously, Nicole had continued to be sick.

'I was ill this morning, but feel all right now,' she said, flicking her brunette hair over her shoulders. 'I'm never doing tequila shots with you again!'

Daniel laughed. 'I warned you that you weren't ready to mix it with the big boys.'

'Well, when I meet some big boys I'll bear that in mind,' Nicole winked, as she stole a French fry from Daniel's hand just as he was about to put it in his mouth. 'Anyway, I've got to run. I've booked myself a hair appointment on Fifth Avenue. I'll see you at the restaurant later?'

Standing up, Daniel put his arms around Nicole's slim waist and kissed her delicately on the lips. 'Sure. See you at eight,' he said, watching transfixed as she turned and walked away. Completely mesmerised by such a sight, he was too infatuated to hear Sam shout over at him, 'Daniel . . . Daniel . . . Daniel!' Finally he snapped out of his trance and turned to look at his partner. 'Come over here, would you,' Sam demanded. 'I want you to meet someone.'

Quickly grabbing another French fry, Daniel wiped his greasy palm on his trousers and walked over. 'This is Ryan Lang,' Sam said, introducing the guy standing next to him. 'Ryan used to work for Neteller processing for online poker.'

'Pleased to meet you,' Daniel said, shaking Ryan's hand, who gripped it tightly, showing off a dazzling smile. Dressed in navy blue slacks and a tight-fitting white shirt, which showed off his chiselled physique, Ryan looked slick. With his short, dark hair and olive skinned complexion, he was a good-looking guy who seemed to have a bit of a swagger about him. If he had worked for Neteller before, then Daniel reasoned he was definitely at the top of the processing game. Neteller was renowned for being one of the biggest processors in the world. They set the standard in a lot of areas, except in fraud control where Daniel was convinced Intabill held a significant edge.

'Your partner here has been telling me all about you guys,' Ryan grinned, as Sam looked on. 'Sounds like you have a good operation going. If I'm being honest, I've actually heard a lot of good things about you on the grapevine. I was hoping I would bump into you here.'

'Oh yeah. Why's that?' Daniel replied, pleased to hear his company's reputation had reached the ears of someone who had worked for Neteller.

'I act on behalf of a number of the top online poker companies these days,' Ryan began, slightly lowering the tone of his voice, and dropping his head down so Sam and Daniel had to lean in to hear him. 'I don't know how much you guys know about that industry, but my guys are all looking for new processors. It's big money, big volume stuff. Do you think you'd be interested in dealing with something like that?'

Glancing quickly at Sam, Daniel smiled, 'Sure. Sounds good.'

'Good,' Ryan answered, casually removing a silver card-holder from his pocket and taking out a business card which he handed to Daniel. 'Why don't I come out to Brisbane to look up your operation with my partner Rodney and we can talk about it all in a bit more detail.'

'Sounds great,' Sam replied. 'Doesn't it, Dan?'

It sure did, Daniel thought. At the moment Intabill was processing for clients in the pharmaceutical, music, travel and dating field;

as of yet they weren't involved with gambling. As far as Daniel was aware, Neteller had that area sown up. If there was an opportunity to get some of that action then he was all over it. It seemed that Ad-Tech hadn't been such a disaster after all.

With the day at an end, Sam had returned to his room at the W Hotel in Times Square to meet up with Jo-Anne and the kids while Daniel had hopped in a cab and directed the driver to take him to Robert De Niro's sushi joint, Nobu, which was a short drive away on West 57th Street.

Already waiting for him at a table for two, in the middle of the bamboo-decorated room, a homage to Japanese culture, was Nicole. Taking a seat, Daniel excitedly told her about the conversation with Ryan Lang. In response she nodded her head and smiled awkwardly. Continuing to try to eke out a conversation, Daniel realised something was up. Nicole wasn't her usual zestful self. Trying in vain to get a reaction from her, asking how Fifth Avenue was, did she buy anything nice, did she go anywhere good for lunch, he soon tired of her one-word, vague answers. 'What is it?' he finally asked. 'Have I done something wrong?'

Staring at the floor, then to the side, Nicole briefly bit her lower lip. 'No,' she tentatively answered, crossing her hands defensively across her chest, as her eyes darted to the floor.

'Then what is it?' he asked again, a sick feeling knotting itself in his stomach as he feared that the relationship was about to be brought to a premature end.

Taking a deep breath she looked Daniel directly in the eyes. 'Do you love me, Daniel?'

Smiling under the candlelight Daniel reached forward and took her hand in his. 'Yes I do,' he answered sincerely. 'Very much.'

'Good. Because I love you too,' Nicole said, taking another deep breath before dropping a bombshell. 'Daniel . . . I'm pregnant.'

'What?' Daniel spluttered in response.

'That's why I've been sick in the mornings. I did a test this afternoon. I did loads of them. They all came up positive. I'm sorry.'

For a moment, Daniel sat in silence. They had been together for only six months. He was just twenty-three years old. Despite adoring Nicole, was he ready for a baby? Just at that very moment, the waiter arrived at the table to take their order. Flustered, Daniel rattled off a list of food, Bigeye Tuna, Yellowtail, Red Snapper, Octopus, Shrimp and King Crab, before asking: 'What's the best bottle of champagne you have?'

'That would be the Ruinart Blanc de Blancs Brut, sir,' the waiter replied.

'Sounds good. One bottle please.'

'Daniel what are you doing?' Nicole asked her boyfriend.

'What does it look like?' he said, his face breaking out into a huge grin. 'Celebrating!'

Reaching across the table to take her small hands in his, Daniel leant over and kissed Nicole on the lips. It may not have been planned, but he was happy. It seemed everything was falling into place. The future sparkled with limitless hope and opportunities. And, without realising it, one of those opportunities was all down to a failed politician who had wanted to run for President of the United States.

5

Los Angeles, California, Present Day

It was the last session of the 109th Congress before the 7 November 2006 US mid-term elections, where it was fully expected that the Republican Party was going to lose control of the House. This late-night session therefore realistically represented the last opportunity for the Republicans to force through any controversial bills they had hoped to enact.

Prior to this final session, Bill Frist, the Republican Senate Majority Leader from Tennessee, had decided he was going to make a run for the White House when George W. Bush's term in office came to an end. If he was going to succeed in his goal, he knew full well that certain deals would need to be cut to attract enough support. One such deal involved getting Jim Leach, a member of the House of Representatives for Iowa, on board.

Frist knew that Iowa, the first state that would vote in the presidential primaries, was strategically very important. And while Frist had no real interest in internet gambling, Jim Leach certainly did. Leach felt that online gambling destroyed the moral fabric of society. So, if Frist wanted his endorsement then he would first have to pass a bill that effectively outlawed this supposed abomination. Easier said than done.

Over the years there had been many attempts to garner federal support to make internet gambling illegal, most notably by Jon Kyl, the senator for Arizona, but none had succeeded. In any event, the Department of Justice continued to claim that the 1961 Wire Act effectively outlawed internet gambling on a federal level, although many legal experts, and even some judges, had ruled that the Act applied only to sports betting. Knowing full well that time was running out, and the difficulty he would face in getting such a bill passed, Frist concocted a plan that may have been extremely unethical but it gave him exactly what he wanted.

As the last session of Congress approached midnight, there remained only a few more bills to vote on, one of which was The Security and Accountability For Every Port Act, known as the SAFE Port Act. This act had been debated for well over a year and was seen as an important anti-terrorism bill. There was no question that it was going to be passed. No one wanted to be seen to vote against something so important in the wake of 9/11.

Given that this would be the case, Frist attached another bill to the SAFE Port Act that had neither been seen nor even debated before that time. It was called The Unlawful Internet Gambling Enforcement Act of 2006 (UIGEA). When Senator Frank Lautenberg of New Jersey, a pro-gambling state where bills of this nature were of huge importance, heard of this new addition he immediately asked Frist for a copy. He was told there was no time before the vote. Besides, if he voted against the UIGEA, he would also be voting against a vital anti-terrorism bill, and did he really want to be known for that?

So, in the early hours of the morning, tired and uninterested senators passed the SAFE Port Act unanimously. Many were not even aware that this act contained an anti-gambling statute. Some didn't care. It seemed that even the prospect of $41.8 billion being raised in taxes over the next ten years, if online poker was regulated and formally legalised, was not enough to make them think twice.

When news of the UIGEA broke the next day there was understandably outrage in many quarters. Some senators complained that they didn't have a chance to read the bill before voting on it, while poker legend Doyle Brunson commented: 'I can't believe the underhand way this new bill restricting online poker was passed through Congress. What does internet poker have to do with the SAFE Port Bill? We Texans don't like this kind of trickery. Texas is a state where you see an enemy coming, a friend is a friend, and you look someone straight in the eyes.'

It seemed that the internet poker boom had just been dealt a fatal blow. When the markets opened on the following Monday morning, the stock of PartyGaming, parent company of PartyPoker, dropped by seventy per cent, while a total of $7 billion was wiped off online gaming operators' value. PartyGaming's lawyers were spooked. They told the operator that in the wake of the UIGEA, which President Bush signed into law on 13 October 2006, it would be best if the company left the USA. It was time for a strategic retreat. It had been good while it lasted.

However, while panic reigned, some experts kept a cool head. After analysing the UIGEA they realised that it hadn't really outlawed internet poker. There was still a chance the industry could stay in the US and prosper.

One such expert on the UIGEA was Professor I. Nelson Rose. A graduate of Harvard Law School, Professor Rose, who now teaches at Whittier Law School, had for the last thirty years been one of the world's leading authorities on gaming law. In addition to having two books and hundreds of academic articles published on the subject, he had also acted as a consultant for governments, been an expert witness in gaming law trials, taught classes on the subject to the FBI, as well as provided legal advice to some of the biggest names in the industry, such as PartyGaming founder Ruth Parasol and Bodog owner Calvin Ayre. With such a stellar reputation in the gaming world, I knew that in order to fully understand the ramifications of the UIGEA Professor Rose should be my first port of call.

A resident of southern California, Professor Rose agreed to meet with me when I was in Los Angeles in the summer of 2012. Having never before visited a casino in LA, I suggested that we met at the Hustler casino in Gardena, just fifteen minutes south of downtown. It was an opportunity for me not only to do some work but also to visit a place that was once considered almost sacred in poker circles.

Before Vegas or Atlantic City were a twinkle in gamblers' eyes, Gardena had built a reputation as a poker Mecca. Billing itself as the 'City of Opportunity', card players flocked to casinos in the LA suburb, which had started to spring up around the time of the Great Depression. Among the first casinos to open during this golden age were the Eldorado Club, the Gardena Club, the Horseshoe, the Normandie, the Rainbow and the Monterey. All focused on providing a fun and friendly environment to play cards and all did brisk business.

While poker initially flourished in this small haven, attracting card-loving tourists from all over the world, much like Vegas does today, Gardena soon attracted something of an unsavoury reputation. As Aaron Brown has commented in his book *The Poker Face of Wall Street*, Gardena was 'not a place to play poker for fun.'

Cheats soon prospered which saw its reputation take a nosedive, particularly when Vegas and Atlantic City came onto the scene. Brown recalled seeing players stealing chips from tourists when they weren't looking, as well as witnessing a small army of mechanics and colluders in league with each other, passing cards, signalling or dealing from the bottom of the deck.

Poker legend 'Crazy Mike' Caro, who was a regular in Gardena, as well as author of one of the game's most popular books, *Caro's Book of Poker Tells*, has said of his time playing in the gambling haven, 'Cheating wasn't the only obstacle. There were also other annoyances, such as murder. We began to think of ourselves as practising the most dangerous profession on the planet. I was robbed at gunpoint twice ... Unsavoury non-players would gather along the rails surrounding the tables and count chips. Yum yum! You'd get followed home.'

Unsurprisingly, Gardena's dwindling reputation, coupled with fierce competition from the glitzy and glamorous casinos of Las Vegas and Atlantic City, as well as from the super casinos that opened in nearby Bell Gardens and Commerce, saw players go elsewhere. Now there are only two casinos remaining in the city: the Normandie and the Hustler, which was built on the site of the old Eldorado and opened its doors to much fanfare in 2000.

When I arrived at the Hustler, expecting it to be gaudy, in-your-face and shamelessly peddling sex, I was very surprised at what lay before me. The building was just a small, beige block, with a conservative red sign out front proclaiming the venue's name. Used to the mega-resorts of Atlantic City and Las Vegas, it almost seemed quaint in comparison. It certainly didn't fit in with the brash and garish public persona of the owner, porn king Larry Flynt.

Upon entering the casino, expecting to be hit by a barrage of scantily clad waitresses and provocative pictures straight from the pages of *Hustler* magazine, I was again startled. The interior décor wasn't exactly fit for an edition of *Southern Living*, with its red velvet walls, huge crystal chandelier hanging in the centre of the room, red, cream and blue patterned carpet and wood-panelled ceiling, but it was still far more reserved than I would have guessed. It seemed that the Hustler was more focused on cards than on sex, although you could still purchase *Hustler* paraphernalia in the gift shop, and the waitresses were certainly easy on the eye.

But I wasn't there to play cards. This was strictly business. I had arranged to meet Professor Rose for a drink in the upstairs Blackjack Lounge so that he could educate me on the UIGEA. Having located the dimly lit bar, I found Professor Rose dressed conservatively in a navy blue suit, his grey hair immaculately swept to the side. He looked just as one would imagine a law professor to look. Straight off the bat we discussed some of the recent legal developments in the world of poker. From the way he talked excitedly about the subject, it was clear that gaming law wasn't just a job for him, it was an obsession.

When I brought up the topic of the UIGEA, Rose winced, almost as if I had brought up a forbidden subject. 'When the bill was passed, I read it over and over,' he told me, 'and I thought, it doesn't actually do much. Under its own title it's just an enforcement act. The act only comes into force if a state law is violated. It also didn't explicitly ban online poker like some initially thought, either. In fact, it didn't mention poker at all.'

'So what did it do?' I asked, knowing that there had been significant confusion about the bill's purpose at the time it was passed.

'It effectively made it illegal for a gaming operator, who engaged in unlawful internet gambling, to process the money it received from its players. That was all.'

Having read the statute I knew just how much controversy this had created. What was unlawful internet gambling? The UIGEA defined it as a 'bet or a wager' which was staked online 'upon the outcome of a contest of others, a sporting event, or a game subject to chance'.

It was clear that when someone was making a bet or a wager on online poker that it wasn't a contest of others or a sporting event, so the only area where the UIGEA might have had an impact on poker was if poker was defined as a game subject to chance. But is it? And if so, what percentage of chance needed to be present for it to be deemed illegal under the UIGEA? The UIGEA didn't make this clear, neither did any other federal or state statute, so with a lack of statutes and case law to go on, it was left to experts, such as Professor Rose, to work out just what it meant for online poker in America.

Some experts believed that the UIGEA outlawed only online bets or wagers on games where there was a significant amount of chance present. Others looked to state law for guidance, which in many cases stated that chance had to be a predominant factor in any game for it to be an illegal gambling activity. Both tests however suggested that chance had to play a major role in the outcome of the game for it to be deemed illegal.

Either way, many felt that a very strong argument could be made that poker involved far more skill than chance, owing to the fact that comprehensive studies had shown that in over three-quarters of hands played it was the player's decisions, such as calculation of odds, reading tells, playing position, bluffing and the size of bets, which accounted for the result rather than the actual cards that were dealt.

However, as Professor Rose told me, 'Congress deliberately made the chance test as vague as possible to make it a catch-all provision.' With no one knowing how much chance needed to be present, no-one could tell for sure if online poker was illegal or not. By drafting the UIGEA this way, legislators didn't have to deal with the hassle and controversy of explicitly outlawing online poker. A vague law such as this could do the job just as effectively by scaring all of the operators and players away.

But while this deliberate, or clumsy, drafting had made online poker a legal grey area, it also put a tremendous new burden on banks that had been processing for operators. 'It called for regulations to be issued by the Department of the Treasury and the Federal Reserve Board, in consultation with the Department of Justice, for banks to identify and block payments between US players and operators,' Professor Rose continued.

Effectively, rather than the Department of Justice policing these new regulations, they had made ill-equipped banks the judge, jury and executioner. Professor Rose said of this, 'The burden was now on the banks to identify and block transactions between players and operators, and they quite rightly said, if you, the federal government, can't do it then how are we supposed to have the resources to work out whether an online gambling transaction is legal or not?'

If the federal law, such as the UIGEA and the Wire Act, on internet gambling was unclear, and internet gambling was legal in some states, and illegal in others, it was an almost impossible task for a bank to work out if a certain transaction could be processed. 'It was estimated it would cost the banks over one million man hours a year to regulate this,' Professor Rose told me, with disgust. 'How could a bank work through everything it was expected to? It couldn't.'

Unsurprisingly, with so much confusion, there was panic. As we have seen, PartyGaming, the parent company of PartyPoker, the biggest online poker site in the USA, almost immediately pulled out of the market. However, other operators, such as Full Tilt Poker, PokerStars, Ultimate Bet and Absolute Poker, opted to continue offering their services, having taken legal advice that they were free to do so. Not willing to take too much of a chance, most of them did, however, move their operations offshore, if they hadn't done so already. Full Tilt was run from Ireland; PokerStars from the Isle of Man; Ultimate Bet and Absolute Poker from Costa Rica.

But even though those companies opted to continue to stay open in the US, there remained the question of how they could continue to do business if the banks refused to process transactions for them, especially when the predominant payment processor in the poker industry, Neteller, also decided to drop online poker.

As Professor Rose told me, 'Just like Prohibition, if you have a vacuum for a product or service that people want that is illegal, then people will find a way to supply it. But you are opening the doors to private, unlicensed operators to get involved, who have no ties whatsoever to the USA.'

Just as had been the case with Prohibition in the 1920s, rather than see off a very popular activity in the US, the ban instead created a free-for-all. If an online poker operator was willing to take a risk then the rewards were plentiful, so long as they could find a way to process their players' money. And with billions of dollars at stake, high-risk payment processors were lining up to help them out. It seemed that the party wasn't over just yet. Not when there was so much money to be made. But just as Prohibition had brought forth bootleggers and gangs controlling the supply of alcohol, the modern-day online gambling ban also caused its fair share of trouble. More trouble than anyone could have ever imagined . . .

6

San Jose, Costa Rica, March 2007

Impatiently standing on the cracked, weed-ridden pavement outside San Jose's Juan Santamaria airport, Daniel Tzvetkoff and Sam Sciacca waited for their transport to arrive. Ryan Lang had assured them he would sort it out. All they had to do was hop on a plane to Costa Rica. That was it. He would take care of the rest. So far there was no sight of him.

Fed up of standing in the oppressive heat, a wilting Daniel sat on his black, hardtop suitcase and pulled out a white panama hat from his Louis Vuitton monogrammed hand luggage. Fixing the hat on his perspiring head he looked up at Sam, whose grim facial expression told Daniel all he needed to know about his partner's current frame of mind.

'Where is he?' Sam cursed.

'Let's just grab a taxi?' Daniel suggested.

'We can't. We don't know where we are going. Try calling Ryan again.'

Pulling his phone out of his shorts pocket, Daniel once again called Ryan only to find that his phone was off. He had arrived in Costa Rica pumped to the max. Now his mood was changing dramatically.

After meeting Ryan at Ad-Tech in New York, Sam had gone to

town on the legal implications of processing for online poker in the US. The big question that needed answering, as best as possible, was: would processing for online poker companies in the USA be legal? Wasting little time, Sam had hired some of Australia's foremost gaming lawyers to look into it for him. He also instructed Intabill's latest employee, their very own legal counsel Michael Hui, who had previously worked as a junior lawyer for Sam at Sciacca's, to conduct some research into the matter. Just to cover all of their bases, Michael also engaged Damien Botterman, a lawyer from the USA, who was regarded as an authority in the gaming world, to provide them with his opinion.

When the verdict came in, it was unanimous. If they were to process for online poker then, as far as the lawyers were concerned, they wouldn't be breaking any laws either in Australia or in the USA. This was the green light they had been hoping for. Following this advice, Sam had called Ryan Lang and told him: 'We're in.'

A few weeks later, Ryan and his business partner, Rodney Robson, another ex-employee of Neteller, had flown out to Brisbane to inspect Intabill on behalf of the poker companies. While Ryan was cool, calm, suave and constantly seemed to have a grin on his face, Rodney was a little more serious. Married with two kids, he looked like an Action Man doll owing to his toned physique and close-cropped brown hair with a small quiff at the front. Ryan had told them beforehand that Rodney had an in-depth knowledge of processing for online poker and would be a good guy to use for advice. However, he wouldn't be able to take too much of a hands-on roll as his young son was currently sick and needed Rodney's full attention back home in Canada.

Sat outside Sam's family restaurant, La Dolce Vita, in the up-market Park Street, just across the river from the city centre of Brisbane, the foursome had discussed business over pizza. Ryan had claimed that should he put in a good word for Intabill then they could expect to be processing $30–50 million a month. Quickly doing the maths in his head, Daniel had realised that this roughly equated to a monthly profit of between $2–3.5 million. This was the motherload he had been waiting for.

However, there was a catch. In exchange for placing this obscene amount of business straight into their laps, Ryan and Rodney wanted a little taster themselves. Getting straight to the point they asked for a thirty per cent equity stake in Intabill. At this request, Daniel and Sam had both quickly glanced at each other and nodded their heads. If contracts were signed with the poker companies guaranteeing a certain volume of business, then they would have no complaints.

Having reached an agreement, Ryan had arranged for the boys to travel to Costa Rica to meet Bob Johnson, one of the top processing guys at PokerStars. While they were there, they would also see Brent Beckley, who handled the processing for Absolute Poker. Following these meetings, all being well, they would together then travel on to Dublin, to visit the head office of Full Tilt Poker in Ireland, where they would meet the chief executive, Ray Bitar. That had been the plan anyway, if Ryan ever showed up.

Just as they were beginning to give up hope, a black stretch limo pulled up at the curb. 'How ya doing fellas?' Ryan shouted as he popped his head out of the window. 'What are you waiting for? Jump in.'

No matter what Ryan did, Daniel realised it was almost impossible to get angry with him. His vibrant personality was infectious. Throwing their bags into the large boot, Sam and Daniel entered the limo to be embraced in bear hugs by their new business partners, Ryan and Rodney.

'I need to grab a shower,' Sam uttered, feeling hot and sticky after the long flight. 'How far to the hotel?'

Thrusting a glass of champagne into Sam's hand, Ryan grinned, 'No time for the hotel Sammy. Bob is waiting for us.'

'We're going to PokerStars now?' Daniel questioned, noticing that Ryan and Rodney were dressed very casually in just jeans and T-shirts.

'Not exactly,' Rodney laughed.

Driving through the impoverished streets of San Jose, Daniel was surprised at the view outside. When he had heard they were going to Costa Rica, he had been expecting a Caribbean island retreat, not the third world. Thousands of shacks, virtually built on top of each other, lined either side of the road while the pot-holed road itself was covered in rubbish. When they entered what appeared to be the city centre, dozens of begging children swarmed around the car shouting in Spanish every time they came to a stop. So much for a break in paradise.

Finally pulling to a stop, Ryan looked out of the window and smiled, 'We're here!'

Following Ryan and Rodney out of the car, Daniel saw a large pink building in front of him, with a red sign on top that showed it was the Del Rey Hotel. Thinking that their meeting must be at the hotel, he set off towards it before Rodney stopped him: 'No. Not the hotel. We are over here.'

Turning towards where Rodney was pointing, Daniel saw what looked to be a beat-up Victorian haunted house. 'You guys ever heard of the Key Largo Bar?' Ryan asked excitedly, putting his arm around a bemused Sam. 'No' Sam answered. 'Well, you're going to love it,' Ryan proclaimed, leading the way through the heavy wrought-iron gates and up a path surrounded by towering bamboo trees.

Upon entering the baroque-style venue, Sam failed to see the reason for Ryan's excitement. 'This it?' he asked, to which Ryan proudly responded, 'Yup. Best bar in Costa Rica.' Sam thought he would hate to see the worst; he thought the place looked like a dump.

Split into distinct rooms, it still looked as if it could be a house. No effort had been made to knock down any of the walls. It was almost as if the owners had just cleared the furniture and placed a bar at one end and cleared the rest for a makeshift dance floor.

Squinting at the musty smell, Sam was far from impressed. He had been expecting to attend a multi-national company's boardroom, not to sit in a place that smelt of weed, stale beer and vomit. It was filthy, and the place was dead. A couple of old gringos hung around at the end of the sticky bar, drinking rum and smoking rolled up cigarettes, while crop-topped waitresses gossiped together in a corner, playing with their tan leather vests, serving only when someone had the temerity to interrupt their chit-chat.

'Are you sure this place is all right?' Sam asked, feeling distinctively uncomfortable as Ryan walked to the bar to get in the drinks.

Smiling broadly Ryan replied, 'It's quiet now but wait until later; then this place is a riot.' This wasn't the answer Sam was looking for. He had been wondering if this was a good place to do business, not if it was suitable for an outbreak of mayhem.

'What do you reckon, Dan?' Ryan asked, swaying to the music while he put his hands on the bar, feeling the vibe in his own little world.

'You can't go wrong mixing business with pleasure,' Daniel smiled, appreciating the more relaxed atmosphere.

As they waited at the end of the sticky black bar for one of the waitresses to drag themselves away from their gossiping, Sam couldn't help but notice that everyone was looking at them. It was as if they had just walked into a bar in the old Wild West. The old men stared in their direction, and whispered in low voices, while the few girls who loitered around the dance floor also eyed them up.

Suddenly a portly figure arrived at the doorway. 'Bob. Over here,' Ryan shouted as the man, dressed casually in loose-fitting jeans, a blue Hawaiian shirt and a red baseball cap, which hid his thinning blond hair, walked towards them. Apparently, so Ryan had told them, the chubby Johnson was the man tasked with finding new processing solutions for PokerStars in the absence of Neteller. He was far from the image that Daniel and Sam had of him in their heads. Nevertheless, this was the guy they needed to impress. The owner of the company, Isai Scheinberg, was based on the Isle of Man and he had put his faith in Johnson to locate suitable processors. In effect, Johnson was now the master of their destiny.

Shaking Daniel's hand, followed by Sam's, he panted heavily, 'Pleased to meet you guys. Thanks for coming all this way to see me.'

'What you drinking, Bob?' Ryan shouted, having finally attracted the attention of one of the barmaids.

'Rum', Bob answered, which saw Ryan order a bottle of rum and five tumblers and lead the group to a table in the far corner. Addressing Sam and Daniel, as everyone sat, Johnson dived straight in: 'Ryan and Rodney tell me good things about you guys and your operation. But processing for poker will be unlike any industry you've ever worked with. So if we are going to go ahead with this, there are a few things I need to ask.'

'Go ahead,' Sam said authoritatively, taking charge, switching instantly into business mode. He could smell the scent of a deal. He was going to eat it alive.

'Firstly,' Johnson began, pulling up his red cap to wipe the sweat from his balding pate with his hands, 'I know all about your fraud control. Very impressive. But if you're going to process with us you need to have access to a bank that is willing to do ACH in the US. No credit cards. No foreign banks. Can you do that?'

'No problem,' Daniel butted in, before Sam had a chance to talk. 'We've got ACH ready to go in the States.' While the lawyers had looked into the legality of online poker, Daniel had spoken to Ryan and Rodney about the practicality of processing for it. They had told him that since 2001 Visa and MasterCard had really clamped down on banks processing for online gambling via credit card. As a result, it was very difficult for poker companies to take customer deposits this way. While processors and poker operators had found certain ways around this, such as issuing incorrect transaction codes that weren't related to gambling and by developing 'stored-value cards' which players could load with funds, credit cards were now pretty much a no-go area in the post UIGEA era.

Now the best method of payment was by ACH, also known as the Automated Clearing House. Daniel had been told that ACH was an electronic network, administered by the Federal Reserve, which allowed for electronic fund transfers to and from US bank accounts through e-checks. The network was usually used to process large volumes of transactions that originated in batches, such as payroll, mortgage payments and consumer purchases. If an online poker company had access to ACH, it could process large volumes of payments quickly and efficiently in and out of a customer's bank accounts, away from the prying eyes of Visa and MasterCard. In principle it sounded great, but finding a bank that was willing to do ACH with an online poker company was extremely difficult.

When Daniel had confirmed Intabill had ACH access, Sam was taken by surprise; as far as he was aware that wasn't the case at all. Right now they had banks in the Philippines and St Kitts who were happy to deal with credit cards, but nothing whatsoever in the US, let alone an ACH facility. Of course, Daniel knew this too, but he didn't want to blow the deal by sounding hesitant. He had already located a California-based processor by the name of Electracash who had direct access to ACH. They would just forward the trans-actions on to them after Intabill had conducted their fraud checks. They may have to split the profits with Electracash for now, but they would eventually find their own bank with ACH in the US, espe-cially with such a massive incentive to do so. At least this way they were in the game, even if they were running a risk by working with their rivals.

While Daniel was bluffing Johnson took him at his word. 'Good.

Now I know you guys mostly deal in travel, music and pharmaceuticals, but online poker is very different. It involves millions of players all over the world that like to be constantly updated about their accounts. Neteller used to have a call centre to deal with this, as they were the guys who effectively dealt with the money. Will Intabill be able to do the same?'

This time Ryan spoke before Sam or Daniel could answer: 'Bob, that won't be an issue. I'll personally move to Brisbane and help the boys get a call centre set up that will be even more sophisticated than the one at Neteller.'

Johnson nodded in satisfaction, before then delivering his final proviso: 'Money will be moving at a lightning pace, as players need to place their deposits into their accounts and be paid their winnings. As so much is going on, there is little point in sending the money on to our PokerStars account as it will only hold things up. You'll have to deal with the float and make sure deposits and winnings are paid on time. It's complicated. You'll need to keep track of it all. Is this a problem?'

This was actually music to Daniel's ears. Thanks to Sam's legal craftsmanship, it was already a standard condition in their contract with merchants that Intabill would hold a ten per cent reserve of the total transaction on account for a period of six months. They had been stung too many times before when a bank had shut down an account and had levied a massive fine, which the merchant refused to pay. At least with the reserve they were covered. What's more, the reserve had also left them with a huge pool of cash, which Intabill believed they could invest as they pleased. All that seemingly mattered was that they could pay it all back at the agreed time. This had been enormously profitable for Intabill. Millions had been ploughed into low-risk investments. It was basically a licence to print money.

Now, not only would they be keeping ten per cent on account, as well as charging their seven per cent fee on each transaction, they were also being told that they could keep tens of millions of dollars of poker players' money in their account for a period of time, the so-called 'float'. With that much cash at their disposal, anything was possible. The interest they would rack up alone just by placing it in a regular bank account would be enormous. PokerStars, of course, were not aware that the float might be used for any other purpose, so it was vital that Intabill kept it on the low down. However, the way Intabill saw it, they weren't doing anything illegal, just taking an easy way to make a little extra money. What PokerStars didn't know wouldn't hurt them.

'Mr Johnson,' Daniel said, breaking out into an enormous grin, 'We can do all that for you.'

'Good,' Johnson replied. 'Now I suppose there's just one more thing we need to do.'

'What's that?' Daniel asked.

'Celebrate.'

With that announcement everyone cheered and raised their glasses in a toast. It was time to party. Intabill had just entered the highly lucrative world of online poker.

The next day the exact same events were carried out at Absolute Poker's offices with Brent Beckley, while Ray Bitar gave the green light just a few days later on behalf of Full Tilt Poker. From out of nowhere, Intabill was suddenly a major player. Daniel Tzvetkoff, the twenty-three-year-old working-class boy from Brisbane, without a qualification to his name, was now going to be responsible for a huge percentage of online poker players' money. What could possibly go wrong?

7

Brisbane, Australia, May 2007

'Put your back into it. Smash it,' Kim Tzvetkoff urged, as his son put all his might into bringing down the wall that divided the room.

'I guess I don't have the Tzvetkoff gene for manual labour,' Daniel laughed, referring to his grandfather who had worked as a carpenter in Australia after emigrating from Bulgaria as a penniless immigrant in the 1940s.

Picking up a sledgehammer, Kim stood side by side with his son. 'OK. On the count of three: one, two, three.' Swinging their hammers, the father and son team crashed into the dividing wall and finally brought it down. 'Guess you still can't do without your old man just yet,' Kim smiled, as he wiped the dust out of his greying hair.

'I'd keep the dust in if I were you, Dad,' Daniel quipped with a straight face. 'It's making your hair darker if anything.'

'Cheeky sod,' Kim laughed. Walking towards the ice cooler in the corner of the room, he shouted over his shoulder, 'Beer?'

'Now you're talking.'

Tossing Daniel a bottle of ice-cold Foster's, the two proceeded to sit on the bare floor up against the window, where they could see the high rise buildings of downtown across the Brisbane River. Pulling off the bottle tops, they sat in silence as they surveyed the new open floor area in front of them. This was it: the new headquarters of Intabill.

With PokerStars, Full Tilt Poker and Absolute Poker officially on board, Sam and Daniel had needed bigger premises to cater for the huge increase in business they were expecting. Spotting the perfect location, a four-storey, lime green office on the corner of Cribb Street, just across the river from the centre of Brisbane, they had quickly signed a lease.

The office was spacious, modern and, with room to expand. Intabill could set up a top-class global operation here which would impress all of their clients. Fifty thousand dollars had already been splashed out on a state-of-the-art conference table, which not only had HD video conferencing technology, but at the press of a button twelve computer monitors would magically appear from out of the table itself. As far as Daniel was aware, only a handful of companies in the world had such a facility. It would be perfect for board meetings or for staff training days, not to mention signalling his intent to be one of the big boys.

Just over half a mile away was the 52,000-seater Suncorp Stadium, where Daniel had also just bought a $25,000 corporate box so that he could entertain Intabill's top clients at Brisbane Broncos' games. Admittedly, Daniel wasn't a big rugby league fan, but he knew it would impress the hell out of some of his clients, not to mention his staff.

Though every effort was made to make the operation the envy of Intabill's clients and competitors, Daniel and Sam also wanted it to be a great place to work. Their aim was to model it on Google's offices in California, not taking itself too seriously and creating a fun environment which excited and motivated everyone who worked there.

Grand plans were in place to install a fully functioning breakout area which would provide free food 24/7, as well as entertainment such as cable TV, a Ferrari simulator arcade machine and an Xbox. The call centre staff would be required to work around the clock, so Daniel wanted to make sure his rapidly growing team were well looked after and never went hungry.

Sam had arranged the hiring of most of the staff and implemented all the regulatory and operations procedures for the office. He had chosen the brightest and hungriest people to head the various departments. Operations members included business analysts, compliance and fraud specialists, ex-policemen and forensic experts, all to ensure Intabill provided the safest and most secure systems to process accounts for their merchants.

Ryan Lang now shared a house nearby with recent Neteller recruits, head of fraud Colin Best and head of operations Mike Oliver. On his recommendation, Sam and Daniel had splashed out on state-of-the-art equipment for the call centre. It was so advanced that it was on a par with CIA technology, as it recorded and analysed all incoming and outgoing phone calls. Furthermore, Colin Best's experience, coupled with Daniel's ingenuity, saw the fraud team now boast technology that was light years ahead of most major banks. They had the ability to scrutinise consumer and merchant's details so that nothing went unchecked. It was flawless.

Swigging his beer, as beads of sweat trickled down his face, Daniel looked at his stocky father. 'This reminds me of the time you helped Jessie and me build that tree house in our backyard.'

'Yeah, I don't remember you doing much then either,' Kim joked. 'As I remember it, you sat in a chair and made Jessie do most of the work.'

It was a fact Daniel couldn't deny. 'What can I say? I'm a good manager.'

Breaking out into a big laugh, Kim shot back, 'I'll give you that. I remember you setting up that lemonade stand when you were five and having all the neighbourhood kids do all the work for you. You must have made close to a hundred dollars that day without lifting a finger.'

'A hundred and twenty-seven dollars, actually', Daniel said, correcting him, remembering the profit exactly.

'Geez. I don't know why I didn't just pack in my job and let you run that lemonade stand.'

Looking at the wall that they had just knocked down, which now provided a huge open space where the Intabill call centre would soon be placed, Daniel took a moment to look at his father. At a moment's notice he had dropped what he was doing to help him knock down some walls, which urgently needed removing before the equipment arrived. Whenever he was needed, Kim had always been there for him.

Throughout his teenage years, when he had taken up his father's passion for motorsport, and in particular motorbikes, his father and mother had travelled all over Queensland taking their son to time trials. Then, when his interest in computers had grown, Kim had extended their home so that Daniel could have his very own office. Daniel knew that his parents didn't have a lot of spare money and he appreciated everything they had done for him.

'Thanks for helping, Dad,' Daniel said. 'I owe you big time.'

'Don't be silly mate. I'm your dad. That's what I'm here for. Besides, you know me, I love getting my hands dirty.'

Just at that very moment the ever-immaculate Nicole entered the huge empty room with a smile plastered across her face. Pushing a buggy, with their new-born son, Hugo, fast asleep in it, she triumphantly held up a set of keys in her hands and announced: 'I've got them, babe. It just went through. We can finally move in.'

Daniel's purchase of a $2.5 million Gold Coast condo, on the luxurious Hedges Avenue, across the road from the white sands of Mermaid Beach, was now complete. He was going to be living among the big dogs. Pulling himself up from the floor, Daniel walked over and gave his girlfriend a huge kiss on her lips. Taking the keys from her, he held them in front of him and turned to face his father. 'What do you reckon, Dad? Day at the beach?'

Kim got to his feet and patted some of the dust from his checked shirt. 'No can do today, mate. I need to get back to help your mother. But you two go ahead. Enjoy yourselves.'

'Sure?'

'Yeah. You go right ahead. We're all done here anyway. Have fun.'

With that, the two lovebirds put their arms around each other and set off for the lift.

'Hey, Dad,' Daniel shouted, quickly turning round to face his father. 'Why don't you come down to the coast next weekend with Mum? We'll have a barbecue on the beach.'

'You're on, mate,' Kim replied.

'I'll get some champagne so we can celebrate.'

'No need for that,' Kim said, while putting his tools back into his bag. 'A few beers will be fine.'

Smiling, Daniel turned back towards Nicole and walked towards the lift. As he did so, he passed the huge open space where his crack fraud team would soon be operating. With so much new technology in place, as well as well-trained staff, he was confident that chargebacks were going to be a thing of the past. But what he failed to consider was that stopping chargebacks wasn't the only way you could lose money in this game, something the players of Absolute Poker would soon come to find out to their considerable cost.

8

Atlantic City, USA, Present Day

If you were a young kid inventing an online poker website, you might be tempted to make your own account where you could see everyone's cards. I'm sure some would at least let the thought briefly cross their mind before deciding to do the right thing. However, there might be others who would just think: What the hell! Who's going to find out? I own the site! And that is pretty much how many believe the Absolute Poker cheating scandal came to be.

Keen to get to the bottom of this story, I contacted Haley Hintze, a leading poker journalist. Not only has Haley had countless articles on the game published in various publications and/or websites, but she has also worked as the editor of renowned website PokerNews. In addition, she also has a very popular blog, Haley's Blog, where she discusses all of the latest poker developments.

However, while Haley has very solid credentials she also has something else: an in-depth understanding of the Absolute Poker scandal. For the past five years, Haley has diligently researched every angle of the story and is now writing a ground-breaking book about it. Unsurprisingly, many fear what she will reveal.

Graciously, Haley agreed to meet with me when I was in the States so that she could give me an overview of the scandal. Hopping on the bus at the Port Authority building in New York, I made my way to my destination, 'The Gambling Capital of the East Coast', Atlantic City. However, it almost seems that these days the town is better known as the setting of the hit HBO show *Boardwalk Empire* than for gambling.

Anyone who has watched the series will know that it focuses on the mostly true story of racketeer and political boss Enoch 'Nucky' Johnson's battle to provide the city with illegal liquor, prostitution and gambling during Prohibition. As one of the few places in the States to turn a blind eye to such activities during this era, Atlantic City became a boomtown. But when Prohibition was abolished the place lost most of its unique charm and declined rapidly.

In an effort to revitalise the city, casino gambling was approved by voters in 1976. This led to huge redevelopment on the Boardwalk area, which overlooked the Atlantic Ocean. One individual who was very keen to get involved with casinos in Atlantic City was billionaire property developer Donald Trump. And when I arrived in Atlantic City, two and a half hours later, I pitched up at the pride of his casino empire, the Trump Taj Mahal, which you won't be surprised to hear is modelled on the Indian palace.

Opening its doors in 1990, the casino immediately became known as a high-stakes gambling haven when Japanese high-roller Akio Kashiwagi lost $10 million playing baccarat. But for me, and many others, the Taj, as it is affectionately known, came to my attention during the Matt Damon and Edward Norton film, *Rounders*. It was the Taj which saw Ed Norton's character 'Worm' say affectionately, 'You know what always cheers me up? Rolled up Aces over Kings, check-raising stupid tourists and taking huge pots off them, playing all-night high-limit Hold'em at the Taj, "where the sand turns to gold", stacks and towers of checks I can't even see over.'

Excited at the prospect of visiting the casino, which is the home of the United States Poker Championship, I have to admit I was slightly underwhelmed once I entered the Taj's palace-style entrance from the Boardwalk. It was almost as if I had stepped back in time. While the curved glass ceiling – intricately decorated with gold squares and boasting several ostentatious chandeliers hanging from it, illuminating the thousands of slot machines down below – was admittedly eye-catching, it all felt a bit old hat now. No doubt when it opened, it was hugely impressive, but while the Taj has perhaps stood still, Vegas has long since evolved from themed casinos to luxury venues that are a match for any hotel in the world.

Having made my way across the tired, dark carpet, I found Haley in Starbucks waiting for me. With cascading brown, curly hair, and glasses perched on the end of her nose, she looked a formidable presence, although, as I knew from speaking to her beforehand, she was very friendly and eager to help in any way that she could. In her eyes it was very important that this story became known to highlight the cesspit of greed the online poker world had become. There was a basic idea held by most, including myself, of what had actually occurred. To my understanding, this was how the scandal had unfolded.

In August 2007, a prominent online poker player, Marcus 'Crazy-Marco' Johnson, lost in suspicious circumstances to his opponent, Potripper, in the final of a $1,000 buy-in tournament on Absolute Poker. Feeling that something was amiss, Johnson contacted Absolute Poker and requested a hand history of the final table for him to analyse. A few days later, Absolute Poker forwarded him a Microsoft Excel file, with over 65,000 rows of information. Little did they know that this file would eventually open up all sorts of problems.

While Johnson sat on the file, not yet having the time to examine it properly, allegations started to emerge on poker forum Two Plus Two that other players on Absolute Poker (namely SteamRoller, GrayCat and DoubleDrag) were also regularly winning games, despite consistently playing a losing strategy.

An online poker sleuth and forum poster Michael Josem decided to look beyond the claims and deal with the facts. Analysing the suspected cheaters' available data, and comparing it to a sample of 5,251 players, he soon found something incredible: the suspects' strategy was an unfathomable fifteen standard deviations above the mean. In other words, it was virtually beyond a shadow of a doubt that they were cheating. And not just standard cheating, such as colluding, but they probably had the ability to see their opponents' hole cards.

Despite convincing evidence to the contrary, Absolute Poker repeatedly denied that the players involved could have seen any cards apart from their own and stonewalled any further questions on the matter. However, at this time Marcus Johnson finally decided to take a closer look at the huge Excel file Absolute Poker had forwarded to him. Within the file he found that the hole cards for all of the players had been included. And when he analysed every hand that Potripper played, he found an incredible pattern. Potripper had raised whenever his opponents were behind and had folded whenever they had him beat. Every time!

Amazingly, in the face of such overwhelming evidence, Absolute Poker still continued to try and play dumb. Enraged at this perceived cover-up, the poker community went on a full-scale offensive to uncover the perpetrators. Delving ever deeper into the vast Excel file, they looked to have finally found some significant clues.

Within the file they found that it also contained the IP addresses and email addresses of all players who had played, as well as those who had just observed the table. Subsequently, Potripper, as well as observer #363, both had their accounts traced back to Costa Rica, the home of Absolute Poker's servers. The email address linked to Potripper was scott@rivieraltd.com. Subsequent investigations found that the owner of that address was none other than Absolute Poker founder, Scott Tom, who had set up the website with his University of Montana friends in 2003. Furthermore, the email address connected to observer #363 was found to belong to another person involved with Absolute Poker, Brian Coffey, who was a minority owner, as well as being a good friend of Tom's father, Phil. In fact, Coffey had even helped build houses for both of the Toms.

It was also found that the rivieraltd.com's mail server IP was allocated to Absolute Entertainment SA at Mohawk Internet Technologies' data centre. Tom had apparently sold Absolute a year earlier to Tokwiro Enterprises, a company that was owned by Joe Norton, former Grand Chief of the Kahnawake Mohawk Territory. If Tom no longer had anything to do with the company, as was claimed, then why was his supposed email address linked to the new owner's servers? As poker forum posters posed this very question, the Domain Name System information at rivieraltd.com was suddenly edited in an attempt to hide Tom's alleged involvement. This only added more fuel to the fire. Rather than investigate players' concerns, it seemed that someone at Absolute was busy trying to cover their tracks.

With these events provoking a furious reaction from players, and realising that their reputation as one of the world's top poker sites was in jeopardy, Absolute finally realised that they had to be seen to be dealing with the mountain of evidence that was emerging. Finally, on 21 October 2007, owner Joe Norton released a statement that apportioned the blame for the incident on a low-level employee who had abused his powers. Norton claimed that this employee (who was later alleged by the media, investigators and poker forum posters to be Tom's good friend, Allan Grimard, who also went by the name 'A.J. Green') had managed to breach the site's security systems to be able to see every player's hole cards. In Absolute's eyes, Scott Tom was an innocent party. He had been set up. The perpetrator would be dealt with. That, according to them, was that. Yet Absolute had once again underestimated the ingenuity of the poker community, who remained unconvinced. Haley Hintze in particular was determined to uncover the true story.

'I was aware of it virtually from the first time the accusations were launched on the poker forums,' she told me. 'I notified the editor-in-chief at the time at PokerNews, John Caldwell, and told him that there seems to be more to this than just normal idle rumours. He told me to keep my eye on it. Here I am, five years later, still keeping my eye on it.'

Over the course of those five years, Haley has engaged in a dogged pursuit of the truth. It hasn't always been easy. At times, she told me, she felt like packing it all in, such has been the strain and stress of it all. But now she is close to finally tying up all of the loose ends. The information she has gathered has provided her with an unparalleled appreciation of what happened.

'How did you first start actively pursuing the truth behind this story?' I asked.

Thinking back, she revealed: 'A poster called Nat Arem sent me Marcus Johnson's spreadsheet files. Nat had already seen a Scott Tom email address in there. But there was another address attached to the account to do with rivieraltd.com domain and that turned out to be the behind-the-scenes email address that the Absolute Poker people were using. After we discovered that, they were frantic to hide this information.'

When I asked Haley about her thoughts on Norton's explanation that it was the work of a junior employee, she laughed. 'They lied,' she said, without a hint of doubt in her voice. 'It was garbage. I absolutely believe that Scott Tom was behind all of this.'

Probing Haley to back up this assertion, she proceeded to explain that she had tracked where in the world the cheating account IP addresses had been logged on and had also managed to track down Scott Tom's whereabouts at the same points. They matched. The IP addresses, which were in Scott Tom's name, linked in to wherever he was in the world, including his home in Costa Rica.

It has been alleged by Haley and other investigators that when

Tom first set up the site he created a number of test accounts, one of which was termed '#363'. While user #363 didn't have the ability to play in real-money games, it could do something that no other user could: it could see the players' hole cards at every table it observed. Many believe that in 2007 Tom and his associates gained control of some old Absolute Poker accounts that had been set up by executives and family members, namely DoubleDrag, GrayCat, SteamRoller and Potripper. It is alleged that Tom proceeded to play real-money games on those accounts, while at the same time either he, or an associate, used #363 on another computer so that Tom could see his opponents' cards. It should have been the perfect crime, but what Tom failed to consider was that if anyone ever managed to track down the IP addresses of all of these accounts then they would lead straight to his home, or wherever he was in the world.

What about the involvement of Brian Coffey? When Haley emailed Coffey regarding his email address being linked to user #363, Coffey immediately responded and claimed that not only did he have nothing to do with it but that Scott Tom and/or Allan Grimard would have had access to his account. In other words, he believed he had been set up. To date Coffey has been taken at his word, although there is no denying that his email address was included in the Excel file sent to Johnson.

'What about the fact that Scott Tom had sold the company to Tokwiro Enterprises a year earlier?' I asked. 'If he wasn't involved with the company any more, why did he have an email address with the domain name of the new owners?'

'You don't really believe he sold the website?' Haley shot back, incredulous that I had taken the transaction at face value. 'After the UIGEA, Absolute Poker spoke to a number of gaming legal experts and the advice they received was to find the biggest Indian Reservation they could, to act as a breakwater against any claims of illegality against US-based owners. The man they found was

Joe Norton. He was a front man. Scott Tom was still effectively in charge.'

The introduction of the UIGEA had of course left any US-based owner of an online poker site vulnerable to criminal proceedings. By 'selling' the site to Tokwiro Enterprises, Absolute would now be under the jurisdiction of an Indian Reservation, the Kahnawake Mohawk Territory in Canada, who were beyond the reach of the US Department of Justice. This move would not only have provided Absolute Poker with some protection, it would have also allowed Scott Tom to disappear into the background, while still pulling the strings and reaping the rewards.

'What about Allan Grimard?' I continued, referring to the employee at whom many had pointed the finger, wondering how he fitted in to Haley's explanation.

Placing her palms on the table Haley hunched her shoulders forward. 'There is no hard evidence that Allan Grimard was a cheater,' she revealed. 'Out of all the people who were at the company at that point, he was the only one who was not an owner. If you were looking for a fall guy – someone who could take the blame and keep the ownership group intact – Allan Grimard made the perfect fall guy.'

With Absolute accusing an employee of being behind such a major scandal, one would have assumed that the individual would have been handed into the authorities, or at the very least fired. It appears not. While the Kahnawake Gaming Commission allegedly took action against Allan Grimard, Absolute Poker appears to have done nothing whatsoever.

'Supposedly the Kahnawake Gaming Commission banned Allan Grimard for life,' Haley told me. 'But he was just moved sideways in the Absolute group and worked out of a different office in Costa Rica. I have photos taken subsequently of him partying it up with the other Absolute Poker employees.'

Indeed, despite Grimard being described as a low-level employee at Absolute Poker, it has been alleged by various investigators that he has still managed to afford a lavish lifestyle. While this is not concrete evidence of him being involved in cheating, or of being paid off to take the fall, the question still has to be asked: how did someone said to be on an average wage afford such extravagant purchases?

At the very least, if an employee wasn't held properly accountable, then surely Absolute Poker would have been heavily punished by the Kahnawake Gaming Commission for not having procedures in place to stop such an event occurring? Once again, apparently not. Absolute Poker was fined the measly sum of $500,000, the equivalent of two days' profits. It is, however, unsurprising that the Kahnawake Gaming Commission dealt with the case leniently. Absolute Poker's 'owner' Joe Norton was not only the former Grand Chief of the Kahnawake Mohawk Territory, he had also set up the Gaming Commission itself. If ever there was a conflict of interest, this was it.

'It was a joke,' Haley said bitterly. 'It was basically just a payment from Absolute to Kahnawake for having to deal with the hassle of it all.'

To date no legal action whatsoever has been taken against Absolute Poker, Scott Tom or Allan Grimard. No investigating authority is even looking into it any more. It is left to Haley Hintze, and others in the poker community, to fight for the truth. While poker news sites, forums and blogs have repeatedly named Scott Tom as the mastermind, and have provided comprehensive evidence for doing so, he has yet to take any steps to deny the claims.

However, while this cheating scandal caused uproar, another one would soon emerge that would rock the poker world to its core. This time the stakes were even higher, and the supposed perpetrators even more high profile.

9

Mount Glorious, Australia, October 2007

The designated meeting place was thirty kilometres north-west of Brisbane, at a small petrol station at the foot of Mount Glorious. With the peak 599 metres above sea level, the forested mountain was one of the tallest in the D'Aguilar range, which also boasted Mount Nebo, Camp Mountain, Mount Pleasant, Mount Samson and Mount Mee.

Taking a long drag of a cigarette in the dark, Sam waited impatiently for Daniel to arrive. They had said 11pm sharp. It was almost 11.15 already and he was nowhere to be seen. Frustratingly, being surrounded by mountains meant that he had no mobile phone reception so he had no way of reaching him. It was a particularly eerie feeling to be alone in the darkness, with just the sound of the crickets, and the buzzing from the faulty light that illuminated the petrol station's yellow sign, for company. If the place had been open he could have at least grabbed a Red Bull, but it had long since shut for the night. Sam was the only person stupid enough to still be out there at this late hour.

In the distance a storm was rumbling, which was also dramatically failing to improve Sam's impatient mood. The wind had started to pick up and amid the moist, humid air Sam could feel specks of warm drizzle fall on his head. If it got any worse, he had half a mind to call it a night. However, he knew that while what they had planned was crazy, he couldn't fail but to feel excited. This was going to be a rush ... if Daniel ever turned up.

Finally, in the pitch black, Sam spotted two headlights in the distance. It was the first car he had seen in ten minutes. It had to be Daniel. Lo and behold, just a few minutes later a black Lamborghini Superleggera, with number plate 'BALLR', screeched into the forecourt. With the gull-winged door swinging open Daniel, wearing his favourite baggy jeans and black V-neck T-shirt, stepped out with a sheepish grin on his face.

'Geez!' Sam semi-jokingly scolded, pointing at the round face of his Omega watch. 'What took you so long, mate? I was about to go home!'

Shrugging his shoulders apologetically, Daniel tried to explain. 'I had to wait for Nicole to fall asleep. She would kill me if she knew we were doing this.'

Sam knew that feeling well. He had told Jo-Anne he was going for a drive to clear his head. If she knew the real reason for his late-night excursion, she would have crucified him.

'So this is the new toy?' Sam said, forgiving Daniel for his poor timekeeping and running his hands over the sleek, black bonnet in admiration.

'Yup,' Daniel smiled proudly, opening the boot so Sam could admire the gleaming engine. 'Fresh from the garage: five hundred and twenty-three horsepower, does nought to sixty in less than three point eight seconds, top speed of one hundred and ninety-six miles per hour.'

Sam whistled his approval. 'How much did it set you back?' he asked, visibly impressed.

'Six hundred thousand dollars. It's fully loaded,' Daniel coolly replied as he watched Sam bend down beneath the door to check out the interior.

The past few months had been good to Intabill. Not only had the poker contracts produced a deluge of cash, but they had also found the holy grail of the processing world: a bank that was willing to process most high-risk credit card transactions. Based in Tbilisi, Georgia, Cartu Bank had actually approached Intabill and had virtually offered them carte blanche to do as they wished. They couldn't believe their luck.

The bank had just been granted acquiring rights by Visa and MasterCard, which allowed them to process online credit card transactions. As such they were desperate to attract some big hitters in the payment processing world. Knowing that Intabill was now an established name in this industry, they figured that the Australians could provide them with a lot of business so rolled out the red carpet for them. For the first time ever, Intabill signed an IPSP agreement, which effectively allowed them to process any merchant that they wished through the Cartu system. They could also issue their own credit card descriptors hassle-free. Furthermore, Cartu had also agreed to give Intabill direct access to their Visa/MasterCard gateway. This was unheard of. Even if they had owned the bank itself they couldn't have asked for more.

With the poker contracts already proving highly profitable, Cartu Bank catered for all the other industries Intabill processed for, such as pharmaceuticals and travel. Now they were the complete operation. Money was flowing in. Times were good. As such the boys had decided that they deserved to savour their success with a few treats.

'So how about you?' Daniel asked Sam, who was now sat in the driver's seat, with his hands on the wheel. 'Where's your new toy?'

Pulling himself out of the Lamborghini, Sam pointed to his brand new, jet-black Porsche 911. Walking over to take a look Daniel shouted, so that he could be heard above the ever increasing wind, 'Nice Sammy. Real nice.'

Sam opened the boot for Daniel to take a better look at the engine: 'Turbo manual, hey?' Daniel cooed, suitably impressed.

'Yeah,' Sam laughed. 'Tiptronic is for pussies.'

Turning his head out of the engine, Daniel grinned, revealing two big dimples in his cheeks as he did so, 'Well that's real nice, Sam, but that's not going to keep up with my bad boy in a race is it?'

'Not only will it keep up but it will beat you.'

'And how do you come to that conclusion?'

'Because I'm a better driver than you,' Sam winked.

At that very moment, a spark of lightning flashed near the peak of the mountain. A rumble of thunder followed seconds later. The storm was getting close. Sam pulled up the collar of his blue sports jacket. 'We could do this another time, though. This weather isn't looking too good,' he suggested, putting his bravado to one side.

'Don't be stupid,' Daniel replied, already halfway into the black leather driving seat of his supercar. 'We both agreed. We'd go out and treat ourselves to new cars and then race them to the top of Mount Glorious. We've been planning it for weeks.'

'Yeah, I know, but the weather isn't great. It's pitch black and there are no lights or barriers up there.'

Starting the engine with a loud roar, Daniel opened his passenger window and shouted: 'Look, if we get going now we'll beat the weather. No worries. Besides, when we reach the top I've got something massive to tell you.'

'What's that?' Sam replied, his jacket already speckled with splashes of rain.

Daniel grinned, 'I'll tell you at the top.'

With that, the Lamborghini shot off. Not wanting to be left behind, Sam raced to his Porsche. Hurriedly jumping into the driver's seat he turned the key in the ignition, slammed his foot on the accelerator, and shot out of the garage and onto the main road. It was on!

Speeding through the winding road, with rows of fern trees lining it on either side, Daniel cranked up the sound system so that the motivating base of 'Lose Yourself' by Eminem vibrated through his car. Refusing to take his foot off the accelerator, the car steadily went through the gears, quickly reaching ninety miles per hour as he fearlessly whipped around corners. In his rear-view mirror he could spot Sam about 150 metres behind him. He also had his pedal to the metal, but the Porsche was going to be no match for the might of the Lambo.

Beginning the ascent up the mountain, a few spots of rain started to splash onto the windscreen. Putting on the wipers, Daniel refused to slow down. He was enjoying testing his new toy to the limit. Behind him, Sam continued to try to keep up, but he was finding the sheer raw power of the Lamborghini difficult to match, even if he was in one of the fastest road cars on the planet himself. In any event, he was quite enjoying seeing what the Lambo could do from behind. As Daniel applied the brakes, Sam could see sparks spit out of the back as the car dropped petrol through the carburettors. When Daniel then took his foot off the brake, Sam shook his head in amazement as it sped away like a jet on a runway.

As they steadily climbed the mountain at a furious pace, the weather continued to deteriorate. A crash of thunder, coupled with a fork of lightning, saw the rain come crashing down, dramatically reducing their visibility. The wind was also now picking up, slamming sticks and leaves into the cars' windscreens.

Realising that conditions had taken a turn for the worse, Sam took his foot off the accelerator and softly applied pressure to the brakes. Visibility was now close to zero. The ferocity of the rain had also left standing water on the smooth surface. He really didn't fancy spinning off the road and careering off the side of the mountain, a fate that had already left fifteen people dead in recent years.

Undeterred by the wind and rain, Daniel kept pushing his car to the max. He was far too busy enjoying himself. But just as he put his foot on the brake, in anticipation of a sharp bend approaching, he saw the central control screen flash in red. *No. Please No.* Desperately slamming his foot onto the pedal, he realised that it was useless, the brakes were gone. The car was going at seventy miles per hour and a corner was approaching, with no barriers to stop it.

Having fallen behind Sam watched on in horror, as through the toing and froing of his windscreen wipers he saw a ball of fire erupt from the back of the Lamborghini. Right about now he should have seen the red brake light come on as the car approached the corner, but instead it just kept on going.

Praying to God, Daniel realised that the brakes had overheated and were now no use to him. There was only one option that could save him from hurtling off the side of the mountain: the hand brake. Grabbing it quickly he jerked it upwards, so hard that his knuckles turned white. It was all or nothing. Frantically turning the steering wheel, he also desperately tried to turn the car so that it would go on its side, which could buy him some vital seconds. He knew there was a real chance he was going to smash into the wall of the mountain, but he had to do everything possible to stop himself going off the edge. If he did, it was certain death.

Watching the car as it screeched on its side, Sam winced as it disappeared from view. 'Jesus Christ!' he cried in horror. 'He's gone off.'

Slamming his foot onto the accelerator, he rushed as quickly as he could to the scene. It was hard to see too much with the rain lashing down, but as he leant forward to look through the windscreen the Lamborghini was nowhere in sight. *What the hell had they been thinking?* Finally reaching the bend in the road, Sam stopped the car and jumped out, oblivious to the ferocity of the wind that almost blew him over. Putting his hand in front of his face to shield himself from the rain and flying debris, he ran towards the bend expecting the worst.

'Daniel!' he shouted trying to be heard above the gale. 'Daniel! You OK?'

No answer.

Fighting his way through the elements, he was in a panic. What would he tell Nicole? Jo-Anne? Hugo? How could Intabill continue without the boy wonder? This was a disaster.

'Daniel! Daniel!'

Again, no answer.

Then, just as he had given Daniel up for dead, he spotted the shape of the black Lambo teetering on the precipice with the shadow of his partner stood outside it.

'Jesus, mate! I thought you had gone off,' Sam shouted, looking at the wheels of the car which were just a few centimetres from the edge of the mountain.

Daniel laughed. 'That was a rush.'

Nervously, Sam looked over the edge into the darkness. 'I thought you were dead,' he said, turning back to face Daniel, who didn't look worried in the slightest.

'You worry too much,' Daniel replied nonchalantly, getting soaked in the driving rain. 'I was always in control.'

Sam shook his head in amazement. The balls on this kid!

'What was it you were going to tell me?' Sam asked after a few moments of quiet contemplation.

'What?'

'Before you set off you said that when we reached the top you had massive news to tell me.'

'Oh yeah,' Daniel replied, as he reached into his sodden jeans pocket to produce a box. 'What do you think?'

Taking the black leather box from Daniel's wet hand, Sam opened it and looked inside. In the darkness he could make out a silver ring with a huge pink diamond encrusted into it.

'I take it you're asking Nicole to marry you and not me,' Sam joked.

'No offence Sammy, but my standards are a little higher than you.'

Laughing as he handed the box back to Daniel, Sam replied, 'Well, either way I was planning to dust the suit down for one event after tonight anyway. I'm just glad it's not your funeral.'

'Yeah well, if I don't get back home soon that may still be on the cards!'

New Year's Eve, Dubai. The big moment was close. As the excited crowd finished dancing to the Latino sound of the Gypsy Kings, who had just finished their outdoor set at the Al Sahra Desert Resort, Nicole and Daniel stood in anticipation of the fireworks display that was about to herald the new year.

Looking every inch the young jetsetters, they happily held hands and gazed up at the clear night sky, which was illuminated by a full moon and a sprinkling of stars. Dressed for the occasion, Nicole was wearing a white halter-neck dress, which showed off her tan, while her hair, which she wore up and parted to the side, fitted in with the Latino theme of the evening. Daniel, on the other hand, had foregone jeans and T-shirt for the night to wear a beige suit, blue shirt and black tie. He looked dapper, but for once he was as nervous as hell. It was almost time.

The countdown was on. The New Year as well as the big question were just moments away. Three, two, one: HAPPY NEW YEAR! At that, the night sky exploded into life as the pyrotechnics began at the stroke of midnight. Greens, yellows and reds crashed into the still air, liberally spraying vibrant colours across the dark canvas, lighting up the sand dunes that surrounded the resort. The crowd cheered in celebration. Daniel felt sick to his stomach. Scrambling nervously around in his suit pocket, he found what he was looking for. Taking a look at Nicole's happy, sun-kissed face, as she looked up at the sky, he knew that this was the moment. Do or die. This was it. Dropping to one knee he tried to be heard above the din.

'Nicole,' he shouted, failing to grab his girlfriend's attention. 'Nicole!' he tried again, still unable to get her to glance away from the mesmerising display.

Conscious that some of his fellow revellers had cottoned on to what he was doing, and that he was drawing a small crowd, Daniel quickly tugged on the bottom of Nicole's dress. Spinning around, Nicole saw her boyfriend knelt at her feet. 'Daniel! What on earth are you doing down there?' she cried.

Opening the small black box in his hand, to reveal the pink diamond ring, he said to her surprise: 'Nicole, I love you very much. Not only are you the girl I have always dreamed of, but you're also a wonderful mother to Hugo. I can't think of anything I would rather do than to spend the rest of my life with you. Would you do me the biggest honour and marry me?'

Putting her hand to her face in shock, Nicole tried to stop the flow of tears. It was a perfect moment. She didn't want to ruin it by making her mascara run. Taking the exquisite ring from the box, she fingered the large pink diamond in awe. As she did so Daniel remained kneeling, waiting for her to answer.

'Well?' he asked, as she took an eternity inspecting the ring.

Nicole looked down at Daniel kneeling on the floor and smiled.

'YES!' she cried, putting the ring on her finger. 'Yes, of course I will.'

Rising to his feet, Daniel embraced his fiancée and tenderly kissed her on the lips. A small round of applause broke out, which saw them pull away from each other and smile with embarrassment. Turning back, they put their arms around each other and watched the fireworks which continued to dramatically illuminate the sky.

'I knew you were up to something,' Nicole said, playfully elbowing Daniel in his ribs.

'What gave me away?'

Squeezing his hand tightly, as she rested her head on his chest, she replied: 'You haven't stopped grinding your teeth all bloody day!'

There had been no question about it, 2007 had been quite the year. It had provided Daniel with a flourishing business, a baby son and now a fiancée. But if 2007 had been a busy one, then the year that followed would be just as dramatic, however this time for very different reasons.

10

The Gold Coast, Australia, April 2008

At $27 million the house was regarded as one of the finest in Australia. Not only that, but it was also a bargain. Situated on four generously sized beachfront lots, on Hedges Avenue, one of Australia's most exclusive addresses, it had unrivalled access to the highly sought-after sands of Mermaid Beach.

While the nearby beach resorts of Miami, Burleigh, Surfers Paradise and Broadbeach throbbed with action, as tourists came to town to surf, drink and misbehave, Mermaid Beach was a tranquil paradise in comparison. The barely disturbed white sands merged with the turquoise ocean, where dolphins could be seen swimming close to shore, and the only noise that could be heard was the lapping of the waves onto the beach. Far from the manic pace of Surfers Paradise, whose gauche high-rise buildings could be seen towering in the distance, Mermaid Beach was a discreet alcove of luxury for Australia's rich and famous.

The pastel-coloured houses that lined the beach represented the very best that Australia had to offer. Every one of them was spacious, modern, unpretentious and, most importantly of all, an escape from the fast-paced world in which their owners invariably worked. It was easy for them to shut themselves off merely by sitting on their verandas overlooking the beach and taking in the spectacular scenery that surrounded them. For this very reason, a Hedges Avenue address was seen by many as the pinnacle.

However, if a resident of Hedges Avenue, inevitably known as Millionaires' Row, wanted to cut loose then they were also spoilt for choice. Just over half a mile away was the Gold Coast Highway, which quickly ferried surfers, backpackers and playboys to the party destinations of Miami, Broadbeach and Surfers Paradise. At these destinations you could find whatever took your fancy: casinos, five-star restaurants, fast food, nightclubs, shopping malls, bars, live music, sport. There was something for everybody.

Daniel had already relocated to the Gold Coast from Brisbane to enjoy the unrivalled options it offered. Every day felt like a holiday. Even though it took him over an hour to drive to work through the rush hour commute in the mornings, it was more than worth it. Besides, if he was in the Lamborghini, he could sometimes cut the travel time down to forty minutes.

His taste for Gold Coast living was by now very well known to all of the high-end estate agents in the area. Apparently, the young tycoon had money to burn and had followed up the purchase of his $2.5 million condo on Hedges Avenue with a $10 million beach-fronted house on Mermaid Beach, as well as spending another small fortune on a rural estate in the wealthy Brisbane suburb of Brookfield. The word was therefore definitely out. If an expensive house was on the market, then agents made sure Daniel was one of the first to hear about it.

It was for this very reason that estate agent Michael Kollosche called Daniel one afternoon. A once-in-a-lifetime deal had come up: Tony Smith, the former AFL star, who had spawned a business empire after his retirement, was in a jam. He was facing a $50 million margin call on shares that had gone bad and urgently needed to raise money. The only way he could do so fast was by selling his pride and joy, the recently purchased 33 Hedges Avenue.

While the house was yet to be finished, with it undergoing extensive construction work, Kollosche told Daniel that the proposed six-bedroom mansion was without a shadow of a doubt going to be the best in all of Australia. With floor-to-ceiling glass windows, fronting onto the beach, the open-plan mansion had plans for a tennis court, basketball court, outdoor Italian mosaic pool, gym, powder room, steam room, massage room, wine cellar and home theatre. In short, it offered everything a young tycoon could want. It would be the ultimate status symbol, and then some.

Better yet, although the house was on the market for $27 million, once the $10 million refurbishment was complete it was estimated it would be worth between $45–60 million. In Kollosche's words, if you had the money available, this deal was an absolute no-brainer, especially as Tony Smith was willing to take Daniel's $10 million Mermaid Beach house off his hands in part-exchange. All Daniel needed to do was to raise $17 million by the end of the day and the house was his. It was as simple as that.

As with all of Daniel's recent property purchases, the bank couldn't approve it quickly enough. He had earned over $20 million the previous year and he was on course to smash that figure in 2008. The kid was one of Australia's up-and-comers and they wanted to make sure they had his business locked in for years to come. However, this was still asking a lot, so while they were happy to loan Daniel $17 million they wouldn't stretch to lending him the funds to finish the refurbishment. Kollosche had told him that the work was going to cost around $300,000 every ten to fourteen days until completion – big money, but nothing that Daniel couldn't handle.

So, with the deal in place, Daniel became the proud owner of one of Australia's most expensive homes. He felt that he had really made it. Having been living with his parents in the working-class district of Camp Hill just five years previously, here he was, the king of Millionaires' Row. Pizza Hut seemed a world away.

The next morning, the story of Daniel's bank-busting purchase hit the news. TV stations and newspapers were all reporting that an unknown twenty-four-year-old had just bought a mega-mansion in Australia. Staggeringly, the Bulgarian media were also reporting the story. In their eyes, Daniel Tzvetkoff was proof that Bulgarian immigrants could come good. To them, he was a real success story, notwithstanding that he had never actually set foot in the country. The only question everyone was asking was: who the hell was this guy?

As soon as Daniel walked into the ground floor office he shared with Sam, he was greeted by his partner angrily holding aloft a copy of the *Brisbane Courier Mail*, which was running the story. 'Have you seen this?' he shouted, not caring that the door was open and that some of the staff could hear.

'Yeah. So what?' Daniel replied, secretly enjoying the attention. He wondered what all of his old teachers and classmates had made of it. Daniel Tzvetkoff, the super-geek who everyone thought was nothing but a daydreamer, had just spent more money than they would make in a lifetime, on one house.

Sam got up from his chair and angrily walked towards his unapologetic partner. 'Have you gone nuts!' he yelled. 'The poker guys specifically told us that if we were going to work with them we had to keep a low profile!'

'Well, don't blame me,' Daniel protested, quickly shutting the glass door behind him. 'All I did was buy a house. I didn't know it was going to make the news.'

'But you didn't just buy any house,' Sam ploughed on, shaking the newspaper in his hand over his head. 'You bought the most expensive damn house on the most exclusive street in all of Australia. What did you think was going to happen?'

As Daniel sheepishly looked at the floor Sam's phone rang. 'Shit!' he exclaimed, looking at the screen, seeing that Isai Scheinberg, the reclusive, billionaire founder of PokerStars, was on the line. 'It's Isai. You'd better hope he hasn't heard of this yet!'

'What the hell is going on with your boy?' the Canadian voice bellowed down the phone as soon as Sam answered, not giving him a second to compose himself.

Sam shot Daniel a look that could kill. Daniel shrugged his shoulders.

'Isai, it's not as bad as it looks,' Sam tried in vain to explain, knowing full well it was just as bad as it looked, if not worse. Now the genie was out of the bottle, everyone was going to want to know how Daniel had made his money. And the poker boys certainly weren't going to be impressed with him spending such extravagant sums.

'Tell your partner if he can't control his spending then I'll pull the plug on the whole operation. I have other processors I use, you know!'

For the next few minutes Sam paced the office, nodding his head and trying to appease the raging Isai. He was pissed. Sam was doing everything within his power to calm the situation. To his amazement, Daniel didn't seem bothered at all. In fact he was breezily flicking through the business pages of the newspapers that were left on his desk every morning without a care in the world. After ten minutes of Sam feeling like a schoolboy being scolded by the principal, the lecture was over. Finally putting down the phone, Sam sighed and sat on the end of his desk, while Daniel looked up from the newspaper, waiting for the inevitable telling off.

'You heard him, Dan. You've got to watch your spending. Otherwise he's going to give all of our business to some of his other guys.'

Daniel smirked. He knew that was never going to happen. 'Sam, he's bluffing. Why do you think he keeps increasing his business with us? We are one of the only processors he's got who can process online poker money on such a big scale and keep chargebacks down. Without Intabill PokerStars is fucked.'

Sam knew that confrontation wasn't going to be the best option. He did, however, have to make his partner see that they were not impregnable.

'I know our fraud system is the best, but he already has other processors working with him who have direct ACH access. Until we get direct access, we are walking a tightrope.'

Leaning towards his computer Daniel switched on the monitor and clicked onto one of his emails. 'I think I may be able to solve that problem,' he announced, beckoning Sam to come over and take a closer look.

'Payday loans?' Sam muttered, as he read the email from Intabill's new US representative, Andrew Thornhill, a bald former stockbroker from Chicago, who had significant experience in the processing world.

'That's right,' Daniel grinned, swivelling his chair around to face Sam. 'This way we can make over one hundred million dollars in three years and have direct access to ACH. What more could you want?'

Sam had to admit the email certainly sold the idea. With access to ACH Intabill would no longer have to split the poker profits with the likes of third-party processors such as Electracash and Teledraft. Indeed, those companies were also technically rivals of Intabill. So far Intabill had managed to keep the source of the money they were passing on to them a secret. However, sooner or later they would find out which online poker companies Intabill was doing business with and could then try and cut out the middleman. That was the nature of the processing world. It was cutthroat.

Sam also realised that this opportunity could give Intabill a more secure grounding in the online poker world. As he had just witnessed, the online poker companies recognised that Intabill had the best fraud control system in the business, but without direct ACH there was still every chance they could walk away at any moment. He knew they had to get ACH as a matter of urgency and this seemed to be the answer to his prayers.

What's more, payday loans were just the type of high reward investment opportunity Intabill had been looking for to invest the poker reserve and 'float'. They currently had tens of millions of dollars sitting in bank accounts around the world. Each account was earning a healthy sum in interest but an investment opportunity such as this could really ramp things up.

On the surface it all sounded great. Perfect, in fact. But as Sam came to the end of the email he still had many questions that needed answering, with the first one being, who on earth was Curtis Pope?

11

Whitsunday Islands, Australia, April 2008

Head tilting skywards, the middle-aged businessman exhaled a large cloud of smoke from the fat Cuban cigar that he had firmly clamped between his lips. Dressed in nothing but loud Hawaiian swimming shorts, he rested his hands on the back of the bubbling jacuzzi, stuck his paunch outwards, then slowly dipped the back of his silver hair into the warm water. Curtis Pope was in his element. As the bubbles relaxed his body, and the sun beat down on his chest, he took in the fantasy scene that surrounded him. Clear blue sky, turquoise water, blazing hot sun, a bucket of ice-cold beers and, best of all, the hot tub he was currently sat in on the back of Daniel and Sam's latest toy, *Maximus*, a luxury 98-foot, $7.5 million yacht.

The partners had taken one look at the extravagant vessel at the Sanctuary Cove Boat Show and had fallen in love. While they had claimed it would be the perfect place to entertain clients, they both knew they would also gain considerable enjoyment from it as well. Boasting two VIP staterooms, each with en-suite bathrooms, two double cabins, self-contained accommodation for four crew, a captain's quarter, a fully functioning kitchen for a chef and an enormous dining and seating area, it was truly the stuff that dreams are made of.

At this moment, *Maximus* was anchored just off the coast of Queensland, in the middle of the multi-coloured natural wonderland of the Great Barrier Reef. Surrounding it was an array of deserted tropical islands, which formed part of the Whitsundays. It was paradise personified, and they had it all to themselves: the ocean, the islands, the boat, the jacuzzi. Daniel Tzvetkoff, Sam Sciacca, Curtis Pope and his two associates, John Scott Clark and Derek LaFavor, were lapping it all up.

It had already been quite a few days. The party had snorkelled through the warm waters of the Reef itself, fished off the back of the boat, explored the white sands of one of the many islands, and had then finally moored at Hamilton Island where they had partied on deck into the early hours. Now, after so much pleasure, it was time for business.

The first half of 2008 had seen Intabill's profits continue to escalate. Cartu Bank had continued to seamlessly process all high-risk credit card transactions, while the poker companies were so impressed by Intabill's processing capability in the US that they had significantly ramped up their volumes. However, Daniel knew that if Intabill could find a way to process ACH directly, as well as find a profitable venture in which to invest the poker money, then things could really explode. When Andrew Thornhill had introduced him to Curtis Pope, who he had met via John Scott Clark, his contact at Utah-based payday loan and payment processing company Impact, he thought all of his Christmases had come at once.

Pope was vice-president of a Las Vegas-based company called Selling Source. As far as Daniel could tell, Selling Source provided payday loan companies with leads and call centre facilities, among other things. In other words, if you had a large chunk of cash, Selling Source had the means to help you loan that money, unsecured, to individuals who would then be charged an eye-wateringly high interest rate. The profit potential was staggering.

And while that was a big draw, Pope also offered something else which was just as tempting: direct access to ACH. Pope and his colleagues already had plenty of banks who were happy to process payday loans via ACH. And Pope had already had preliminary discussions with some of the banks about processing online poker money. They were in. This venture was win-win. It offered Intabill with direct ACH access and the opportunity to make a fortune.

After speaking to Pope on the telephone, it had been arranged that he would travel to Brisbane, along with his boss Derek LaFavor and associate John Scott Clark, so that they could discuss it further. LaFavor had actually been the founder of Selling Source, but he had recently made a killing after selling out to private investment juggernaut London Bay Capital. Despite this, he was still one of the main men at the company and was very keen to get Intabill on board as a new client.

On the other hand, John Scott Clark was already one of Selling Source's biggest clients. His Impact company, based in Utah, was not only a payment processor but had also been in the payday loans business for years. Pope and LaFavor had felt that Scott Clark could not only help sell the huge potential of setting up a payday loans portfolio, but that he could also offer his guidance to Intabill, for a slice of the profits of course.

Now Pope, LaFavor and Scott Clark, along with Daniel and Sam, were all sat in the hot tub, each with a Cuban cigar in their mouths, courtesy of Pope. Contentedly puffing away, Pope hit the group with another tornado presentation. The well-built Las Vegas-based businessman had energy to burn; everything he did seemed to be at a million miles an hour.

'Listen, fellas,' he barked. 'Payday loans is a great fucking opportunity. You've seen the figures and you've heard from John, we can triple your dough in three years. Three fucking years. Ain't that right John?'

Scott Clark, the slow-talking Mormon from Utah, who was in his mid-fifties, but whose portly, balding figure made him look years older, continued: 'That's right, Curtis. With the top-quality leads Selling Source provides, it makes things real easy for you. I can guarantee you won't regret it. Typically, loans will be for between two and five hundred dollars, and the interest rate we can charge varies between three hundred and ninety and seven hundred and eight per cent APR. It's all real sweet.'

Already infected by Curtis's swashbuckling attitude, Daniel looked at LaFavor, the straight-talking CEO of Selling Source, 'This all sounds great. How do you see it working Derek?'

'What I propose to you gentlemen,' LaFavor began, smiling knowingly at Curtis, 'is that you set up a new entity and Curtis here will run it for you from Vegas, with Scott Clark overseeing it all from his base in Utah. We've actually got a spare unit in our building, so you can run it right next to Selling Source itself. We will provide you with leads and Curtis here can help you close them.'

Sam raised his eyebrows. *Curtis run the portfolio?* He couldn't deny that he was a fun guy to be around, but for some reason something just didn't sit right. He couldn't put his finger on it, but he certainly didn't feel comfortable having Curtis handle so much of their money. He had hoped that Intabill would be directly involved with Selling Source, where Derek would run the show. Selling Source was a top-class operation and Derek LaFavor was a man who Sam trusted. But Curtis Pope? Sam wasn't too sure.

'I'll even bring my gang from Selling Source over with me as well,' Curtis chipped in. 'Mike Lane, Gordon Jones, John Andrews, Chad Elie and Dave Majcher. That way, we can hit the ground running.'

'That sounds great,' Daniel smiled at Curtis, his new best friend, as Sam glowered at him. 'So how much would we need to put into a portfolio to make this all work?'

'Daniel, you can put a pot of piss in there if you like buddy and I'll turn it into a pot of gold,' Curtis laughed, leaning forward, sensing that the deal was close. 'But if you put up thirty-two million dollars, then in three years I'll have turned it into a hundred and twenty-three million. If all goes like I expect it to, I'll be making you two million dollars a week in profit, which we split right down the middle. I make coin like nobody's business!'

LaFavor slapped Curtis on the back: 'This guy is a machine. He will kill it for you.'

'I'll fucking demolish it. No question. John knows this business back to front and I know better than anyone how to run a sales team. Selling Source will provide the leads to us and I'll get the staff whipped into a fucking frenzy. By the time I'm through with them, they'll be trying to sell their own mothers.'

'But what happens with the poker money?' Daniel asked.

There was a brief silence before the motormouth from Tampa rode roughshod over any of his colleagues who may have wanted to speak.

'No problem,' he grinned. 'You route all of the poker money to the new entity in Vegas, and the banks we use will be happy to process it. It's a done deal. They all know me. They know I don't fuck about. I do big business. Everyone will be on board, and if they're not I'll flip 'em.'

'Flip 'em?' Sam enquired, unsure of the lingo.

'Yeah. Flip 'em,' Curtis explained, opening his eyes wide. 'I'll pay the bastards off. And if they still don't play ball, then I'll have them whacked.'

There was an awkward silence before Curtis suddenly broke out into a big grin, 'I'm joking. I'm joking,' he said, slapping Sam on the back as everyone laughed. 'You don't have to worry. The banks we use will be happy to process for poker. It's all good.'

While everyone laughed along with Curtis, Sam was still uneasy. He had done his research. There was no doubt that Selling Source was a top-quality company, one of the fastest growing in America in fact. That part of the equation was solid. Indeed, Derek, Curtis and John were all respected high-end corporate guys, apparently stellar businessmen with impressive track records. But in the back of his mind he had just felt that something wasn't right. Daniel had laughed when he had told him of his concerns. He liked Curtis and felt it was a unique opportunity. Now they were being told that they could triple their investment and have direct access to ACH, there was no way Daniel was going to back out.

'All right, guys,' Sam started tentatively, not wanting to rain on the parade. 'That all sounds great, but if we are investing our poker reserves with you then we need to have the ability to withdraw some of that money at any time we like. We can't have it tied up for three years with no access to it.'

For a moment there was silence while everyone considered this conundrum, before Curtis smiled and said: 'Sam, the lawyers can sort all of the technicalities out for us. I just make the dough.'

Looking on, as Curtis high-fived Daniel, Sam then broached another subject that had been bothering him: 'Daniel and I have been advised by our lawyers not to have our names on any official documents in the USA which are in some way linked to online poker.'

Curtis nodded, while blowing smoke out of his mouth, 'Ain't lawyers a pain in the ass?' he joked as he elbowed Daniel in the ribs, knowing full well that Sam was a lawyer himself.

Ignoring Curtis's jibe Sam continued. 'Our lawyers are convinced that processing for online poker is legal but we've been told to be careful. So, if we are going to commit to this one of you guys will have to put your name down for the US entity and we will set up an offshore entity under our name which will effectively control everything. You will be holding all the money on trust for us. That's the way it's got to be if we do this.'

As Sam finished speaking he knew this had the potential to be a deal-breaker. In fact, he almost wanted it to be one. Effectively he had just asked the Vegas boys to carry the risk in the US, if indeed there was any. But amazingly it appeared that Curtis and Scott Clark were quite happy with this arrangement.

'Like I said, I let the lawyers deal with this stuff,' Curtis replied. 'But if you want one of us to front up the operation in the US, then John here is your man. No one knows the payday loan and processing game stateside better than him.'

Scott Clark grinned at his buddy's endorsement. 'It won't be no problem, boys. I'd be happy to put my name down. There ain't nothing here to worry about.'

Daniel looked hopefully at Sam, praying that this would answer his concerns. Sam pursed his lips together and reluctantly nodded. So long as the lawyers agreed to everything on paper, it seemed a go.

'Guys, this all sounds great. I'm going to get a bottle of champagne to celebrate,' Daniel announced, as he hopped out of the tub, and made his way to the nearby bar. Sam quickly followed behind him, hoping to grab a quiet word with his over-eager partner.

As Daniel pulled a cold bottle of Cristal from the fridge, Sam whispered: 'Let's take a moment to think about this before we commit. I'm not feeling too comfortable about the whole thing. I think we need to give it more thought.'

Popping the cork from the bottle Daniel laughed: 'C'mon Sam. We've just been presented with an opportunity to triple our money and have direct ACH access. We can take the money out at any time we want and there is nothing to connect us to poker in the US. What's there to worry about? We're golden.'

'I just don't think we should rush into anything. That's all. I know these guys check out, but I would just like us to take a step back for a bit to think things through.'

This was typical Sam: overly cautious about everything. Sometimes you just have to bite the bullet and dive right in. That was Daniel's line of thinking, anyway.

'Look, the longer we use other processors to get access to ACH, we are missing out on profit,' Daniel said, frustrated with Sam's inability to grasp the moment. 'Plus you heard the projections for the payday loan portfolio, two million dollars a week!'

'I know, mate. I know. But we don't really know these guys. They are going to be on the other side of the world controlling all of our money. How can we trust them?'

'Because I'm moving to Vegas,' Daniel replied, smiling from ear to ear, shocking Sam in the process.

Curtis had already offered to sort him out with a house next to his at the magnificent gated community of Southern Highlands, on the outskirts of the city. He would also help him settle in, take him to shows, restaurants, clubs – anything Daniel wanted. Sure they were there to work, but there was no reason why they couldn't have a little fun at the same time, so long as they remembered Sin City's official motto: *What happens in Vegas stays in Vegas!*

12

Las Vegas, USA, July 2008

When Daniel had moved to Vegas, he had been looking forward to spending his days living it up at the monolithic, debauched resorts that lined The Strip: the Bellagio, the Venetian, Caesars Palace, the Wynn. Sadly, the headquarters of his new payday loan and processing operation, Trendsact, offered none of the glitz he had been eagerly anticipating.

Located just off the south end of The Strip, past the Mandalay Bay Hotel and McCarran Airport, Trendsact shared office space with Selling Source in a light brown, two-storey, nondescript building. The bland architecture of the building fitted in perfectly with the lack-lustre area that surrounded it. While just half a mile away tourists were treated to every temptation known to man, the Trendsact office was virtually located in the obscurity of the desert. The only real highlights in the vicinity were a 24-hour liquor store, a dry cleaners, and a half-empty residential area situated behind the office. In fact, the only sounds that could be heard, other than the drone of traffic from the freeway, was the soaring of low-flying airplanes overhead as they shepherded tourists to and from the nearby airport.

The actual office space was almost a football field in length, and judging by the rowdy noise erupting from inside, any innocent bystander may have surmised that its one hundred or so inhabitants were partaking in the Super Bowl itself. It was clear that in this windowless, rectangular room testosterone and aggression ruled.

'OK. Stop talking for one second!' one high-strung, eye-popping individual screamed down his headset as he paced, his white shirt opened wide to reveal a glimmer of his sweaty chest. 'You called me. Not the other way around. Now you're flat broke. We are doing you a favour. No one else is going to give you an unsecured loan at such a low rate, so you either stop dicking me around and sign the contract I'm going to send you, or your kids don't eat this week. Makes no difference to me.'

This was the reality of the world of payday loans, where the weak and desperate were willing to sell their souls for a sniff of cold, hard cash. Sky-high interest rates of up to seven hundred and eighty per cent a year were currently of no concern to them. Their need was immediate. They had to have the money in their account now. Some needed the cash to feed the kids, pay the bills, whereas others had heard of a hot tip at the track, and having squandered everything they had on other bets, needed cash quickly to take advantage of this 'sure thing'. It was a merry-go-round. Many of these customers would be back on the phone again next month with the same problem, with their repayments continuing to escalate at a frightening pace.

All of this was the end result of the meeting in Australia. The complicated corporate structure which held the whole thing together saw Sam and Daniel hold ultimate beneficial ownership of Angsana, a British Virgin Islands corporation. Angsana in turn funded the Hugo Payday Lending Portfolio, which was incorporated in Nevada and had Curtis's associate, Chad Elie, named as general manager. Hugo then provided the funds to Quasar Corporate Services, which traded by the name Trendsact, who were the end servicing company, of whom John Scott Clark was named as the sole shareholder. It was a complex arrangement, but at least it allowed Sam and Daniel to control all of the money without putting their names on anything official in the US. As far as the US authorities were concerned, John Scott Clark was the man behind Trendsact.

A contract had also now been agreed upon, if not yet signed, following an email by Selling Source's general counsel John Hancock, who, along with Intabill's Michael Hui, was helping to piece everything together. Hancock had settled Sam's nerves when he had confirmed in writing that 'Angsana can exercise and assume complete control of its funds at any time. It was organised in this manner in consideration of the fact that Angsana/Intabill is funding this venture'.

While John Scott Clark was the man named as president of Trendsact, there was absolutely no doubt that Curtis Pope was the man in charge on a day-to-day basis. Standing on a raised platform in front of his army of staff, he surveyed his worker bees, ensuring that everyone was giving it their all. He was their general, they were his soldiers, each of them willing to die for the cause of his payday loan crusade.

Stood to the side, Daniel watched in awe as Curtis aggressively chewed his favourite tobacco before marching towards the rail in front of him. 'You all heard what I said this morning, didn't you?' he yelled at his disciples below him. 'First person to hit their target today gets my Rolex. I'm not fucking about. First person in the building to hit their target today walks out of here with a fifty-thousand-dollar solid gold Rolex. So if you want it, you'd better get a move-on because time's ticking.'

The words sent a renewed jolt of electricity around the room as the staff erupted into a feeding frenzy: voices got louder, movements more exaggerated. The fish on the other end of the line were going to take the loans, whether they liked it or not.

Having moved to Vegas with Nicole and Hugo a few weeks previously, Daniel was now used to the drill. If a person in the USA wanted a loan they could apply for one online, usually via a Selling Source website. Once they had entered in their details, Selling Source would apply a value to it; for instance, someone looking to borrow a large sum of money, who had a good record of making loan repayments, was regarded as a Category A lead. To get hold of this information it would cost a loan provider, like Trendsact, $100 a pop. As soon as Trendsact had purchased that information, it would be filtered through to the sales staff who would waste no time in immediately calling the loan applicant to persuade them to borrow the money.

While the payday loan operation was moving along seamlessly, the poker processing had hit a few snags. Although Trendsact had direct ACH access via certain banks, Daniel soon realised that he would still have to continue to use other processors, who had their own ACH deals with banks in place. This may have seemed strange as these processors were rivals, and Intabill finally had their own ACH pipe, but as always things were complex in the processing game.

The banks would only let processors process a certain volume through their ACH system per day. So although Trendsact was pumping a huge amount of cash through the banks they were working with, there still remained plenty more which couldn't be processed as quickly as they would like due to the volume cap. Until they had more banks willing to process poker money, Trendsact would have to continue to rely on using other processors to get everything through. However, even this wasn't that simple. Finding a processor who was happy to process online poker money through their own network of banks was a tough ask. Everyone was very nervous about handling online poker money, even if some legal experts decreed it safe.

There was also something else to consider. In the past Daniel had learned the hard way that if you put all of a merchant's cash into one pipe, and it got shut down, it would take everything with it. It was therefore vital that they spread the risk around as many pipes as possible. One pipe getting shut down would be a blow but at least it wouldn't be a knockout one.

Despite all of these initial issues Daniel was in the process of putting a genius plan in place. While some banks, and processors, were more than happy to process, knowing full well the money was from online poker, the vast majority didn't want to have anything to do with it. If Trendsact was going to have the ability to process all of their money through ACH then Daniel realised he would have to dress it up a little. As such, Daniel was in the process of creating a network of shell payday loan companies, all with real websites. He would forward the poker money on to the banks, or other processors, under this guise. They would think they were dealing with payday loans, so would be happy to process, while Trendsact could process huge volumes of poker money, spreading the risk through the various shell companies, banks and processors. It was foolproof.

'Come on. Come on,' Curtis urged his staff, as he turned to spit a wad of tobacco in the bin next to him. 'Who wants to get rich today, huh? These people are desperate for money. Fucking give it to them!'

The end of the day was fast approaching. The oval clock on the far wall read 4.45pm. Curtis's incentive would soon expire unless someone hit their target soon. Frantically the staff pounded through their calls, each getting more aggressive, more desperate to do anything that was required to get the contracts signed. Suddenly, a shout erupted from the back of the room as a well-built black employee stood up: 'BOOM y'all! Elvis has left the God-damn building.'

'Yes. Yes. Yes! That's what I'm talking about!' Curtis gesticulated wildly to his champion. 'You're the fucking man, Leon. Come up here and grab your prize.'

Leon had smashed his target. Triumphantly making his way through his co-workers, high fiving and getting pats on the back as he did so, he finally walked up the steps where Curtis was stood.

Taking the gold watch from his wrist, Curtis put it onto Leon's and then held his arm aloft, as if he was a boxing referee declaring a fighter the winner of a world championship bout.

'Take a look people. This is what you get when you deliver. Curtis Pope doesn't fuck about. Deliver for me and I'll make you all fucking millionaires!'

Daniel watched in amazement as the staff whooped and hollered. He had never seen anything like it. It was almost as if they were a religious cult and Curtis was their master. He wasn't so sure if his no-nonsense approach would work at Intabill, but he couldn't deny that in the world of payday loans he was a maestro.

Not only was Curtis proving to be as good as his word on the business side of things, he had also helped Daniel to settle in. Having arranged for Daniel to move in to the house next door to him at Southern Highlands, Curtis had also helped him to become a member of the $90,000-a-year golf club that their two homes backed on to. He had also taken him out to the best restaurants and clubs Vegas had to offer: Joel Robuchon's, Picasso's, Carnevino, PURE, The Bank and Tryst.

His beautiful blonde wife, Christina, who looked like a former beauty queen, had also been great to Nicole. The two girls spent their days shopping at the Bellagio, Caesars Palace or the Fashion Show Mall, or they would sit at one of their swimming pools watching the kids. Nicole had initially been reluctant to relocate to Vegas, especially with Hugo just turning one, but so far she had thoroughly enjoyed the experience. It certainly helped that Daniel had bought her a run around, a white Bentley, so she could get about the vast sprawl.

Later that night, Curtis and Christina continued with their hospitality when they took Daniel and Nicole to dinner at their favourite restaurant, Wolfgang Puck's high-class Beverly Hills steakhouse, Cut. Located at the Palazzo, the Italian renaissance-themed shopping area of the Venetian Hotel, the restaurant was regarded as one of the finest in Las Vegas. In fact, customers usually had to book weeks in advance to get a table, unless of course you were Curtis Pope.

Upon arrival the party had been disappointed to learn that the restaurant was fully booked. After summoning the manager, Curtis had managed to 'flip' him by passing him a couple of hundred bucks to ensure they got the best seat in the house. Soon they were sat at the corner table, which surveyed the whole restaurant, with Curtis holding court.

'I'm telling ya,' Curtis laughed as he finished another one of his stories, 'I was literally living in the mountains of Wales with the sheep. Me!'

Christina gazed at her husband adoringly as he spoke. 'You're a city boy, aren't yah hun?' she said.

Just at that moment a waiter arrived at the table with a trolley containing sumptuous slabs of raw meat.

'Damn that looks good', Curtis said hungrily. 'How much is the Wagyu?'

'$145 dollars a cut, Sir,' the waiter answered.

'Yeah, give us four of those bad boys. Make 'em nice and juicy. All of them rare. I like the blood.'

'Hun, Daniel and Nicole may not want theirs rare', Christina interrupted.

'Actually', Nicole said, managing to get a word in edgeways for the first time that night, 'I'd prefer mine medium'.

'Very good, Madam. And you, Sir?' the waiter said, looking at Daniel who was happily drinking another glass of wine.

'I'm happy with the blood,' Daniel answered. 'And what is this wine?'

'That's the Elderton Riviera, Sir.'

'Bring us two more bottles of that.'

At this Curtis laughed as if he had just heard the funniest joke in the world. Grabbing Daniel playfully around the shoulder he looked at Christina and said, 'Waddid I tell ya? This is the kid!'

Suddenly Nicole stood up. 'Where are you going?' Daniel asked. 'Bathroom,' she sullenly replied. 'I'll go with you,' Christina said, getting up from the table, which saw Curtis also rise to attention before sitting back down.

While any night with Curtis was full of fun and energy, Daniel was surprised at just how much he toned his demeanour down in front of his wife. Sure, he still spoke and acted like a kid in a candy store, but he refrained from using profanities in front of her and he always stood up for the girls whenever they got up. He was quite the gentleman, in certain circumstances. There was obviously more to him than met the eye.

Having got through the best part of three bottles of wine between them, Curtis and Daniel were now feeling a little worse for wear. With his eyes glazed over, Curtis pushed his way round to Daniel's side of the booth. Leaning back, he put his arm around him, 'Told ya Vegas was where it's at, huh?'

'It's going great, Curtis,' Daniel replied, reaching for his glass. 'Really great. Thanks for looking after me and my family so well.'

'Family...,' Curtis muttered softly under his breath, his demeanour instantly switching from excitement to sadness. 'Ain't nothing more important than that ... Do you know I never had a father?'

'What? Never?' Daniel replied, struggling to maintain an image of sobriety.

'No. No, I had one. He was in the air force. I was actually born at Scott Air Force Base in St Claire County, Illinois. Imagine me, a military man!'

Daniel laughed, while Curtis continued.

'But the bastard walked out on us when I was four. Yup. Never saw him again.'

Daniel felt a pang of sympathy for him. He had always counted his blessings that he had enjoyed a strong relationship with his father.

'My mom tried her best,' Curtis continued, looking into the distance misty-eyed as he reminisced. 'Worked as a book-keeper for years to help raise me and my kid brother, but it wasn't no good. You see, she had different men coming into our house all the time. Boys can't live like that. So I moved out when I was just fourteen years old. I left with nothing.'

'So what did you do?' Daniel asked, interested to hear his new partner divulge some of his past for the first time.

'Hustle,' Curtis recalled, without giving too much away. 'I had to fight my way out of the projects and make things happen. Sometimes I got up to no good. Y'know what I mean? I had to make money any way that I could. I was flat-ass broke. It was survival of the fittest, and I had no education. I left school at sixteen and basically moved all over trying to make a go of it: Dallas, Baltimore, Florida, and like I said before, I even moved to Wales in the UK for a time. Sometimes it was pretty rough, but you know what?'

'What?'

'It all made me the man I am today.'

Nodding, unsure of what to say, Daniel waited for Curtis to carry on.

'And you know, now it's not just me I got to look out for,' he said proudly. 'I got a family: Christina, step-kids, grandchildren. If I don't earn, then we all burn.'

'I don't think there's any chance of burning just yet,' Daniel grinned. 'We made half a million dollars this week. You got the family and the dough. You're made.'

Curtis smiled and nodded. 'Sure. But you know what I don't have no more?'

Shaking his head, Daniel spotted the two women walking back from the bathroom, which saw Curtis quickly try to wrap up what he was saying: 'I don't have a brother. My own, Barry, died a few years back. God rest his soul.'

Grabbing Daniel's hand, Curtis suddenly looked him dead in the eye, 'It's me and you out here pal. Vegas don't take no prisoners. We gotta have each other's backs. Just like brothers. You hear me?'

'You can count on me, Curtis,' Daniel promised, staring intently right back at him, moved by his partner's speech. And he truly meant it. He knew that if they continued as they had started, and backed each other up, then absolutely anything was possible.

As the two women sat down Christina looked at Curtis, who had tears in his eyes. 'Is everything OK, honey?' she asked.

'Perfect sweetheart,' Curtis answered. 'Just perfect.'

13

Las Vegas, USA, July 2008

'Listen lady, I will fucking kill you or any other bastard who's keeping our money. You got that!' Curtis Pope bellowed, as he marched angrily around his office, speaking through his headset, while chewing tobacco. He couldn't believe it. They had just lost $3 million. Out of nowhere, E-Z Bill, a processor Trendsact had been using, had just frozen their account.

'Mr Pope,' the risk manager from E-Z Bill shot back in a harsh Texan accent. 'Please do not threaten me or my company. There are irregularities with the account and therefore all funds are frozen until they are fully investigated.'

Scratching his head in frustration, Curtis looked out of his window, which had a view of the desert stretching towards the dark brown mountains in the distance, while shouting, 'What do you mean "irregularities"? I told you, this is all to do with payday loans. What's your problem?'

'That may very well be, Mr Pope, but we have reason to believe that some, if not all, of the money is not connected with pay-day loans.'

At this statement Curtis stopped briefly. Were they on to them?

Did they suspect the money was to do with poker? No, surely not. That was impossible.

'What are you trying to say?' he finally countered, deciding aggression was the best way to fight back. 'You think this is gambling money or something. Huh? Is that what you think?'

There was silence on the end of the line. The risk manager took a moment to choose her words carefully before saying: 'I am not permitted to discuss this with you any longer, Mr Pope. The account is frozen for a maximum of two years. If we decide within that timeframe that the irregularities can be explained legally, then we will of course transfer the funds back to you. If not, then they will be seized. Good day.'

Gritting his teeth together, as his face turned an alarming shade of violet, Curtis exploded: 'Unfreeze that fucking account or I'll be coming down to Dallas with a posse and you'll rue the fucking day you fucked with Curtis Pope! Do you hear me!?'

But it was too late. The line was dead.

Smashing his fist against his mahogany desk, Curtis snarled in frustration. 'Goddamn it!' He couldn't believe that just like that he had lost $3 million. Trying to compose himself, he pressed a button on his headset, which connected him with Daniel, who was based down the hall with his Intabill gang, Michael Hui and Andrew Thornhill.

'Daniel,' Curtis growled gloomily once his partner had picked up. 'Just got off the phone with E-Z Bill. It's bad buddy. They've frozen the money. All three million bucks of it.'

Daniel's heart sank: 'Did they say why they froze the account? Did they mention poker?'

'No,' Curtis replied. 'They're dickless. They don't have a clue. There is no way they can find out. It's foolproof.'

On paper it certainly should have been. They had processed the money with E-Z Bill under one of the shell payday loan companies that Daniel had set up. So far no other bank or processor had raised any questions about the system they had used. However, E-Z Bill was a different animal altogether. In the past they had processed a lot of payday loans and poker money, so they knew the average pattern of both industries. True repayments of payday loans were typically for smaller-dollar amounts and took place at regular periodic intervals. The repayments Trendsact were putting through were for wildly different amounts and were usually made several days in a row, the typical pattern of an online poker player.

Suspicious of such irregular patterns, the risk manager had decided to investigate further. Looking up the supposed payday loan website, she had noticed that it was not actually fully operational. Upon asking Curtis to provide 'proof of authorisation', i.e. some sort of concrete evidence that the customer had authorised the payday loan company to make the debit from their account, they had swiftly been stonewalled.

What had then confirmed E-Z Bill's suspicions was that, as they had previously processed large sums for the online poker companies themselves, they still held a customer database that listed hundreds of thousands of US-based online poker players. Cross-checking that list with the customer names provided by Trendsact, they quickly found a significant correlation. A huge percentage of these supposed payday loan customers had in the past been regular online poker players. Coincidence? Maybe. But it certainly warranted a full investigation.

If it had just been E-Z Bill investigating Trendsact, with the end result being the seizure of the funds, then that would have been manageable. But this was far worse. What Trendsact couldn't have known was that E-Z Bill had been busted for processing online poker themselves. To avoid further punishment, they had signed up to a cooperation agreement with the FBI. As soon as they had suspected Trendsact to be involved with poker, they had immediately informed Special Agent Rebecca Vassilakos. As a result of this, Agent

Vassilakos had been listening in on the risk manager's conversations with Curtis Pope for several weeks.

Confident that Pope was involved with online poker, Agent Vassilakos had stepped up her investigation by paying one of the supposed payday loan customers a visit. Unsurprisingly, when questioned, the customer had no idea about any payday loan. In fact, they quite openly told Agent Vassilakos that, as far as they were concerned, the money was connected to their online poker account. This was the smoking gun she had been looking for.

Subsequent follow-up calls to the other payday loan 'customers' also revealed the same thing. The supposed payday loan customers were all online poker players. Further investigation of the shell payday loan company, and Curtis Pope, led her to Trendsact. It was now clear that Trendsact was the new big dick of the online poker-processing world. And the FBI now had it within their sights, but as far as they were concerned, John Scott Clark and Curtis Pope were the guys behind the whole operation. So far they had not heard of Daniel Tzvetkoff or Intabill. All Daniel had to do was to lie low and he would be out of the firing line, but it seemed that lying low was the last thing on his mind . . .

14

London, UK, August 2008

Buying banks had been Daniel's idea. First they'd do it in Europe, to deal with credit card purchases, and then in the US, to get unrestricted ACH access for online poker. This would not only allow the company to keep far more of the profits, as they would stop using third-party processors, but there would also be no more shell companies, no more fake descriptors, no more risk – they could process whatever they liked.

The first port of call for such a deal had been the City of London. It had been arranged for Daniel and Sam to meet with several brokerage firms who had prospectuses on banks in Europe that were available for purchase. Having spent a few days looking at various institutions, Daniel finally spotted one that he liked. HKB Bank in Germany was a small, conventional, deposit and loan business that was set to make a small loss of 100,000 euros for the year. The purchase price was in the region of a million euros – chump change compared to the potential profits.

Daniel had big plans for the bank. Not only did he intend to process high-risk credit card transactions through it, but he also wanted to roll out credit and debit cards for customers, as well as expand into 'card not present channels', i.e. accepting payments from websites and call centres. All being well, he was hopeful that he would eventually be able to expand the bank throughout Europe. It was a real cash cow.

By the time Sam and Daniel made their way back to their suites at the Ritz Hotel in the heart of London, the due diligence on HKB was already underway. If everything went according to plan, and the takeover was approved by the regulators, then Daniel was told he could expect to be the owner of the bank within nine to twelve months. This would then mark the next phase of Intabill's worldwide expansion.

Having been driven through Piccadilly Circus rush-hour traffic by their private chauffeur, Winston, who was provided by the Ritz, along with the use of a Rolls Royce Phantom for the duration of their stay, Sam and Daniel wearily retired to their luxurious suites on the top floor. It was time to get some sleep before Daniel went back to Vegas in the morning and Sam returned to Brisbane.

As usual, Daniel wasn't doing things by halves. He was staying in the Prince of Wales Suite, a traditionally decorated, apartment-style penthouse, which within its 2,000 square feet of floor space included its own hallway, two king-sized bedrooms, a dining room, a drawing room, a butler's kitchen and two marble bathrooms. What particularly pleased Daniel was that each of the two bathrooms boasted plasma televisions. It was truly a room fit for royalty – or Daniel Tzvetkoff.

With a long, hard day behind him, Daniel had been particularly looking forward to ordering room service and watching some TV while he soaked in the bath. Undoing his tie, and throwing his Armani black suit jacket on his four-poster bed, he walked on the plush carpet towards the bathroom to run the water. Yet, just as he turned on the gold taps, and cracked open a beer, he heard his mobile phone ring from his jacket pocket. Walking briskly back to the bedroom, he picked up his phone and saw that the call was coming from Intabill's legal counsel, Michael Hui, who had been sent to Tbilisi to sort out a small issue with Cartu Bank.

'All right Michael,' Daniel answered, as he belly-flopped onto the huge bed. 'How we looking, mate?'

'Not so good, Dan,' Michael shot back in a panicked tone. 'They've shut us down.'

'What!?' Daniel shouted, his head spinning at the thought of such a disaster. 'Why?'

'Some other processor Cartu have been using has been busted by Interpol for processing illegal pharmaceuticals. Visa and MasterCard have frozen everything in their accounts.'

Everything. At Daniel's last count there was at least $10 million in Cartu. Losing that much money would be a significant blow. Back on his feet, Daniel realised that he just couldn't let this go. 'Stay where you are Michael,' he ordered. 'I'm scrambling the private jet and we will be with you as soon as we can.'

'I wouldn't do that if I were you, Dan,' Michael warned. 'Word over here is Russia is gearing up to invade Georgia. Everyone is bricking themselves. In a few hours this place could be a war zone.'

Taking this warning on board, Daniel was still determined to go to Tbilisi. He couldn't face losing so much money first to E-Z Bill then to Cartu all in the space of a month. 'War zone or no war zone,' Daniel huffed as he paced the suite, 'we are not leaving Georgia until we have our money.'

15

Tbilisi, Georgia, August 2008

It was barely 5 in the morning when the Intabill private jet touched down. Tbilisi Airport was shut. But, as with all the other luxuries that a private Gulfstream jet (costing a total of $1.8 million a year in rent, as well as extras such as fuel and staff) provided, special privileges was one of them. Customs staff were dragged wearily from their beds and the airport lights were switched on. It wasn't very often that the run-down Tbilisi Airport had a private jet on its tarmac, and therefore a special effort was made to accommodate it and its passengers.

Rumours of a Russian attack were now gathering pace in the news. Just a few days earlier, Georgia had started a military campaign to re-claim South Ossetia from Russia, an area that had been heavily fought over since the 1991 South Ossetia War. The Russians had reacted to Georgia's attack by deploying the army and air force to hit back. As South Ossetia was just 55 miles from Tbilisi, there was a real chance that the fighting would soon spill over into Georgia's capital city. It appeared that the Russians certainly weren't counting anything out.

Due to this unrest, it had been decided that the pilot, Neil, would stay with Daniel and Sam at their hotel, so that they could leave at a moment's notice, although there would be no Ritz-style luxury suites on this occasion. The only half-decent hotel in Tbilisi was the Marriott and that was fully booked. At last-minute notice, Michael had only been able to book them into a small bed and breakfast, and they would all have to share rooms. Daniel dreaded to think what a bed and breakfast looked like in Tbilisi; a city that Michael had told him was at least twenty years behind the western world.

Greeted at the airport by Michael, and Andrew Thornhill, who had flown in especially from Vegas as he could speak fluent Russian, the party made their way, via taxi, into the centre of Tbilisi. Since the breakup of the Soviet Union, the capital of Georgia had suffered from frequent bouts of instability and turmoil. Crime and corruption had become rampant at most levels of society, with many mafia clans violently guarding their patches. With mass unemployment and a crumbling economy, the average citizen of Tbilisi was impoverished. And as Daniel looked out of the taxi window, he could spot signs of poverty everywhere.

Travelling on the motorway alongside them were numerous horse and carts, which caused havoc as the cars swerved to avoid them. It was clear that normal traffic rules didn't apply here, something which saw an uneasy Sam grip his battered leather seat in terror. The people they saw walking on the hard shoulder were mostly dressed in rags. Many didn't even have proper shoes, their feet were either bound in cloth or they had strips of tyre wrapped around them.

As they entered the medieval city, driving along the banks of the murky Mt'k'vari River, in the shadow of the Saguramo mountains, Daniel was surprised to see that many of the buildings looked Arabic in nature. Situated just 700 miles from Tehran, the capital of Iran, it was clear that this proximity had not only rubbed off on the local buildings but also on the people, who looked more of middle-eastern descent than Eastern European. Notwithstanding this, there were still significant signs of the country's more recent communist past. Huge, grey, concrete, featureless, Stalinesque blocks peppered the landscape, as did several ill-placed, half-finished buildings, the result of the government's failure to curb unsanctioned building projects since the end of communism.

The mood in the car was downcast as they drove through the depressing streets. They weren't due to meet the officials of Cartu until later that morning, so as the sun slowly began to rise over the mountains that surrounded the city, Daniel thought it would be best for them to all grab some breakfast and map out a plan of action.

'Where's good to go around here for breakfast, Michael?' he asked the slight, boyishly handsome legal counsel who was sat in the front seat.

'McDonald's,' Michael laughed. Sadly the rest of the group didn't find the suggestion quite so funny.

Yet when the driver pulled up at the nearest McDonald's, everyone was pleasantly surprised. Far from the cookie cutter design that was seen throughout the world, this McDonald's looked from the outside to be something else altogether. Situated in a huge stone building, which had a balcony surrounding a large dark grey dome on top, with a glass frontage stretching all the way from the floor to the top of its six storeys, it looked like a monument to American fast food. If ever there was a five-star fast food establishment then this was it.

Once they had all hungrily marched through the entrance, the familiar waft of American fast food hit their nostrils. However, despite its grand façade, they could quite have easily been in any other McDonald's on earth so familiar were the surroundings. Even though the menu was written in indecipherable Georgian, Andrew Thornhill told them that it was pretty standard. Speaking in fluent Russian, Thornhill proceeded to order an arsenal of McMuffins, hashbrowns and pancakes to feed the troops. Michael was, however, the only one with any local currency on him, so he was left to pick up the bill.

Devouring their breakfast, the Intabill gang sat quietly as Daniel outlined how the meeting would play out.

'At the end of the day, Visa have shut down the pipe, not Cartu, so they are going to claim it's nothing to do with them,' he said, between bites of his sausage McMuffin. 'But we've put a shitload of business their way and in my eyes they owe us. They've made huge profits off the back of us.'

'That's right,' Sam chipped in. 'When we've had money frozen by banks or processors before, we've agreed to pay back those customers who we have made a lot of money from. It's just good business sense. So what we do for our big customers, then they should do for us.'

Slurping his coke, Daniel continued from where he had left off: 'We all know how these things work. In the past we've had Visa pull the plug on banks in St Kitts and the Philippines. Within a few months, they get back on their feet and everything is back to normal. We need to make it clear to Cartu that if they don't reimburse us the ten million now, then that's the last they will see of us. This isn't the type of money we can just write off. It's meant to be passed on to some of our biggest pharmaceutical and travel clients. We've promised them Cartu is secure and they are depending on it. If they lose a load now, there is no telling what they will do.'

So that was the plan. In fact it was the only plan. The odds were certainly against them but they had to try everything they could to get the money back, and fast, before the Russians unleashed hell. Once they had filled up at McDonald's, the party was soon in transit to Chavchavadze Avenue, where the headquarters of Cartu was based. The building looked just like any other on the street when they arrived, a nondescript, grey stone, five-storey building with the only distinguishing feature being the blue Cartu sign emblazoned across the front.

Waiting in the drab lobby for them was the manager, Nona, a smiling, red-haired, olive-skinned lady in her early forties, who was wearing a plaid navy blue skirt coupled with a white blouse. Alongside her was the assistant manager, Vladimir, who with his black suit and military haircut looked like a KGB agent. If ever a duo were bad cop and good cop, it was these two.

With pleasantries out of the way, Nona shepherded them all into the boardroom on the ground floor, which consisted simply of a wooden table and plastic chairs. Having been poured a cup of stale coffee, the negotiations began, with Sam putting forward a formidable case for why Cartu should reimburse Intabill. Outlining the huge profits Intabill was currently making, and the exciting new plans for expansion, he hammered home just how foolish it would be for Cartu to upset one of their biggest customers.

'I am sorry but there is really nothing we can do,' Nona said after listening to Sam's pitch. 'Visa has shut down the accounts. Not us.'

This comment enraged Daniel. 'Do you realise how much money your bank has made off Intabill?' he began. 'I don't give a shit if Visa has shut the accounts down. You've made more than enough in profits to reimburse us.'

'Again, I am sorry, but there is nothing I can do.'

'That's bullshit Nona,' Daniel snapped back. 'If you don't repay us our ten million in full today then we're through with you.'

'You've got to think of the long term here Nona,' Sam added.

Suddenly Vladimir, who had been quiet up until now, spoke: 'Does it look like we give a fuck?'

Everyone turned to look at the hulking assistant, shocked at his outburst.

'What did you say?' Daniel asked.

'We ... Don't ... Give ... A ... Fuck.'

For a moment Daniel and Vladimir eyeballed each other before Nona stepped in to try and calm things down.

'Please' she said, 'there is another issue here. Our bank is affiliated with the Georgian politician Barzan Ivanishvili. He has made it very clear to us that we cannot continue to process for high-risk processors, and must make every effort to sever our ties with them. With elections on the horizon, it could be very embarrassing if anything unsavoury was to emerge.'

'He's embarrassed!' Daniel said mockingly. 'He wasn't too embarrassed to take our money was he?'

Sam realised that not only were things in danger of getting out of hand but they were also losing the initiative. He had to act fast. 'I understand, Nona,' he said, playing their last roll of the dice. 'But we don't deal with any illegal products. We make sure of that. Is there any way you could set up a meeting for us with Mr Ivanishvili so we can explain?'

'There will be no such meeting,' Vladimir barked, with his square jaw jutting hostilely forward.

'I'm getting tired of listening to this dick,' Daniel said irritably, a comment which saw Vladimir cast aside his chair, stand up and march menacingly towards him. Daniel also stood up. He was in no mood to be messed around. Yet just as Daniel geared himself up to launch into Vladimir, a loud rumbling, almost like a crash of thunder, shook the room. 'What the hell was that?' Andrew exclaimed, as everyone jumped up to look out of the window.

In the distance they could see a plume of smoke rise into the sky. A fighter jet suddenly pierced through the air. It was the Russians. They were coming. As everyone else peered out of the window in shock, Sam quickly started to gather his belongings. They didn't have a second to lose. 'Don't just stand there!' he shouted, haphazardly pushing papers into his black leather briefcase. 'We need to get out of here!'

Breaking out of their daze, Daniel, Michael and Andrew hurriedly snatched their suit jackets off the back of their chairs and were soon running towards the entrance with Sam. Peering up into the now clear blue sky, they could see other Russian fighter jets on the horizon. This was really happening. A full-blown war looked set to breakout. And they were slap bang in the middle of it. Thankfully, their Georgian driver was still faithfully waiting for them in the battered Lada. Jumping in, Andrew Thornhill shouted to him in Russian: 'The airport! The airport!'

Weaving their way through the manic traffic, as people desperately tried to get to shelter, the Intabill gang were thrown around the car. 'Doesn't this thing have seatbelts?' Michael shouted, which saw Andrew pull his one up. It was torn. They all were.

As they navigated their way through the madness of Tbilisi, Sam called the pilot, who had already checked into the bed and breakfast with their bags. 'Neil, it's Sam. We need you to get to the airport with our bags. We are getting out of here. Pronto!'

Neil was on his way. But as they raced along the motorway, hopefully towards the safety of the airport, another black cloud of smoke rose in the distance. Another bomb. *Shit.* Things were really starting to heat up.

'Here, mate. You can't go any faster can you?' Daniel asked the young driver, who was clearly terrified himself.

Looking wide-eyed at Daniel, he turned and pointed at the speedometer. They were going at seventy miles per hour. It was almost off the gauge and the car was rattling as if it could fall apart at any moment. What he wouldn't give for his 196 miles per hour Lambo right now, Daniel thought.

Pinned back to their seats in terror, the young driver took his terrified passengers on a short cut across the muddy hard shoulder, owing to the horse and carts blocking their path on the motorway. Bouncing around in their seats they travelled in silence, each praying that they could get out of this Godforsaken place before things got any worse.

Bouncing and weaving their way over potholes and rubbish, the car managed to keep itself intact and finally pulled up at the airport, battered, but still in one piece. Thrusting a wad of British notes into the driver's hand, the only currency Daniel was currently holding on him, he threw open the car door and sprinted towards the entrance, with Sam, Michael and Andrew urgently following him.

Once they were inside the terminal, there was a mad frenzy. Travellers dashed about, each frantically trying to escape. Incomprehensible announcements were being relayed over the tannoy. Staff struggled in vain to keep up with developments. The place was sheer bedlam. Casting his eyes desperately at the overhead monitors, Daniel saw red Russian writing next to all of the flights.

'What does that mean?' he asked, turning to Andrew.

'All the flights are cancelled!' he replied.

'Yeah commercial flights', Daniel said desperately. 'But we're on a private jet. We might be ok.'

Just at that moment, Neil the pilot ran towards them, pulling a trolley with all of their bags on it. 'Sorry guys,' he panted, struggling to catch his breath. 'Just spoken to the officials. No planes are getting out of here. They've gone into lockdown.'

This was not news anyone wanted to hear. They were stuck.

'Well, what are we going to do?' Sam said, not wanting to spend another moment in this hell hole.

'We have three options,' Neil outlined, trying his best to maintain a professional, calm, considered approach. 'One, we stay here and wait it out. Two, we go back to our hotel in Tbilisi . . .'

'So what's the third option?' Michael asked, echoing the thoughts of the group, all of whom didn't want to spend another second in Tbilisi.

'We get down to the hangar and just get the hell out of here.'

Sam looked puzzled. 'I thought you said all planes were grounded.'

'They are, but in these type of places money talks.'

The group looked at each other. *Fuck it* seemed to be the general consensus. Do whatever needs to be done to get us out of here.

'Does anyone have any money?' Neil asked.

Digging deep into his luggage Daniel pulled out several thousand American dollars, gold dust in a place like Tbilisi. 'Will this do?' he replied, as Neil quickly snatched it away. 'Perfect.'

With time of the essence, Neil marched across to a customs official and pulled him aside.

'I don't like this one bit,' Sam said.

'Yeah, but I also don't like the idea of being stuck in a bloody war zone,' Daniel replied.

After a few moments of animated chat, Neil gestured over for everyone to follow him. 'Quickly! Quickly!' he shouted. It seemed he had struck some sort of deal. Frantically picking up their luggage, the group ran towards him. There wasn't a second to lose.

Following the official, everyone raced towards the private hangar where the jet was stored. Scampering up the stairs to reach the entrance, they all piled into their cream leather seats and fastened their seat belts while Neil dived into the cockpit.

'Buckle up guys,' he announced over the intercom. 'This could get bumpy.'

Within seconds, the plane was reversing out of the hangar, and making its way onto the runway. No one spoke. No one was willing to curse this giant slice of luck. If they could get out of here in one piece then they would all be eternally grateful. Nervously gripping the leather armrest of his chair, Sam closed his eyes as the plane zipped across the tarmac. *Please God get us out of here*, he silently prayed.

'Guys,' Michael nervously said, looking out of the window, where he could see more plumes of black smoke rising in the distance. 'I don't know if this is such a good idea.'

'Why?' Daniel asked.

'Because those fucking fighter jets are still in the sky! What if they shoot us down?'

No one had thought of this. As they all looked out of the window they saw exactly what Michael did, a handful of jets circling Tbilisi, dropping bombs at will. Anything and everything seemed fair game. Perhaps even their jet.

But as they feared the worse there was a loud thrust of the engine, as the plane suddenly left the ground. It was too late. They were airborne.

'Nothing we can do about it now,' Daniel shouted, as they soared into the clouds.

Sam sat perfectly still with his eyes closed, barely breathing through fear. Michael curled himself up into a crash position while Daniel and Andrew continued to scan the skies for trouble. But there was none. It appeared as though they had managed to escape in one piece.

As the plane continued to hurtle out of Tbilisi Neil broke the tension with an announcement, 'We are out of Georgian air space boys.' A sigh of relief reverberated around the cabin. They had made it. Shortly before they had feared being shot down in the sky or having to spend the night in a war zone, with no guarantee of when they would be able to leave. Now, they were jetting back to civilisation. London first, so that Sam and Michael could catch a connecting flight back to Brisbane, and then onto Vegas for Daniel and Andrew.

'Jesus that was close!' Andrew shouted to the relieved cabin, as the plane continued to speed its way out of hell. Everyone was shattered. The events of the last twenty-four hours had pushed everyone to their limits.

As Michael and Andrew sat in silence, still rocked by the events of the day, Sam knocked back a large whisky to steady his nerves.

'Hey Sammy,' Daniel said. 'It's ok. You can stop bricking it now.'

Everyone laughed. 'Jesus that was intense,' Sam smiled.

'I told you not to come out here,' Michael said. 'Even for ten million dollars.'

Daniel's face suddenly dropped. He had forgotten about the money. 'Fuck!'

'Forget about it now Dan,' Sam said, just relieved to be out of Tbilisi. 'It's gone.'

'That's easy to say Sam but how the hell are we going to cover a loss like that?'

'We'll just have to replace it with some of our profits. It's not ideal but we are well covered.'

This was not what Daniel wanted to hear. He had big plans for that money. This escapade was going to cost him dear. 'I need a drink,' he finally said, reaching over for a miniature bottle of vodka. At least he could console himself with the profits Trendsact was making. Thank God for payday loans, because right now, without that money, Intabill would be in serious shit. They could just about take a hit like this, but any more and things could get out of hand.

16

Las Vegas, USA, September 2008

For once in his life Curtis Pope was lost for words.

'Are you just going to look at it all day or are you going to take it for a ride?' Daniel asked, as he opened the door to the gleaming, $250,000, red Ferrari which was parked in the Trendsact parking lot.

'You bought this for me?' Curtis replied, still in shock.

'Yeah. It's all yours.'

Fighting back his tears, a clearly emotional Curtis somehow managed to utter, 'Why?'

'It's a thank you gift,' Daniel smiled, tossing Curtis the keys. 'You've been as good as your word. We are making a lot of money together and you've been a good friend.'

And it was true. Despite the occupational hazard of losing money to processors and banks the Trendsact/Intabill partnership was still highly profitable. All in all, Daniel was now making around $3 million profit a week. Things were ticking along very nicely.

Sitting in the black leather seat, Curtis turned the key in the engine and smiled as he heard it roar for the first time. Putting on his sunglasses, he revved it up so everyone in the office could hear it. He wanted them all to see him in his very own Ferrari. As staff from

Selling Source and Trendsact looked out of their windows to see where the noise was coming from, Curtis placed his foot on the accelerator. But, just before he shot off, he pulled down his sunglasses and said to Daniel: 'Haven't you got your boys in town tonight?'

'Yeah, why?'

'I'm going to make sure you guys have the best fucking night of your lives!'

And with that the Ferrari, driven by the happiest man in Las Vegas, kicked dust behind it as it screeched out of the parking lot and made its way towards The Strip.

Hours later, Curtis proved as good as his word. With Ryan Lang, Michael Hui and Sam's younger cousin Joe Mannino, (who was 'researching' Vegas nightlife for Daniel and Sam's latest venture, a nightclub in Brisbane, which he was going to run on their behalf) in town, Curtis had laid on a convertible Rolls Royce for the night. Not only that but his office assistant, twenty-one-year-old David Majcher, was also on hand to drive the boys wherever they fancied. VIP tables had also been arranged at one of the finest nightclubs in Las Vegas, The Bank, at the Bellagio Hotel.

The boys sat in the Roller's back seats, with the roof down, as they cruised along The Strip. Chatting excitedly while downing shots, they passed the black pyramid of the Luxor Hotel on their left, which was shining a light from its tip all the way into the night sky, while on their right they soon saw the glowing green neon lights of the enormous MGM Hotel, which was situated on the corner of Las Vegas Boulevard and East Tropicana Avenue. No matter how many times Daniel went out in Vegas, he could never get over the sheer size and garishness of it all. From the desert, The Strip looked insignificant but when you were among it all, the scale was truly astonishing.

Continuing north they passed the New York, New York Hotel, which was shaped to look like Manhattan's skyline and had a roller-coaster wrapped around the Chrysler and Empire State Buildings. On the streets, a swarm of men in baggy white T-shirts were slapping the calling cards of hookers against their wrists, hoping to catch the attention of the thousands of tourists who walked past them, drinking cocktails, laughing and joking as they made their way to the casinos. There was even a giant slot machine on the street itself, which had attracted a row of hopeful punters, all lining up for the chance of a free spin and a $1 million prize.

Admiring a group of scantily clad girls in tiny, tight-fitting dresses, Ryan jumped up onto one of the seats. 'Hey, you girls want to join us?' he hollered.

Of course they did. What group of girls in Vegas wouldn't want to join a bunch of young guys in a convertible Rolls Royce where shots of Patron were being passed around as if it were Christmas? But just as they walked towards the car, Joe stuck his head out of the window. 'Ew', one of the blondes cried in disgust, as Joe suddenly threw his guts up. Tequila had never been his strong point.

As the girls turned to walk away, Joe managed to shout: 'Hey! Not even a kiss?'

Cranking up the hip-hop music, Dave Majcher continued to drive Daniel and his entourage past the dancing, synchronised fountains of the Bellagio, which were set in an eight-acre lake on The Strip. Crowds were gathered around the lake to watch the show, but the boys were too busy downing shots to care.

'Leave us out front,' Curtis directed, as his assistant swung into the Bellagio's driveway. Having parked at the entrance, one of the Bellagio's front-of-house staff opened the doors for everyone to get out. 'I'll wait in the car park for you,' Dave said to Curtis, as his boss slipped a $100 note into the doorman's hand, his tip for opening the door.

'Follow me, fellas,' Curtis said, leading the way, eager to show Daniel and his mates the best night of their lives.

Entering one of the finest hotels in Vegas, the gang, looking like the stars of *Ocean's Eleven*, laughing and slapping each other's backs in their dark suits, strolled across the cream marble floor, and walked through the stone archways into the lobby area. Paying no attention to the 2,000 hand-blown glass flowers that were suspended from the ceiling, they followed Curtis into the vast gaming area to their right.

Locating the nightclub at the back of the dimly lit room, which was quieter and more reserved than most of the raucous casinos in Vegas, Curtis walked up to the head doorman and announced his arrival. Seeing Curtis's name at the top of the list, the hulking doorman lifted the red rope for the group and ushered them into the club, past the huge line of partygoers who queued outside.

Escorted by a brunette hostess, they walked into the grand foyer where the flashing strobe lights from the club reflected off the hundreds of bottles of Cristal that were stacked from floor to ceiling in the lobby. Striding past the hundreds of young, drunken revellers on the dance floor, the boys were led up a flight of stairs to their VIP table.

'What did I tell ya?' Curtis laughed, as he waved everyone past him. 'Best table in the club.'

Everyone had to admit. It really was. Overlooking the dance floor, they could see everything that was going on. And better yet, everyone could see them. Like three over-excited kids, Ryan, Michael and Joe looked over the balcony and began pointing out hot girls to each other. Just at that moment, the hip-hop music that had been booming through the club stopped mid-track. In its place came the *Rocky* theme tune, 'Eye of The Tiger'. Daniel looked over the balcony to see what all the commotion was about. Down below he could see a group of stunning girls, dressed in nothing but bikinis and black boxing robes, saunter sexily through the crowd, each holding aloft huge bottles of Grey Goose vodka and Cristal champagne while at the same time waving sparklers.

'Let's make some muthafucking noise for Daniel Tzvetkoff and the

Brisbane mafia boys up in VIP!' the DJ suddenly bellowed to the crowd, as over $30,000-worth of booze was brought up to their table. A huge roar reverberated around the club as the patrons signalled their approval.

Grabbing a bottle of Cristal from the ice bucket that had just been placed on their table, Daniel stood up on his seat, shook the bottle vigorously before spraying it on everyone down below. To the cheers of the crowd, he took a huge swig from the bottle and held his arms aloft victoriously. He was revelling in it.

'Daniel! ... Daniel!' a familiar voice suddenly shouted in the darkness. Daniel turned to see it was coming from Mick Doohan, the Australian five-time former world motorbike champion. Not only was he Daniel's childhood idol but these days Mick ran a jet leasing company on the Gold Coast from where Daniel had rented his private jet. Embracing his idol in a bear hug, Mick broke away to high-five the guys around the table, who were all excited to see him.

'Daniel,' Mick said, pointing to two guys who were walking in the shadows behind him. 'I want you to meet two good friends of mine: Michael Schumacher and Mike Tyson.'

'Oh my fucking God!' Joe shouted, as he saw the two former world champions shake Daniel's hand.

'Guys, come sit with us. We've got more alcohol than we can handle,' Daniel said to Mick and his friends.

'That's what you think,' Ryan laughed as he began pouring everyone at the table a drink.

'Not for me,' Tyson shouted above the music, in his familiar New York lisp. 'I'm banned from drinking in Vegas.'

'Really?' Michael Hui questioned, looking comically slight next to the hulking figure of Tyson.

'It's a long story,' the champ answered, flashing a grin that showed off his gold teeth.

Michael grinned goofily, unable to play it cool, 'I can't believe there are three world champions sat here right now.'

'Don't you mean four?' Daniel said with a straight face. 'I'm the world champion of processing,' a statement that saw Curtis grab Daniel around the shoulder, drag him in close and kiss him on the cheek.

Feeling his phone vibrate in his pocket, Daniel took it out to see that it was Sam. 'Sammy! How you doing mate?' he answered, putting his finger in his ear to drown out the noise.

'Did you buy Curtis a Ferrari?' Sam cursed down the phone.

Daniel ignored the question, instead handing the phone to Tyson: 'Hold up Sam, I want you to speak with someone quickly.'

'Hey Sam. It's Mike Tyson. You better get your ass over here. Your boy is making it rain!'

Handing the phone back to Daniel, who was busy knocking back shots with Mick Doohan, Schumacher and Curtis, Daniel laughed down the receiver: 'Sammy! You need to get out to Vegas soon, mate. It's crazy. You'll love it.'

'Daniel! Did you buy Curtis Pope a fucking Ferrari?' Sam shouted, disregarding Daniel's obvious high spirits.

'Yeah, it's a bonus. He's done good for us!'

'Is that Sam?' Curtis shouted over the music. 'I called him earlier to thank him for the present. Send my regards.' Daniel nodded, not quite sure if this was what Sam wanted to hear right now.

'For crying out loud, Daniel. Didn't you think to run this by me first? You can't spend money like that on the company without checking with me.'

Daniel knew Sam was unsure about Curtis, but he didn't expect him to be so jealous. So what if he had bought him a Ferrari. The guy was helping them make millions of dollars in profits. A $250,000 car was nothing in the big scheme of things. In fact, it was probably just under one day's profits the way things were shaping up. Big fucking deal!

'Relax, Sammy,' he replied. 'These days $250,000 is a day's pay. And if you are jealous I'll buy you one as well. In fact, fuck it, everyone who works for Intabill should drive a Ferrari. Let's make it the company car.'

'Jesus, Daniel! I'm not jealous. You just need to run all company expenditure by me. I am your business partner after all. Please tell me you're not using the company credit card tonight? I'm sick of opening statements to see thousands of dollars being spent in nightclubs.'

It was true. Daniel had gone a little wild in the clubs recently with Curtis. But it was all in the name of business. That's what he told himself anyway. 'No, I'm not actually,' he countered, sounding suitably hurt by the suggestion. 'Curtis has sorted us out. Anyway, what do you care? If I want to spend my half of the profits on nights out then it's nothing to do with anyone but me.'

'Yeah, well, technically that's not quite the case any more,' Sam bluntly interjected. 'I've been trying to speak to you about this. ASIC [Australian Securities and Investments Commission] have been in touch. Now we're doing more than twenty-five million dollars in turnover, we need to do an audit on the books.'

An audit? Daniel didn't like the sound of that one bit. Up until now he had been looking after all of the accounts himself, alongside his financial director, Sonya Rowe. He had masterminded a software system that had allowed him to keep track of what banks and processors owed Intabill and what Intabill owed its clients, including the reserves and the floats held for paying the poker players. While *he* had a handle on all of that, he didn't want anyone rooting around Trendsact, which was kept separate from Intabill, and was where the bulk of the money was held these days.

'Listen Sammy,' Daniel said defensively. 'The numbers are fine. Just give the auditors what I've prepared. It's been checked by external accountants already.'

'That's not good enough. We need to do a thorough audit, so I've hired a new CFO to do it for us.'

'What?'

'She's called Shelley Courtney,' Sam explained. 'She's worked for processing companies in the past so really understands the business. From now on all expenditure has to go through her. No money can be spent unless she approves it.'

Daniel grinded his teeth together angrily. While it was all well and good heading up a successful business of over 200 employees, he was getting sick to death of everyone telling him what to do. At the end of the day, he was the majority owner of Intabill. And under his watch it was close to becoming a billion dollar operation. Why should more and more people stick their noses in to his business?

'Get rid of her Sam. We've done fine by ourselves so far. The numbers are solid. You've seen them yourself.'

'That may well be, but it's the law. We need to do things this way now, otherwise ASIC are going to start hitting us with fines or they could even shut us down.'

Watching as the boys challenged Schumacher and Mick to a vodka shot frenzy, Daniel abruptly ended the conversation. 'I'll speak to you in the morning about this Sam!'

Hanging up the phone, Daniel refused to let Sam's news put a dampener on the night. They had money to burn; they were in the VIP room with oceans of alcohol, and had three of the greatest sportsmen the planet had ever produced for company. *Fuck it*. He had worked hard to earn his money and he was going to enjoy it any way he pleased.

Noticing that Daniel was perturbed, Curtis saddled next to him, 'Sam's not like us Dan. Don't get me wrong. I freakin love him, but he's a 9-5 guy. He needs the rules. He's a lawyer for Christ sake. Guys like us, we say fuck the rules. We make things happen.'

Daniel smiled. He could always rely on Curtis to back him up when Sam was trying to shoot him down. Curtis understood.

'Say Daniel,' Mick Doohan shouted across the table. 'I've been meaning to speak with you about a new club Billy and I are putting together right here in Vegas.'

Mick was referring to his business partner, Billy Cross, the brain-child behind one of Vegas's most popular male revues, *The Thunder from Down Under*. The two of them already owned the Cat House nightclub at the Luxor Hotel and by all accounts were doing very well out of it.

'Billy has just got permission to build the biggest nightclub in the world,' Mick continued, as the group carried on knocking back shots of Grey Goose, surrounded by swarms of admiring girls. 'It's going to be at the new City Center Plaza that's going to be built slap bang in the middle of The Strip. We are going to call it Society. We were wondering if you fancied being an investor with us?'

The biggest nightclub in the world! And in Las Vegas. Of course Daniel was interested.

'How much are you looking for?' Daniel replied.

'Fifteen million dollars.'

'I'm in,' Daniel blurted, excited not only about being part of the biggest nightclub in the world but also of going into business with his idol.

As the night wore on, and Mick, Schumacher and Tyson had departed, Daniel decided it was time to mix things up a little bit. 'Let's get out of here, guys,' he said to gasps of obvious displeasure.

'Why do you want to leave, Dan?' Ryan questioned, gesturing to the two very interested blondes who were sat either side of him. 'It's only midnight and the party is just getting started.'

Signalling for everyone to gather closer, Daniel announced: 'I've just called the Palms. I've booked the Playboy Mansion Suite for us. It's a duplex penthouse with its own infinity pool on the balcony.'

Watching everyone's faces light up, Daniel put his arm around Joe's shoulder: 'And seeing as Joe here thinks he can run a nightclub for me in Brisbane, let's put him to the test.' Looking Joe in the eye he said:

'Joe you've got one hour and a one hundred thousand dollar budget to throw us the biggest and best party in town. What do you say?'

'I'd say I'm going to get you guys shitfaced,' Joe grinned.

True to his word, Joe delivered. Within one hour the luxurious Playboy Mansion Suite, on the top floor of the Palms hotel, was pumping. It was almost staggering what he had managed to achieve in such a short space of time. One of Vegas's top DJs had stationed his decks in the large, open-plan living-room area, while PVC-clad cocktail waitresses pranced around in high heels carrying drinks. Perhaps Joe's most inspired idea had been to speak to the head bouncer of the Playboy Mansion Club downstairs and offer him $100 for every pretty girl he sent up to the room. Suffice to say, the club was now just a cock-fest, and some of the best-looking girls in the city were queuing to get into Daniel's room.

Ryan and Michael had taken it upon themselves to act as doormen and they went about their job with relish. In fact, Ryan had made it a condition that if the girls wanted to get in they had to wear a bikini. He had even managed to purchase some swimming costumes, which he handed out only to the prettiest of girls. Some were so keen to get in that they happily stripped in front of the boys on the door. Just another perk of the job.

Curtis, on the other hand, had decided to play Santa Claus with a giant bag of coke. Holed up in the bathroom, he was joined by a host of girls who were all lining up to do lines off the counter. Half the party were now walking around the place with their eyes popping out of their skulls.

While mayhem was breaking out, Daniel sat in the infinity pool at the back of the balcony, which had views of all of Vegas, drinking Cristal champagne straight out of the bottle. Sat all around him were four naked girls, two of whom had started to make out in the corner while the other two were doing lines of coke off each other's breasts. All it would have taken was for Daniel, the self-styled king of the party, to click his fingers and he could have had any one of them, or indeed all of them. But that wasn't his style, no matter how tempting. Despite his playboy bravado, Daniel remained fiercely devoted to Nicole, and he never touched drugs. Ever.

As guests disappeared into the bedrooms and bathrooms to cavort, Daniel remained sitting in the pool speaking to Ben Gourley, the brother of T R Gourley, one of John Scott Clark's business partners, who was currently in Vegas and had been invited by Curtis to get involved in the party. A good-looking, clean-cut guy who seemed like the archetypical high school jock, Ben had an easy-going manner and a dazzling Hollywood smile. And that was just where he was working these days, Tinseltown. In fact, he told Daniel, as they sat in the pool in the early hours of the morning, smoking cigars, that he was just in the process of finishing editing the latest film he had written and was looking to get another one off the ground.

His next project, he explained, was to be a romantic comedy, and he hoped to attract actor Matthew McConaughey to play the lead. The only problem was he needed some investors to help stump up the cash in order to attract the A-list star. This was music to Daniel's ears. He had always been a huge film buff, and in his younger years had dabbled in scripts and animation.

'Why don't you come out to LA with me?' Gourley proposed, sensing Daniel's eagerness to get involved. 'I'll show you my latest film in my private cinema and we can go over my new script.'

'Michael!' Daniel yelled to his legal counsel, who was now virtually comatose on the wraparound sofa in the lounge, 'Call the airport and tell them to get the jet ready. We're going to LA first thing.'

Processing was all well and good, but now Daniel thought it was time to have some fun with business. And what better way than owning clubs in Vegas and Brisbane and producing movies!

17

Las Vegas, USA, October 2008

Money being frozen by processors and banks was par for the course. Having it stolen by an associate was not.

'That motherfucker,' Curtis Pope bellowed from behind his desk, as Daniel entered the room, dressed in his casual office attire of jeans, black T-shirt and flip-flops. 'I brought that little cocksucker into the business and this is how he repays me.'

'What's up?' Daniel wearily replied, having spent the last few days working around the clock to get his Brisbane nightclub, Zuri, ready to open in time for his twenty-fifth birthday. The last thing his head needed right now was for Curtis to blow up over something. He had seen him lose his temper before. It wasn't a pretty sight.

'Chad has cleared out the National Bank of California account,' Curtis cursed, standing up and pointing at his computer screen.

'What?'

At this, Daniel raced round to see the source of Curtis's ire. It was true. The account was empty.

Chad Elie was one of Curtis's boys. Born and raised in Springfield, Massachusetts, the twenty-five-year-old had set up his own processing company, Viable, as far back as 2004. Since then, he had become involved with Selling Source, where he had helped them process payday loans as well as offer various other services. Having met Chad at Selling Source, Curtis had drafted him in to help find processing solutions for Trendsact. He had also suggested that Chad should be officially named as the general manager on all documents relating to Hugo Services LLC. That was how much faith Curtis had in the good-looking, red-haired kid from a hard background, much like himself.

But why would Chad do such a thing, Daniel thought? For the first few months of Trendsact, Chad had been a key part of the team. Based in Las Vegas, he frequently spent time at the office going over processing solutions and had enjoyed many a night out with Daniel and the gang. He seemed like a good guy who had already made a lot of money. It just didn't make sense.

'How much was in the account before?' Daniel grimaced, fearing the worst as he went to take a seat on the opposite side of Curtis's mahogany desk.

'Four point two million dollars,' Curtis growled, suddenly slamming his fist against the table. 'I swear I'll kill that son of a bitch when I get my hands on him.'

Daniel closed his eyes in disgust. It was worse than he thought. Not only was it big money, but the National Bank of California was one of the PokerStars accounts. Isai Scheinberg was already complaining of slow processing turnarounds. He would not take kindly to this news.

Besides antagonising Scheinberg, there were only so many hits the company could keep taking. So far Intabill had agreed to repay the poker companies over $12 million which had been frozen or seized by banks and processors. Contractually the money was at the poker companies' risk, but Daniel and Sam felt it was good business to take the hit. They had to keep the poker boys sweet at all costs. However, with the banks increasingly cracking down they couldn't keep swallowing up the losses forever. But in this particular situation they certainly could not expect PokerStars to take the loss when it appeared to be down to one of their own employees. Isai was hardly going to like hearing that.

Reaching into the pouch of tobacco on his desk, Curtis proceeded to shove a large, brown mound into his mouth.

'How did he steal the money?' Daniel enquired, furiously wiping his forehead in frustration, feeling a migraine coming on.

'He was the account signatory,' Curtis spat out between chews.

'Do we know where he is? Have you spoken to him?'

'No.'

Sam was already on the warpath over what was going on in Vegas. As far as he was concerned it was just one big party out there, even though the payday loan portfolio continued to sky rocket. Once he heard one of the Vegas crew had stolen some of the PokerStars money, Daniel knew that he would hit the roof.

'Curtis, mate. We need to track down Chad and get that money back.'

'Don't worry,' Curtis scowled from across the table. 'I'm already on it.'

'How? It's not as if we can call the police.'

Leaning back in his chair, a small smile suddenly flickered across Curtis's face. 'Remember I told you I grew up with some rough guys,' he said, spitting some tobacco into the bin under his desk.

'Yeah,' Daniel replied, not quite sure where this was going, as he watched Curtis wipe away the tobacco juice on his chin with the back of his hand.

'Well, I've made some phone calls. They are tracking down Chad as we speak.'

'What will they do if they find him?' Daniel asked.

'Use your imagination,' Curtis smiled in return.

*

Sat at his desk in his small Tampa office in Florida, Chad Elie was hard at work. He had left Trendsact under a cloud. There had been various disagreements and he was now glad to be shot of the place. While he had some money to fall back on, it was important that he kept his company, Viable, up and running. He needed new clients, and new processing solutions, if he was going to have a long-term future in this business.

Focusing on going through his emails, Chad's concentration was broken when he saw two men walk around the back of his building. Standing up he looked out of the window to get a better look at them. One looked to be in his early fifties, built like a fridge and had slicked-back dark hair, olive skin and wore a dark suit that looked fit to burst at any moment. The other one was younger, no more than in his early thirties. He was skinnier, although still muscular, and had the same dark looks as his older partner. Watching as the men walked towards the back door, he saw them peer inside before banging on the glass.

'We're closed,' Chad shouted, not sure who the hell these guys were, and in no mood to find out.

The older man shot Chad a look and gestured with his head for him to come to the door.

Once again Chad shouted to him: 'Hey buddy. Office is closed.'

But the two men refused to budge.

Getting up from behind his desk, Chad walked tentatively over to them, unlocked the bolt and slowly opened the door, leaving only enough room for him to speak through.

'Sorry guys. Office is shut,' he said for the third time, looking at the two men, only for the older one to suddenly stick his foot in the gap of the door, leaving Chad unable to close it.

'Hey. What are you doing?'

'Curtis Pope has sent us. We are here to have a little chat,' the older man warned in a New York-Italian accent. In other circumstances,

Chad might have laughed. They both looked and sounded like extras from *The Sopranos*. Worryingly, they both acted like them as well. And if Curtis had sent them, then Chad knew these guys had every chance of being legit. Barging their way into the office, Chad backtracked into his room terrified.

'We are here about the money,' the younger one said menacingly.

'What money?' Chad stuttered, still backtracking into his room.

'Don't play stupid,' the younger one yelled, walking aggressively towards him. 'Curtis told us you ripped off four million dollars. Now it's time for you to pay it back.'

'I didn't rip it off,' Chad replied, his voice shaking, his heart racing. 'He owed that to me.'

'Course he did sweetheart,' the younger one mocked.

'I swear,' Chad stuttered. 'Seriously. Let me show you the documents.'

'We're here for the money not the bullshit excuses.'

Holding his hands out behind him, Chad found he had come to his desk. Walking back towards his chair, never taking his eyes off the men for a second, he reached into his open draw and found what he was looking for. His gun. But the clip wasn't in it. *Shit*. As quick as he could, he fumbled around blindly for the clip before trying to load it, all the time trying to make sure the two goons couldn't see what he was doing. The only problem was his hand was shaking so much he couldn't get the damn thing in, and they were almost on top of him.

Click. The clip was in. But just as he went to raise the gun, the older man pulled it from his grasp. Looking down at Chad, the fridge smiled: 'We don't need to go there . . . yet!'

18

Atlantic City, USA, Present Day

Back in the old Wild West, or on the Mississippi riverboats in the 1800s, cheating at poker was part and parcel of the game. For many it was a badge of honour to be termed a 'cardsharp' or a 'cold deck artist'. Cheating was so rife that sensible players didn't dare play without utilising some kind of edge to try to tilt the odds in their favour. To play fairly was to see a player labelled 'a sucker', and suckers were there for the taking.

During this time a whole host of inventive schemes were concocted to help relieve a sucker of his money. Standard schemes involved marking certain cards with a thumbnail or needle, dealing well-placed cards from the bottom of the deck to a partner, playing in teams where the partners could work together to signal or bully a player out of a pot, and some even used well-placed mirrored objects, such as rings, snuff boxes or cigarette cases so that they could see their opponents' cards as they were being dealt. There was even a device invented which was hidden in a cardsharp's sleeve. When required the device could take a specific card out of the cardsharp's hand and when they should later wish to call upon that card it could deliver it back to them, with the rest of the players none the wiser.

However, for some, cheating was just the basics. In order to make a real living as a cardsharp, you had to have more up your sleeve than just an ace of spades. In order to be invited to play the big-money games on Mississippi riverboats, where rich Southern plantation owners tended to play the highest stake games in town, a cardsharp had to blend in effortlessly if they weren't to draw unwanted attention to themselves. Much like Paul Newman's character, Henry Gondorff, in the film *The Sting*, a cardsharp would be seen wearing a well-tailored suit, top hat, ruffled white shirt, and speaking with the refined air of someone who had been born into privilege. More often than not these 'actors' had been born in slums and had hustled their way out. Their 'acting' had to be of Academy Award standard if they were to appear as just the type of person the rich gentlemen would like to play at their table. Many of them would have given Daniel Day-Lewis a run for his money such was their convincing character transformation.

All of this chicanery was of course high reward, high risk. If a cardsharp was ever caught in the act of cheating then there was often a significant price to be paid. Opponents often thought nothing of shooting them dead or throwing them overboard. In Vicksburg in 1835, five suspected cheaters were even lynched.

When the game moved online in the mid-1990s, it was thought that most forms of cheating would now be eradicated. Sure, players could still work in teams and collude, but the days of marked cards, mirrored objects and devices up sleeves now seemed relics from the past. Players didn't even have to dress up any more to try to get an invite to the biggest games in town. Now they could find them while sat in their pyjamas in their bedroom at any online poker site. The big games were now open to anybody, no matter what their background. All that mattered was that they had a big enough bankroll to deal with the action.

Perhaps the clearest sign of just how determined most in the online community were to ensure that this new breed of game was clean came in 1999 when researchers cracked the code on website Planet Poker. This allowed them to predict hands that were being dealt with one hundred per cent accuracy. Amazingly, rather than use this information for profit, the researchers made their findings public to help ensure that Planet Poker improved their software. Nevertheless, as was seen in the Absolute Poker scandal, cheating online was still quite possible. It had, however, been hoped that this was just an isolated case. Sadly, it proved to be the tip of the iceberg.

Just as the Absolute Poker scandal was starting to die down, an even bigger one had erupted at its sister site, Ultimate Bet, which had also been under the control of Tokwiro Enterprises since 2007. The story goes that in January 2008 several posters on Two Plus Two began to question an Ultimate Bet player going by the name NioNio. He appeared to be clearing up. No matter the odds, or how badly he played a hand, it seemed that he always emerged victorious. With the Absolute Poker scandal still at the forefront of their minds, some posters opted to look into this themselves, unconvinced that a Tokwiro Enterprises company could be trusted to do so.

Trambopoline, who had lost $300,000 over the course of 3,000 hands to NioNio, looked up his opponent on www.mypokerintel.com, a website that provided a summary of a player's last fourteen sessions online. The information showed that NioNio had beaten the games at a rate of 114 big blinds per 100 hands.* To compare, the best players in the world consider themselves to be doing well if they win the equivalent of 15 big blinds per 100 hands. Furthermore, Michael

---

* The blinds are compulsory bets which are usually made by the two players directly to the left of the dealer. The small blind is firstly placed by the player immediately to the left of the dealer while the big blind is then placed by the next player to their left. A round of betting will then follow where other players have the opportunity to fold, call the big blind or to raise, before the action comes back to the player who first placed the big blind. To win the equivalent of 114 big blinds per 100 hands NioNio was inflating the pot each time by constantly raising every hand, causing the other players to wager more in order to defend their initial big blind.

Josem, a poker professional as well as an accomplished mathematician, created a chart which compared NioNio's results against a large sample size of average players. He found that NioNio's win rate was off the chart. It was the equivalent of winning a one-in-a-million lottery ... four days in a row.

After this evidence was shared on Two Plus Two, posters became suspicious of other accounts. Soon the usernames Flatbroke33, ilike2win, monizzle, nopaddles, nymobser, nvtease, sleepless, stoned2nite, utakeit and whackme were all identified as having the same style and winning percentage as NioNio. What's more, most of these users had stopped playing in September 2007, around the same time the Absolute Poker scandal was first reported. This certainly seemed suspicious and alarm bells really started to ring when, after these usernames were made public in January 2008, the two accounts that were still operational suddenly closed down or changed screen names.

Two Plus Two poster and renowned poker investigator Nat Arem went on to scrutinise the pattern of these accounts. Soon he had discovered how it had worked. Put simply, an account would be created that would clean up, that account would then disappear but would later return with a different username. This pattern continued indefinitely, apparently sweeping all who lay before them.

Brett 'Gank' Jungblut, a poster on PocketFives, went even further in his investigation. He looked into the IP address that was linked to many of the offending accounts. That led him to 1725 Glenview Drive, Las Vegas. The owner of the property was none other than 1994 World Series of Poker Main Event champion, and one of Ultimate Bet's early owners, Russ Hamilton.

Hamilton was already regarded by some as a dubious character. The year he won the World Series, Jack Binion, who owned the tournament at that time, had pledged that whoever won the Main Event would not only pick up $1 million, they would also receive their body weight in silver. When Hamilton emerged victorious, he was invited to step on the scales to weigh in. When he did so, it was found that he had stuffed his pockets in order to make himself appear heavier than his already considerable 360 lbs.

On 11 September 2008, with Hamilton's name now out in the open, the Kahnawake Gaming Commission, following its belated investigation into the matter, released its findings. A statement confirmed that between May 2004 and January 2008 Russ Hamilton had defrauded players out of $22,100,000. Ultimate Bet was subsequently ordered to reimburse its wronged players that amount, as well as pay a $1.5 million fine. Unsurprisingly, Ultimate Bet's current owners Tokwiro Enterprises sued previous owners Excapsa Software, as they had owned the site when most of the cheating devices had been put in place. Eventually the parties settled the case out of court for $15 million. Yet, just like the verdict in the Absolute Poker case, the alleged perpetrator, Russ Hamilton, emerged from it all relatively unscathed. He may have been disgraced, but he remained a free man.

Unsatisfied with this, and the investigation into the matter, poker journalist Haley Hintze once again dedicated herself to uncovering the truth. She explained to me that while Hamilton was one of the parties involved, there were others who were not named by the Kahnawake Gaming Commission. 'There's no doubt in my mind that Russ Hamilton did not act alone,' she told me. 'He was a good poker player, but he couldn't have circumnavigated the site's security without help from a person connected to the software. And the person who provided the software to Ultimate Bet was Greg Pierson.'

Pierson was a successful software developer from Portland. He was held in such high esteem by some in the poker community that Phil Hellmuth, an Ultimate Bet pro, and the then youngest World Series of Poker Main Event champion of all time, said of him: 'Greg Pierson is the man! No, you haven't heard of him yet, but mark my words: GP's new company, Iovation internet security company, will have a billion dollar evaluation by 2008.' Whether Pierson actively

helped Hamilton or unwittingly provided him with some information is unclear, but it does seem highly probable that he was
Hamilton's source, whether or not he knew about it.

Another name that has been linked to this affair is that of Travis
Makar, who not only sold 1725 Glenview Drive to Hamilton in 2006,
but owned other properties that were also linked to IP addresses
behind suspect accounts. However, as this story broke Makar seemed
to have disappeared. With little known about him, many rumours
were floated. Those with the most credibility alleged that he was
Hamilton's right-hand man who had also worked as a computer con-
tractor for Ultimate Bet.

Then, out of nowhere, in February 2011 Makar called up the
Donkdown poker forum podcast. The alleged ex-cheater had now
suddenly turned whistle-blower. He claimed that while he had never
worked directly for Ultimate Bet, he had managed to obtain a
number of incriminating documents after working for one of the
alleged perpetrators of the scam. One of the documents he shared
was dynamite: it was an email from 2005 that forwarded on the 'God
Mode' tool to be used for the purposes of cheating. He had, however,
blacked out the names of the three people who were included in the
email. Haley has, however, seen the unedited email, and knows who
they are. Yet before naming them, she has been trying to give them
all a chance to give their side of the story. As with most things in the
online poker world, it is dangerous to jump to conclusions. Things
are not always as they seem.

Makar also revealed another interesting fact during his chat with
Donkdown host Bryan Micon. Following the scandal, a poster by
the name of 'Brainwashdodo' had briefly appeared on Two Plus Two.
Slowly but surely he had started to drip-feed Ultimate Bet cheating
stories to the masses. It was clear from the high level of information
he provided that Brainwashdodo had to be an insider. But who?
Makar now revealed that Brainwashdodo was an Ultimate Bet

customer service representative by the name of Zoltan Rozsa. Apparently Rozsa had hoped that, by posting these stories, he could persuade the company to pay him off so he could open a doughnut shop. It was a ploy that was doomed to fail.

Whether the complete story behind the scandal will ever emerge, Haley isn't sure. But by the time she publishes her long-awaited book on both the Absolute Poker and Ultimate Bet cheating scandals, she hopes to have at least revealed all of the main perpetrators. Many are also hopeful that her exhaustive research will also lead to all of the guilty parties finally facing justice. In any event, the Absolute Poker and Ultimate Bet cheating scandals, which came one after the other, caused significant damage to online poker's reputation. It seemed the game had reached its nadir. However, this would soon pale into insignificance compared to what lay in wait just around the corner. Armageddon was on the horizon.

19

Brisbane, Australia, October 2008

It had arrived in a pink rectangular box: no note on the top, no explanation – nothing. After untying the crisply tied black bow that adorned it, and prising off the top, the curious recipient could finally cast their eye on what lay inside. There, on black velvet, was a perfectly cut row of diamond-drop crystals to which an invitation on white parchment paper was attached, which read:

'On 10 October 2008, at 1/367 Brunswick Street, Brisbane, Daniel Tzvetkoff requests the pleasure of your company from 7.30pm onwards at the opening of his opulent new nightclub experience, Zuri. Please bring the enclosed crystal droplets with you so they can be attached to our chandelier. And remember, dress to impress!'

Zuri was the nightclub everyone had been talking about. No expense had been spared to make the new club one of the most lavish experiences in all of Australia. Materials had been sourced from all over the world for the gold, black and red Moulin Rouge-inspired, $4 million fit-out. Rare fabric that had been used in the Palace of Versailles was utilised as drapes, wallpaper and upholstery, gothic gates were shipped in from Buenos Aires, marble from Italy, antique gold mirrors from England and chandeliers from Paris. The attention to detail had also not escaped the hiring of the staff.

Daniel, Sam Sciacca and Joe Mannino wanted their new club to be far more than just a place that looked good. It was vital that the staff were trained to the highest standard possible, hence Joe creating what became known as 'Zuriversity'. All staff were subject to an intensive six-week induction period where they would not only be taught by experts about how to deliver unparalleled service, they would also become masters of the products by undertaking cheese-making and wine-tasting classes.

While the staff would be of the highest calibre, Daniel was also determined to serve his patrons the very best food and drink. Therefore one of Europe's top mixologists, Barry Galloway, was hired to stock the bar with an awesome arsenal of alcohol. Fine wines, vintage champagnes, boutique beers and noxious shots all now stood invitingly on the black marble back wall of the dimly lit bar. Whatever the fancy of the invited guests – a 1988 Dom Perignon or Daniel's own personal favourite, Lemon Drops – they would not be disappointed, especially as for the opening night he had decreed it to be a free bar, owing to the fact that the requisite licence had not arrived in time.

The food, which would line the guests' stomachs in between bottles of Cristal, was also of the highest quality. Renowned sushi chef Taichi Ito had been hired to design an inviting menu, which included delicacies such as Tempura Prawns, Wafu Wagyu Steak and Salt & Pepper Squid. And if the opening of Daniel's latest indulgence wasn't reason enough to celebrate; it also happened to coincide with his twenty-fifth birthday. Everything was in place for the party to end all parties.

For the opening, guests were flown in from all over Australia, business class of course. Alex Dimitriades, Gyton Grantley and Damian Walshe-Howling, stars of Daniel's favourite show, *Underbelly*, the popular TV mini-series about a gangland war in Melbourne, were all treated in such a fashion. As were actor Hugh Sheridan, MTV host and model Ruby Rose, and Sydney party impresario Toby Osmond.

Although not everyone could be in town for the opening, it had already been arranged for some of Daniel's favourite stars from the world of entertainment to receive the red-carpet treatment when they eventually arrived in Brisbane on their world tours. Already lined up for future appearances were Snoop Dog, Ice Cube, Chris Brown, Stevie Wonder, will-i-am and Vince 'Vincent Chase' Grenier, star of the hit HBO show *Entourage*, whose band had been booked to play on New Year's Eve.

The chance to get a glimpse of Queensland's most talked-about venue, and also to learn a bit more about the man of mystery himself, was too much for the media to resist. Reporters from iconic fashion magazine *Vogue* arrived with photographers in tow, as did presenters from TV stations Channel 9 and Channel 10, as well as a host of newspaper writers from all over Australia. No one had managed to nail down more than a few words from the elusive Tzvetkoff, but with an ocean of alcohol likely to loosen his tongue this would be their best chance yet to ask the many questions that remained unanswered. Number one being: how on earth had one so young, from a working-class background, with no academic qualifications, become quite so wealthy so fast?

As the guests escaped the clammy summer heat, and were whisked from their limos into the sanctity of the air-conditioned club, they walked up a flight of red carpeted stairs to be greeted by Daniel Tzvetkoff's fantasy come to life. The club was packed with the young and the beautiful, who either gyrated on the dance floor to the beat of Daniel's favourite hip-hop music or sat on plush gold thrones quaffing vintage champagne. But while the great and the good continued to flock into the packed venue, the man of the moment was nowhere to be seen.

Watching from behind a one-way tinted mirror in his own private room, the Salon, which was adjacent to the VIP area, the host for the evening sat on a red velvet sofa having his own private party within a private party. Wearing a pristine Dolce & Gabbana two-buttoned white suit, which showed off his Vegas tan, and a tight-fitting black V-neck T-shirt, which revealed the paunch he had developed from eating and drinking the best steak and wine on offer in Vegas, Daniel was revelling in being the centre of attention. The models, actors, musicians, socialites and reporters were all there for him. It was a scenario he had long coveted. Ever since his days as a quiet, unspectacular student at the Catholic boys' school, Villanova College, he had dreamed of one thing: popularity. Now, at last, it was his. Everyone was here to see Daniel Tzvetkoff.

Nodding his head to the sound of the Notorious B.I.G's 'Big Poppa', Daniel saw the door open and a bald head appear from behind it. It was Sam.

'Daniel, mate, whatcha doing?' his partner asked impatiently. 'Everyone is waiting for you.'

Looking up towards the door, Daniel couldn't help but muster a grin. Sam was as usual dressed in his trademark navy blue suit, well-cut white shirt and grey tie. He was even wearing his square glasses. It was his staple choice for all occasions – even the opening of a nightclub. It seemed that Sam was either too old at thirty-eight to indulge in club attire or he was too set in his ways after his fifteen years working as a lawyer.

'Didn't anyone tell you it was a party?' Daniel grinned, a remark that made some of his guests break out into laughter.

Ignoring the remark, Sam continued to press his partner: 'You need to get out there, Dan. Press the flesh and all that. After all, this is your party.'

Reluctantly standing up, Daniel buttoned up his white jacket and looked into the oversized gold mirror to the side. Quickly brushing his cropped jet-black hair into shape with his hands, biting his lower lip as he did so, he winked at Sam: 'How do I look?'

'Very pretty, mate,' Sam sighed, getting increasingly impatient. 'You ready?'

Puffing out his chest, Daniel nodded before picking up a shot of Lemon Drops and knocking it back for Dutch courage. 'Let's do this.'

Striding out of the tranquil peace of the Salon and into the throbbing VIP area, which smelt of sweat, champagne and smoke, Daniel spotted a familiar face coming towards him. Dressed in a well-tailored black suit the well-tanned figure slapped Daniel on the back and let out a roar of laughter. 'Dan! How you doing buddy? Great party, mate.' It was Mick Doohan.

'We'll be having a bigger and better one in our club in Vegas soon,' Daniel laughed.

'You better believe it buddy,' Mick said excitedly, as he handed Daniel a shot of Patron. 'Get this down you.'

But just as Daniel was about to take the shot from Mick's hand, he was stopped in his tracks. Nicole, wearing a tight-fitting white dress, which showed off her post-pregnancy workout success, strode up to him. 'Where the hell have you been?' She was angry, a state she had been in for most of the past two months since Daniel had broken it to her that he didn't have time in his busy schedule to get married any time soon.

'I've been in the Salon with some of the boys,' he said, shrugging his shoulders, as Sam and Mick backed away from the ensuing argument.

'Were there other girls there?' Drink could go two ways with Nicole, it either made her the happiest person in the world, or it made her jealous. It seemed tonight jealousy had won out. Despite this, Daniel didn't care less. 'Yeah. So what?' he replied. 'I wasn't doing anything.'

As he spoke some of the photographers noticed the boy wonder

On top of the world. Daniel Tzvetkoff and Sam Sciacca pose for the media after Daniel was named in the *Business Review Weekly* Young Rich List.

Deep in thought. Curtis Pope looks ready for business in his trademark cigar smoking pose.

From left to right: Michael Hui, Sam Sciacca, Curtis Pope, Andrew Thornhill, John Scott Clark, Derek LaFavor, and Daniel Tzvetkoff celebrate their new partnership outside of Intabill.

Daniel's prized possession, his top of the range, fully loaded Lamborghini, with 'BALLR' number plate, a homage to his love of hip-hop.

Still on friendly terms, John Scott Clark, Daniel and Curtis Pope with their partners after another night of Las Vegas gastronomic indulgence.

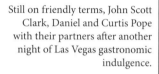

Nicole Crisp looking happy next to Daniel's latest gift to her, a top of the range Bentley.

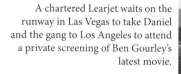

A chartered Learjet waits on the runway in Las Vegas to take Daniel and the gang to Los Angeles to attend a private screening of Ben Gourley's latest movie.

Love at first sight. Maximus, the $7.5 million 98-foot yacht which Sam and Daniel snapped up after seeing it on display at the Sanctuary Cove Boat Show. They opted to do without the Audi R8 that came with it.

The luxurious cream and walnut interior of Maximus, a sight which greeted many of Intabill's top clients.

Happy families. Daniel, Nicole and Hugo celebrate Christmas at Lake Tahoe.

Daniel tests out his V8 racing car driver, Marcus Marshall, on the track.

From left to right: Michael Hui, Ben Gourley, Joe Mannino, Daniel and Chad Elie get ready to depart for Los Angeles.

Andrew Thornhill and Chad Elie play up to the cameras on a night out in Las Vegas.

From left to right, Chad Elie's girlfriend Darby, actress Jaime Pressly and Nicole party in the VIP room of a Las Vegas nightclub.

Intabill wasn't just a money-making machine, it also supported many charities, such as the Make-A-Wish Foundation.

MAKE·(A·)WISH. & *intabill*

WOULD LIKE TO INVITE YOU TO...

TRACK DAY
2008

Join us on Saturday, October 4 at QLD Raceway and put a smile on your dial

Date: Saturday, October 4, 2008

Venue: **QLD Raceway**
             Champions Way Willowbank QLD 4306

PLEASE RSVP BY SEPTEMBER 24 TO REGISTER FOR YOUR TICKETS. EMAIL JADA@INTABILL.COM

A fun day for all Make-a-Wish kids and their families to view and ride in prestige performance cars.

Catering will be supplied.
Face painting, jumping castles!

Time blocked itinerary of prestige cars, Japanese drift cars & V8 cars and utes will be on display and available for rides.

Below: John Scott Clark shows off a tie that Sam Sciacca bought for him in Brisbane, after the party went for dinner at the Tattersall's Club and none of the Americans had ties or jackets with them.

Daniel and Andrew Thornhill travel in style to a Playboy fancy dress party at the Palms in Las Vegas.

The Access Cash Ford
Falcon V8 racing car.
The car went further
than the product that
sponsored it.

Curtis Pope happily poses
in the car park of the Las
Vegas Four Seasons Hotel
in front of his gift from
Daniel, a Ferrari.

Where it all began. Daniel Tzvetkoff
mans the Intabill booth at the Ad-Tech
Exhibition in New York.

Getting ready to roll. The office at
Trendsact being prepared.

With a little help from Nicole, this Marie Antoinette inspired advert for Daniel's nightclub Zuri was shot in the club's VIP area.

The crowd gather in Daniel Tzvetkoff's suite at the Palms in Las Vegas for the room party to end all room parties.

A room with a view. The infinity pool in the Playboy Suite at the Palms Hotel had unrivalled views over Las Vegas, and was where Daniel spent most of his time swigging champagne.

From left to right: Nicole Crisp, Daniel Tzvetkoff, Chad Elie, Chad Elie's girlfriend Darby and Michael Hui at a Playboy sponsored fancy dress party.

Daniel and Curtis Pope meeting with a potential ACH provider in Las Vegas.

Joe Mannino and Daniel brave their hangovers following the party in the Playboy suite at the Palms Hotel, to travel to Los Angeles.

Nicole and Darby party the night away in a Las Vegas nightclub.

From left to right: Michael Hui, Daniel and Curtis Pope stand proudly outside Intabill's latest acquisition, a private jet.

was in the VIP area and started to snap pictures. Daniel turned around and gave them a quick smile while Nicole looked on seething with anger, 'I've hardly seen you in weeks and . . .'

'And it's been great,' Daniel shot back, tiring of the argument already.

Suddenly, Nicole reached her hands back and pushed Daniel in the chest with all of her might. 'Fuck you, Daniel. Fuck you. Who do you think you are?'

Gritting his teeth together, Daniel tried to keep his cool. This was his party and Nicole was going to blow it. He knew she had been frustrated lately, having quit work to move to Vegas, so he had suggested she take an active part in Zuri. As such, Nicole had sourced all of the barmaids' outfits from lingerie shops in LA, as well as helped to design the advertising campaign, which was based on Marie Antoinette, her idol. At the same time, Daniel had also told her to help supervise the redevelopment of 33 Hedges Avenue. He had also given her carte blanche to buy whatever she wanted – handbags, shoes, dresses, jewellery, cars, interior design – anything at all, just so long as it kept her quiet. Yet, despite embarking on a massive spending spree, she still wasn't happy.

'If you don't calm down I'll have you thrown out,' Daniel threatened under his breath, with a smile still fixed across his face.

'Dan,' Sam interrupted awkwardly. 'We need to get going.'

Grateful for the intrusion, Daniel shot Nicole an angry glance before leaving her to put on a charm offensive with the media.

'That's right!' Nicole screeched, oblivious to people watching. 'Just leave. That's all you ever do. Fucking leave!'

Ignoring his fiancée's cries, Daniel high-fived Mick Doohan before confidently navigating his way through the throng to meet the press. He was pumped with adrenalin. His big moment was coming up. Flashing his trademark grin to his guests, who had by now stopped what they were doing so that they could get a better look, he nodded his head to the hip-hop music as he strolled up a flight of stairs. As he did so he took a momentary glance at the carnage below him. Lines of well-dressed socialites were at the black marble bar downing a row of shots while beautiful girls danced on tables. It was going off.

'Sorry to keep you waiting,' Daniel cheerfully announced to the waiting press-pack, as an incessant flashing of cameras suddenly went off in his face. Holding a flute of champagne in his hand, Daniel grinned as the photographers shouted out directions. 'Daniel. Daniel. Smile this way, mate.' Joined by Sam on one side and Joe on the other, Daniel posed in front of a black wall which had 'Zuri' emblazoned in gold on it, feeling every inch the star.

Laughing and joking, he chose to ignore the sight of Nicole dancing with a group of guys in the VIP area by herself. It was just an attempt to make him jealous – two could play at that game. 'Hey, darling,' he beckoned to one of the barmaids, who was dressed in nothing but lingerie. 'Why don't you come here with your friends and have some pictures with us?' Grinning from ear to ear, surrounded by a bevy of lithe, perky beauties, Daniel beamed for the cameras, noticing Nicole looking on in disgust. Right now he was the man of the moment. The whole nightclub had virtually come to a standstill, including the VIPs, in order to catch a glimpse of the golden boy who was living the dream.

Joe walked to the edge of the stairs and waved his hands downwards, signalling for everyone to be quiet: Daniel was going to say a few words. Grabbing a microphone, the young tycoon remembered he was under strict instructions from Sam not to say too much. Such had been the intense focus on Daniel after he had bought the Hedges Avenue mansion that they had fed the media a few lines on how Intabill was a general e-commerce processing company. They had been happy with that. And most importantly, so were the poker guys.

Taking the microphone from Joe's hand, Daniel looked down below and said the only words that seemed appropriate: 'Let's get this party started, bitches.' And with that the revellers cheered as the DJ wasted little time in spinning 50 Cent's 'In Da Club'.

Watching on, Nicole ran to the toilets, mascara running down her face. What had happened to the shy guy who would have done anything for her? Stood to the side, Sam also looked on in amazement. The cocky and brash, post-Vegas Daniel was very different to the young kid who had first come to his office, sheepishly looking for help, just three years earlier. But as Daniel took to the dance floor, surrounded by hangers on, he couldn't have cared less. He was the king. Nothing was going to stop him, not even the chaser emails for payment from PokerStars, Ultimate Bet and Full Tilt that had started to arrive in his inbox.

20

Las Vegas, USA, December 2008

'It doesn't look good,' Daniel announced grimly, addressing Curtis Pope and John Scott Clark, who joined him around the board-room table at Trendsact, each trying desperately to get to grips with the situation.

Although the payday loans may have been flourishing, the processing side of the business was struggling. More and more banks, as well as third-party processors, seemed to be catching on. If they weren't freezing accounts, they were just flat-out refusing to process. While Daniel wasn't panicking just yet, he was well aware that the once-lubricated pipes were now gradually getting shut off. What was more, most of the ACH pipes that were still in action had strict volume caps of around $1 million a day. As such, a backlog of poker transactions was building. If something wasn't done soon then things could start getting messy.

'I've had the poker boys going crazy,' Daniel proceeded to explain. 'Their customers have authorised us to take money out of their accounts, but we don't have enough pipes to process all of it. Right now some of the poker sites are having to credit their customers' accounts without actually having received a penny themselves.'

'So what do you suggest?' Curtis asked, chewing on a pen, while he rested his Ferragamo loafered feet on the table.

'I don't know. That's why we are here. But we've got to think of a new processing solution. The old ways aren't working so well any more.'

Curtis knew the pipes were drying up, but something else was also concerning him: 'Whatever it is, I'm telling ya, it needs to cut down on the risk. Some of these processors are close to blowing the whistle on us. It won't be long. We're making a shitload of money, but it won't be worth it if we end up in the slammer. This is a time-bomb waiting to explode right in our damn faces. First things first, we've gotta cover our own backs.'

John Scott Clark nodded in agreement. His own processing operation, Impact, which Trendsact used for one of its pipes, was also finding it more and more difficult to force the poker money through.

'Why don't we just buy a bank?' Curtis suggested, taking his feet off the table, sitting upright at the thought of an answer to their prayers. 'That way we can do what we want.'

But Daniel shot the suggestion down in seconds. It was an idea that could work, but as he had found with HKB Bank in Germany, buying a bank took time – something they didn't have right now. They needed to do something new, think outside the box. They had to dispense with the old methods and come up with a solution that was going to keep the pipes flowing without any interference or risk. Easier said than done.

As the unseasonably chilly Las Vegas morning wore on, little progress was made. Sat around the table, the three munched their way through an In-N-Out burger feast hoping for inspiration to strike. It looked hopeless. Maybe it was time to get out of online poker. They had had a good run. Maybe the future was just to focus on payday lending.

Lately, several very wealthy businessmen had expressed an interest in investing in a portfolio at Trendsact, which would see Curtis and Daniel split fifty per cent of the profits. One such businessman was Jason Galanis, a New York-based financier, who was flying into Vegas shortly to discuss making $30–60 million available for Trendsact to put on the street on his behalf. If they could attract more payday loan investors in that ballpark then they could definitely consider getting out of online poker processing.

John Scott Clark's company, Impact, had also been contemplating putting more focus on the payday lending. In fact, he had been spreading his net far and wide making new contacts in the payday lending universe and now had a few things on the go, one of which had huge potential.

'How's things going up in South Dakota with Butch?' Curtis asked during an impasse, referring to Scott Clark's link-up with Chief Martin 'Butch' Webb's Western Dakota Bank, which was based on the Cheyenne River Sioux Tribe reservation.

'Real good,' Scott Clark said slowly, taking an age between each word. 'Everything's a lot easier dealing with the Indians. They just want to do business and not tie your butt up in red tape.'

Scott Clark went on to explain that he had recently set up new payday lending entities on land owned by the Cheyenne River Sioux Tribe. His pal, Butch, was named as the owner of the entities, and Butch's bank, Western Dakota, which was also on the reservation, was processing all of the loans on behalf of Scott Clark's business.

This partnership allowed Scott Clark to offer payday loans to all of the states across America, even those states where such a service was illegal. This was the benefit of doing business in Tribal areas. Their laws, compared to most states, were incredibly lax in some areas, such as loans and gaming. Businesses in such areas could operate on a reservation and have sovereign immunity, meaning they didn't have to follow state and federal rules. They could even advertise in those states where such businesses were illegal so long as they serviced the customers from the confines of the reservation, something that was very easy to do in the cyber age.

That was it, Daniel thought, as Scott Clark continued to speak of his success with Butch. Suddenly everything seemed so simple.

'You got a contact who owns a bank in an Indian reservation?' Daniel probed.

'Sure I do. Butch is a good buddy of mine and Curtis's.'

As Scott Clark uttered those words, all three of them stopped and looked at each other, their minds fizzing with opportunities. Indian reservations! This was the answer. Why the hell hadn't they thought of this before?

If an American Indian reservation could operate under its own laws, and remain immune from prosecution in the payday loan world, then why shouldn't that also apply to processing for online poker? A lot of reservations already had strong links to gaming, with a number allowing casinos to be based within their borders, as well as regulating online poker companies, as the Kahnawake Tribe did for Absolute Poker and Ultimate Bet. With such legal flexibility, and a pre-existing relationship with gaming, there could be an incredible opportunity which could solve all of their problems, and this would be all the easier if they had a contact there already.

'Could you set up a meeting with Butch?' Daniel urgently asked.

'Sure, no problem,' Scott Clark replied, hurriedly standing up, already fishing his phone out of his pocket to make the call. 'When do you want to go?'

'Now!' Daniel urged. This couldn't wait a moment longer.

With the Gulfstream jet scrambled at nearby McCarran Airport, David Majcher dropped Daniel, Curtis and Scott Clark at the private terminal. Within one hour of Daniel's request, they were airborne. Two hours later they touched down on the tarmac at Mobridge Airport, where they were picked up by a taxi, which proceeded to take them to see Butch in Timberlake itself, which was a thirty-minute drive away.

With a population of just 443, Timberlake was one of the smallest towns situated in the Cheyenne River Indian Reservation, which was created by the United States in 1889, after the government had broken up the Great Sioux Reservation following its victory over the Lakota in a series of wars in the 1870s. These days the reservation was the fourth-largest in terms of land area in the United States. However, within its confines, it had only a little under 10,000 residents, many of whom were unemployed or who were surviving on just $22,000 a year per family, less than one-third of the American average income. Indeed, many of the thirteen small communities on the Cheyenne River Reservation didn't even have water systems, such was the abject poverty in some areas.

As they drove up the straight-as-an-arrow highway, with desolate, snow covered, prairie land stretching either side, Daniel spotted a small gathering of houses up ahead. This was it: Timberlake, one of the poorest towns in the United States. It certainly didn't fail to disappoint. They most definitely were not in Vegas any more. Southern Highlands, the Vegas housing community where Curtis and Daniel both lived, looked bigger than the entire town. It was certainly more luxurious.

Situated in the middle of nowhere, it seemed to be just a square block of houses all built on dirt. There wasn't another town for miles. This was what the residents of Timberlake had to put up with, day in and day out, with the only thing to occupy them being the nearby lake, the small local museum or drinking themselves into oblivion.

Turning right on 7th Street, the taxi took them past seven featureless blocks of houses before turning right on East Street. There, on the corner, was their destination: a white wooden house with a blue roof, surrounded by dirt, which was covered in a thick layer of frost and snow. Stepping out of the car, and taking a look around him, Daniel couldn't believe that this was it. This small, nothing town could potentially become the epicentre of online poker processing in America.

Already waiting for them outside the shabby building was Butch, a short, bald, podgy Native American, who wore an Aztec-patterned red waistcoat over a baggy white shirt, which had a cowboy string tie hanging from the collar.

'Well, well, well', Butch laughed as Scott Clark got out of the taxi. 'Look what the cat's dragged in.'

'Butch!' Scott Clark exclaimed, as he embraced his friend and patted him on the back. 'You already know Curtis, of course.'

Putting his arm playfully around Curtis's broad shoulders, Butch laughed: 'It's about time you came to see me, you son of a bitch. It's been too long.'

'I know, buddy. I know', Curtis grinned as he slapped Butch in the belly. 'What ya been feeding yourself down here?'

'A man's gotta eat' Butch quipped, which brought on more back slapping and laughter.

'This here is Daniel, our good friend and partner at Trendsact in Vegas,' Scott Clark said, as Butch grabbed Daniel's freezing hand in a vice-like grip and shook it vigorously. 'So this is the Wizard of Oz y'all been telling me about,' he smiled, his crow's feet stretching like river tributaries towards his temples.

'This guy is a smart son of a bitch,' Curtis said, a cloud of cold air spiralling from his mouth as he spoke. 'And we think we may have come up with something that a hound dog like you will appreciate.'

'Oh yeah?' Butch grinned. 'Well, you guys better come inside and tell me all about it.'

Sat in a small wood-panelled kitchen at the back of the house, the four men crowded around a rickety wooden table as a heater spewed out intermittent blasts of hot air. Handing them all cups of steaming hot coffee, Butch sat back in his chair. 'So what do you have in mind for me then, boys?'

'Payment processing for online poker,' Daniel said, cutting straight to the chase, as he quickly took Butch through the basics of the industry before outlining how he envisioned it would work.

He explained how the three of them would set up new entities, as well as base all of the servers required, on the reservation. The first set of entities would be called High Country Ventures, Lone Mountain and Sierra Ridge. Those three entities would be linked to the poker sites. Whenever a player on a site wanted to make a deposit or a withdrawal, then that information would be passed on to these entities. The entities would then pass the information on to a new processing entity set up on the reservation called CybrCollect, who would then forward it all on to Western Dakota Bank, who via ACH could pull and push the money in and out of the players' accounts when required. It was that simple. And if it went ahead there was virtually nothing the American authorities could do about it.

'That sounds real interesting,' Butch said thoughtfully, taking all of this information onboard, as he crossed his arms across his chest and slowly leaned back. 'So what sort of money are we talking here?'

'Around one billion dollars a year,' Daniel casually replied. 'Western Dakota Bank would become the main processing centre for online poker in America.'

Upon hearing such an amount, Butch choked on his coffee and began spluttering. This Australian kid was crazy. Standing up in order to catch his breath, Curtis laughed at his friend: 'What did I tell you, buddy? Told you this would interest you.'

'But how could we do so much on the reservation? We don't have the infrastructure in place for so much business.'

'Let us worry about that,' Curtis said, grinning at Daniel. 'We will get our asses down here and help you set everything up. It will be beautiful buddy. Beautiful.'

'I don't know,' Butch answered, as he paced the room. 'I know we are an Indian reservation and all, so normal rules don't always apply, but the Feds are sure to get involved in this.'

Curtis shook his head. 'Fuck the Feds. They won't notice shit. On the reservation, we are all untouchable. It's all perfectly legal. Besides,

Daniel has been doing this for over a year now and I've been helping him for six months. We got the game sussed. Do you know what the worst thing that can happen is?'

'What?'

'You make so much dough, you don't have room to store it!' Curtis said, deadly serious, 'looking Butch straight in the eye. 'We would pay you a small fortune. And this wouldn't just be good for you. The whole town would benefit. Hell Butch, this place could sure do with it. What other industry is going to come here and drop this much money straight into your lap?'

Looking towards Scott Clark for reassurance, Butch was greeted by his friend's bald head nodding. 'It's all true, Butch. Every word of it. We go way back now. You know I wouldn't bust my behind coming up here if I didn't think it was possible.'

Teasing his lips together in thought, Butch leaned against the wall. It was extremely tempting. And Curtis was right: this town was dying a slow death. Online poker could completely reinvigorate it. Surely it was worth looking at further?

'OK, Curtis,' Butch said. 'You did what you usually do to me?'

'What's that?' Curtis replied, grinning widely, standing up to seal the deal with a shake of the hand.

'You flipped me.'

21

Adelaide, Australia, February 2009

While the wheels were being put in motion on the tribal processing deal, Daniel was soon concentrating on another set of wheels altogether, namely his very own V8 racing team in Australia. And there was a bonus: he could even pass it off as a business expense!

With the payday loan operation in Las Vegas continuing to rake in a mountain of cash, Daniel and Sam had decided to expand, first in Australia and then on to the UK. Their new company was to be called Access Cash and would be ready for launch by May 2009. When it came to how to market the new brand, Daniel had the perfect idea: they should buy their own V8 racing team and cover the car in the Access Cash logo.

Initially, Sam had been reluctant but Daniel had been prepared for this. He had done his homework. As a result, he had shown Sam that racing teams in NASCAR had long-standing sponsorship arrangements with payday loan companies. The demographic of the average race fan fitted in perfectly with those who predominantly applied for payday loans. And the V8 Racing Championships in Australia boasted similar demographics to NASCAR. It was the perfect way to launch Access Cash. When Sam looked into it further, he had to agree; this actually made perfect sense.

However, if Daniel was going to own a racing team then it had to be the best. He had no intention of showing himself up by being among the also-rans, but putting together a competitive V8 racing team wasn't going to be cheap. The racing licence alone cost $1.5 million, and that was before he had splashed out on buying a car, hiring a driver, assembling a team and kitting out a garage.

For Daniel, the car was all-important. Before anything else, he just had to have the very best machine on the market. But there was a problem: he didn't have enough time before the first race to get one custom built. So, what do you do when you need to buy the very best second-hand racing car on the market? You buy the car that won the championship the previous year.

Conveniently, the 2008 championship winning Ford Falcon, which was ridden to glory by star driver Jamie Whincup, was owned by Brisbane-based team Triple Eight. When Daniel made them an offer they couldn't refuse, they couldn't sell it quick enough.

Having bought the Ford Falcon for $500,000, Daniel also commissioned Triple Eight to build him a new car which would be ready by July. In such a short space of time, he couldn't have done any more. He had bought the previous year's championship-winning car and had that team building a new one for him as well. Triple Eight's star driver, Jamie Whincup, was so dismayed by his team's decision to help out Daniel that he criticised the move in the press. It was clear he was worried that the new kid on the block was going to soon be a serious contender. But he had no need to worry: in good time, Daniel was planning to snap him up as well.

But for now Daniel had the perfect driver in mind, Marcus Marshall, a vastly experienced performer, with over 12 years of racing behind him, at a variety of different levels. Daniel and Marcus were in fact firm friends having met socially on the Gold Coast. While they enjoyed socialising together, Daniel had also got him involved at a Make-A-Wish day, which Sam had organised for terminally ill children, at Queensland Raceway. All of the kids had a day to remember as they were driven around the track by Marcus in Daniel's Lamborghini. Daniel had been the biggest kid of the lot. He had loved it. Daniel knew that his friend could more than hold his own in V8 racing. And not only was he a capable driver, Marcus was also interested in building a team from the bottom up. All things considered, he was the perfect fit for where the team was right now.

Quickly Marcus set about putting together a team that could help him be competitive. From experience he knew a solid team manager was a must, so he hired Keith Evers, his old boss from his Formula Ford days. As well as build a solid team around him, Marcus also helped Daniel spend close to $3.5 million on renting a garage on the Gold Coast as well as purchasing trailers, wheel rims, tyres, racing suits, spare car doors, bonnets, tool boxes, a drill press and racing fuel. No one said winning came cheap.

Adelaide's Clipsal 500, a street track which had once hosted Formula 1, was to mark the debut of the fledgling team Daniel had coined, Team Inta-Racing. At 3.2 km a lap, with fourteen brutal corners, the race was considered to be one of the hardest on the circuit. Despite wanting to be a championship-winning team in the long run, Marcus told Daniel that first time out it would be an achievement just to get some points on the board.

As the team prepared for their debut race, Daniel was determined to throw the mother of all launch parties. Travelling by private jet from Brisbane, he had invited a handful of business associates, some of whom had expressed an interest in investing in a payday loan portfolio, to join him on the trip to Adelaide. Once there, they would be taken on a VIP tour of the Team Inta-Racing garage before heading to one of the track's Gold Boxes, from where they would watch the race, wallowing in luxury.

Yet while Daniel was looking forward to partying and selling payday loan opportunities, he realised that there was one person that just had to be there for the day to be perfect: his dad. During his teenage years, the two had bonded over their love of motorsport. Such was their fascination that Kim had even bought an old Austin A30 so he could teach Daniel how to put together an engine. Now they would get the chance to bond over their own team in Australia's premier racing competition. It was the perfect way for Daniel to pay back his dad after all he had done for him.

However, with the jet sat humming on the runway in Brisbane, and with champagne already flowing freely, Kim Tzvctkoff lowered his tall frame through the doorway, took one look inside, and promptly walked off. 'Dad!' Daniel cried, unbuckling his seat-belt, racing along the aisle and towards the tarmac. 'Where are you going? We're about to take off.'

'You go ahead, son,' Kim replied, his grey hair ruffled by the wind. 'I'll make my own way there.'

'What are you talking about? You've got a seat on a private plane with me!'

Turning his eyes away from his son, Kim took a moment to choose his words carefully. 'I would just be more comfortable in a normal plane. That's all,' he finally said, putting one hand on his son's shoulder to reassure him.

Removing his over-sized aviator sunglasses, Daniel looked his father in the eyes. 'Come on, Dad,' he pleaded. 'Come with us and have some champagne. We will have a laugh.'

'No. Seriously, mate. You go ahead. I'll see you there.'

With that, Kim turned his back and made his way to the terminal. Daniel watched on bemused. He couldn't understand why his father couldn't enjoy the finer things in life. It almost seemed like it was a chore to him. Shrugging his shoulders he re-boarded the plane. This wasn't quite what he had in mind, but no matter; so long as his dad was there for the race that was what really counted. At the end of the day, Daniel just wanted him to be happy.

Two hours later, after the party had gone through the best part of a crate of champagne, a limo was waiting at Adelaide airport to take the rowdy group to the race track. For close to half an hour, the limo waited for Kim Tzvetkoff to arrive but it was to no avail. He was a no-show. With time ticking away, it was decided that they would just have to make their way to the circuit without him.

Shortly afterwards, the raucous party pulled up at the circuit. Making their way through the pits, where the smell of oil and rubber dominated the humid air, and the sound of highly tuned engines made the floor vibrate, they were happily distracted by an array of Grid Girls, who were dressed provocatively in black hot pants and crop tops. As photographers surrounded the group, Daniel stood triumphantly in the middle, with his arms around two of the beauties. Laughing and joking, it was clear that he was in his element.

Continuing to march their way excitedly through the paddock, with VIP lanyards hanging from their necks, Daniel and his impressed associates rubbed shoulders with the sport's top drivers – Jamie Whincup, Craig Lowndes and Mark Skaife – before they finally saw the Team Inta-Racing red, number 77 Ford Falcon parked in front of a garage.

'Marcus!' Daniel shouted upon seeing his driver in the team's trademark red Access Cash overalls.

'Hey Dan. How's it going?' Marcus smiled, shaking his boss's hand, slapping him on the back as he did so.

'All set for today?' Daniel asked his driver hopefully, as everyone gathered behind him to listen in. 'I saw we start at twenty-first on the grid. Any chance of getting some points on the board?'

'You bet. We may be at the back of the grid, but that's where I'm at my most dangerous,' Marcus winked, laughing.

'Marcus!' the team manager, Keith Evers, suddenly yelled from the back of the garage. 'Come over here, will ya. I need you to take a look at this.'

'Excuse me,' Marcus apologised, as he disappeared into the back.

While Marcus went off, Daniel took his phone from his pocket and tried to call his father. Again, no response. Where was he? 'Let's get up to the box guys. Race starts soon and we've got a ton of champagne to get through,' Daniel announced to the group, a bit perturbed that his father was still nowhere to be seen. It was only twenty-five minutes until the race got underway. At this rate he would miss it.

Leading the group into his box, which was situated on the top of the Grand Stand, and had unparalleled views overlooking the first chicane, Daniel finally caught sight of his father wandering aimlessly down below. Finally, he had arrived – just in the nick of time. 'Dad!' he shouted, which saw Kim look up towards the box. 'We are up here.' Kim nodded, 'Be right up.'

With the waitresses liberally pouring yet more glasses of champagne, John Anderson, a wealthy friend of Jason Galanis, the New York financier who was very interested in having his own payday lending portfolio at Trendsact, sat down next to Daniel on the balcony.

'Jason sent me through the projection charts,' Anderson began, putting on his sunglasses to shield his eyes from the glare of the sun reflecting off the oily track. 'I'm impressed. If I were to pump fifty million into the portfolio, how would it all work?'

This was music to Daniel's ears. Excitedly he set about outlining the incredible opportunities of payday loans and the type of profits Anderson could make. Anderson was entranced. Smiling at every word, Daniel knew that he had him. As he continued to reel him in Kim walked onto the balcony.

'Where can I get a beer, mate?' he asked, only to be blanked. Daniel was too caught up in his pitch to answer. Going back inside, Kim helped himself to one from the fridge and stood awkwardly. Everyone seemed to know each other. And everyone appeared rich and important – at least they acted that way. He felt like a fish out of water. He didn't have any portfolios to discuss. He just wanted to talk about the racing.

Suddenly a huge roar emanated from the crowd outside. The cars had lined up on the grid. The start of the race was imminent. As everyone hurriedly rushed to the balcony to take their seats, Kim was left standing alone at the back. Daniel was too caught up in his conversation with Anderson to notice.

Cheering and hollering, the crowd spiralled into a frenzy as the cars hummed their engines. Red light. Green light. A roaring crescendo of power. A huge cheer. They were off.

'Come on, Marcus!' Daniel screamed as his driver passed the box on the Senna Chicane, overtaking on the inside corner to go up to twentieth place. Cruising through the gears, the party watched in awe as the Access Cash-sponsored car powered its way through the field. Clipping bumpers, spinning corners, jostling for position with rivals, it was all happening. Jumping out of their seats every time Marcus passed them, the group, led by Daniel, roared him on. And after two hours of racing, Team Inta-Racing had its first points on the board. The red 77 had crossed the line in fourteenth place. It was a more than commendable debut. That was certainly what Neil Crompton, V8 analyst for Channel Seven, told millions of viewers. It was clear that Team Inta-Racing had the potential to be a serious player.

Cheering himself hoarse, Daniel raised his arms in triumph. 'Get in there!' he screamed on the edge of the balcony, grabbing a bottle of bubbly, shaking it vigorously before joining his guests in spraying each other in champagne. He had conquered the world of business, his nightclub was killing it, a film was in the pipeline – and now he was making his mark in the world of sport. He felt indestructible. But as he wiped the champagne from his eyes, Daniel looked around to realise his father was nowhere to be seen. In fact, he realised he hadn't seen him in over half an hour. He was gone. And suddenly, so was Daniel's feeling of invincibility.

22

Brisbane, Australia, February 2009

Bumper to bumper. The beeping of horns. Exhaust fumes mixing with the humid air creating a foggy mirage. Tiredness, frustration and over-heating affecting almost everyone involved. It was Brisbane rush hour. The race to escape the city was on. Sam Sciacca in particular was looking forward to getting home after a day spent trying to placate the poker boys. Processing was currently like wading through thick sludge. Daniel had told them that trying to move tens of millions of dollars in and out of the US each month was becoming more and more difficult, but the poker boys didn't want to hear this. Intabill was well behind on the processing and passing payments onto them. As such they were very concerned that they weren't going to get their money. The time for excuses had come to an end. Now they were just interested in results.

So, as Sam finally pulled out of the city and got onto the freeway, the last thing on earth he wanted to do was to discuss any more work, let alone see the name Shelley Courtney, Intabill's CFO, flash up on his car phone. He had spent weeks with her trying to get to the bottom of the accounts while Daniel, who knew all of the nitty-gritty, had effectively stonewalled her. It was starting to get embarrassing.

But when Sam answered the phone, expecting to have Shelley ask more questions he was unable to answer, he was pleased to hear that she had finally managed to make some sense of the numbers. This should have been a load off his mind. Now they could at least get the audit into ASIC and get on with their lives. However, it seemed that rather than the end of a nightmare it was just the beginning.

'What do you mean the numbers are wrong?' Sam shouted towards his car phone as Shelley broke the news.

'I mean they are wrong, Sam,' Shelley bluntly replied. 'You're not making as much money as you think you are.'

Pulling over onto the hard shoulder, Sam tried to digest what Shelley was telling him. 'Well, how much are we making?'

Clearing her throat Shelley hit Sam with the news he was dreading: 'Daniel's figures say that Intabill is making approximately thirty-two million dollars profit per year. My figures suggest that you are actually only making eight to twelve million.'

It was bad. The company, and Daniel, had been spending money based on his figures. If they were wrong then they were in deep shit. 'And you owe more money than you think as well,' Shelley continued, offering another blow.

Gripping the steering wheel in frustration Sam meekly asked: 'How much?'

As Shelley paused, Sam shouted: 'Come on, Shelley. Don't mess about. Hit me with it.'

'Sam,' she said, wishing she didn't have to be the bearer of bad news, 'Intabill currently owe the poker companies at least seventy million dollars.'

Sam's mouth dropped open wide with astonishment.

'That's the amount you need to repay within twelve months.'

'Shelley,' Sam said, his voice slightly quivering in shock. 'I need to call Daniel. Let me get back to you.'

Hanging up the phone, Sam immediately tried to contact Daniel who was in Las Vegas. With Vegas being seventeen hours ahead of Brisbane, it was always difficult to reach each other, but Sam was prepared to do whatever it took to get hold of his partner. Finally, after a few tries, Daniel answered the phone as he walked the floor at Trendsact. 'Sammy,' he cheerfully answered. 'How you doing, mate?'

'Look, Dan. I've just spoken to Shelley. We've got a big problem.'

'Oh yeah. What's up?'

'The accounts are wrong.'

Daniel laughed: 'Of course they're wrong. She hasn't had access to the books at Trendsact. That's where all the money is now. On paper Intabill may look fucked but in reality we are sitting on a mountain of cash out here in the desert.'

Sam realised Daniel may be right. As there wasn't an official link between Trendsact and Intabill, Shelley hadn't been required to look into the payday loan books. Sure, she had tried, but Daniel had closed that door in her face. He didn't want her snooping around. The fewer people who knew what was going on with Trendsact the better. At that moment in time, even Sam didn't know the true situation in Vegas.

Feeling slightly better about the situation, Sam started to calm down, 'OK, mate. I'm going back to the office right now. I'll send you the accounts and you see what you think, but it looks like we may owe the poker boys more than we thought and ...'

'Don't worry about that,' Daniel interrupted. 'Some of the money we "owe" is money that was seized or frozen. They're lucky we said we would reimburse them because we sure didn't have to. If they have to wait for it, then they have to wait for it. And we are still owed money from a number of processors. Shelley doesn't have that figure.'

This was all true, Sam couldn't deny it, but he also couldn't deny that they were now behind on the reserve and some of the float. 'The fact still remains that we need to pay something up right now. Isai and Ray are going nuts, especially as processing is so slow at the minute.'

'Tell them to relax. When we hit them with the Indian reservation solution all their worries are over. And the reserves are right here at Trendsact. No need to worry.'

'I know, mate. I know,' Sam answered, trying his best to get across to Daniel that wherever the money was, it still had to be repaid as of now. 'But the Intabill books currently show a massive deficit and we need to get the accounts to ASIC sharpish. We need to start pumping money over from Trendsact into the Intabill account and then repay the reserves and some of the float. That way we get ASIC and the poker boys off our backs.'

For a moment, there was silence as Daniel considered this conundrum. While he appreciated some of the poker money needed paying back, he was also conscious that as of late processing had been getting harder and harder. The main solution to this problem was of course the Indian reservation processing deal, but this wasn't cheap to set up. To get it up to the required standard, as quickly as possible, they needed all the cash they had. However, once that was in place, then the processing floodgates would once again open. They could process poker money hassle-free and everyone would get their money. It wasn't too far away now, either. Butch and Curtis hoped to have things ready to roll in a matter of weeks.

Furthermore, the purchase of HKB Bank in Germany was also close to being sealed. This would allow Intabill to process credit card transactions at will. With unrestricted ACH access in the US and the ability to process credit cards hassle-free, they would finally have complete control of the operation, one of the only processors in the world with such a capability. In addition, they had also recently set up IB Global, a new subsidiary which was looking into other profit channels in the processing world.

In order to give IB Global some real clout, they were on the verge of appointing two real heavy hitters: Andrew Pipolo, former CEO of PayPal in Australia, and Paul Lilley, who was a top executive at one of Australia's largest banks. With these two guys on board, Daniel fully expected to be able to push on to the next level. Indeed, they were already looking into opening a new office in New York – Long Island to be exact – where they would join up with Merrick Bank, processing accounts for low-risk merchants. This would keep things ticking over if there were ever any major issues with the high-risk stuff, as there had been with the poker money lately.

However, while these deals were all in place, and costing a fortune to set up, they were not yet ready to go. In the meantime, all the poker boys saw was that they were owed money, and processing was slowing down significantly. While they waited to be repaid, their own businesses were suffering. As such they were on the warpath.

Recognising that while they waited for all of this to take off, they may have to plug a few holes, Daniel asked: 'How much do we need to pay up right away to keep the poker boys happy?'

'I'll have to double check,' Sam answered. 'But I reckon all in all it's around forty million dollars.'

Daniel knew there was no way he could take $40 million out of Trendsact at once, not in one big chunk, as it could seriously slow down the portfolio. And they needed the portfolio to carry on hitting target to keep Intabill afloat while they waited for everything to take off.

'We have the money,' Daniel began. 'But we are really going to struggle if we take that out in one go.'

'You're just going to have to square it with Curtis then, mate.'

'Square what?' Daniel shot back, not quite sure what Sam was getting at.

'Withdrawing some of our money gradually from the payday loan portfolio. If we can't take it all out in one go, then we need to at least start paying some of it back as a sign of good faith.'

'I don't know, Sam,' Daniel said, while watching Curtis through his blinds motivating his troops on the call-centre floor. 'Curtis isn't going to like that one bit.'

Sam had to bite his tongue. He was sick to death of everyone pandering to Curtis Pope. Curtis Pope was just their employee. Technically, he should have no say in the matter.

'I don't give a damn what Curtis likes,' Sam snapped, trying in vain to keep a cool head. 'He's our employee and he will do as he is Goddamn told. If we don't take some of the money out right now then this whole thing could collapse. We need to buy ourselves some time. It's all very well saying we have a mountain of cash in the portfolio, and when all our deals are finalised we can process hassle-free, but Isai and Ray are going berserk. They want their money. NOW!'

Daniel sat down in his black leather chair, twiddling a pen in his hand as he thought everything over. The payday loan portfolio was flying, and they were also close to agreeing a $60 million investment from Jason Galanis, which would really ramp things up. Taking money out gradually shouldn't necessarily be a massive problem. The profits Trendsact was making, coupled with the Galanis investment, certainly should keep everything ticking over.

But Daniel also knew that Curtis wasn't going to take this well. Everything was working like a dream. Money was flying in. The portfolio was on steroids, and then some. If they took some money out now, it could temporarily slow things down. For a few weeks they may not have large enough reserves to enable them to make as many loans as they had been doing recently. But, at the end of the day, the initial capital was the poker reserve. If they wanted to continue processing in the future, and to have the money to make available for more payday loans, then first and foremost they had to make sure the poker boys were happy.

'I'll speak to Curtis,' Daniel finally answered.

'Good,' Sam replied, understanding that they were in the middle of an extremely delicate balancing act. Keeping the poker boys sweet on one hand and buying the business some time on the other.

'So what are you going to do in the meantime?' Daniel asked.

'I'm going to see Isai Scheinberg,' Sam ominously replied. It was time to do or die.

23

London, UK, February 2009

Sam felt like shit. Standing in the grey drizzle, taking a drag of a cigarette, he waited outside London's Royal Garden Hotel, a five-star establishment which backed on to Kensington Palace, once the home of Princess Diana, and tried to get his head together. Just over an hour earlier, he had touched down at Heathrow after a twenty-five-hour flight from Brisbane. It had now been over thirty-six hours since he had managed to get any sleep. For the duration of the flight, he had worked tirelessly. This meeting had the potential to make or break Intabill. He needed to buy them some time. That's all they needed, time, then this whole mess would blow over.

As soon as he had finished speaking to Daniel, he had got straight on the phone to Isai Scheinberg, the chief of PokerStars. Isai was a guy who appreciated honesty, even if it was bad news. If he was upfront with Isai, and had a sensible plan of action in place, then Sam hoped that he would grant them a stay of execution. At the end of the day, as Daniel had said, once the reservation processing solution was up and running, then Intabill could solve all of the poker companies' problems in one big swoop. Sam just needed to make Isai see that. However, that was easier said than done when they owed his company tens of millions of dollars, some of which was payable immediately.

Isai had been in Toronto when they spoke, but he was due to catch a plane to London later that day. It had therefore been agreed that Sam would meet him at the Royal Garden Hotel. Now, just a day later, Sam was there, cursing the shitty weather, ready for action. As of yet, there was no word on when Daniel could wire through some of the payday loan money, but Daniel seemed to think it would be OK. It had better be OK, Sam had thought. It was all very well him trying to broker some sort of deal with Isai, but if the money from Trendsact didn't come through then they wouldn't be able to honour it. And that really would be the end.

Throwing his cigarette into a puddle on the wet concrete, Sam stepped on it with his Gucci loafers. It was time. Putting up his suit jacket collar to shield himself from the driving rain, he made his way to the hotel's entrance. Squeaking his wet loafers across the beige marble floor, Sam marched determinedly through the bustling lobby, fully focused on the mantra reverberating through his head.

Seal the deal. Seal the deal. Seal the deal.

Entering the lift, Sam pressed the button for the eighth floor to make his way to Isai's suite. While the hotel was regarded as one of London's finest, Sam had little doubt that Isai wouldn't have splashed out on an overly extravagant room. Sure, Isai had a lot of money, but when Sam had previously met him, at PokerStars' Isle of Man headquarters, he had been surprised at the billionaire's frugality. Rather than lay out a fancy spread, the lunch that he had served had consisted of a tray of soggy sandwiches. And his office was far from what you would expect from a poker kingpin. The only thing slightly memorable was the signed movie poster of *Ocean's Eleven* that hung on his wall. Isai loved that movie, as he never tired of telling everyone who he met. He was certainly a shrewd guy who looked after his money and drove a hard bargain.

As Sam thought everything through, the ring of the lift bell told him he had reached his destination. Stepping out, he navigated the hotel's long corridors, before he found what he was looking for: Isai's room. Taking a moment to compose himself, Sam fixed his tie before taking a deep breath. This was it. Knocking on the door, Sam tapped his foot nervously as he waited for it to be answered. Suddenly the door swung open. A familiar face stood behind it. It was Isai.

Short, slight and with parted grey hair, Isai looked nothing like the few pictures said to be of him on the internet. Isai often laughed that most of them weren't even close to any sort of resemblance. It was quite astonishing that the poker billionaire had managed to stay under the radar for so long.

'Sam,' Isai greeted, as he shook Sam's hand. 'Come in. Come in.'

Entering the spacious living room area, Sam took a seat across from Isai.

'Thank you for coming all this way to see me,' Isai began. 'Would you like some food? A drink, perhaps?'

'No thank you, Isai. I'm good.'

'Very well. So, what is the purpose of your visit?'

Sam and Daniel called Isai 'The Matrix'. He had an uncanny ability to start a conversation with basic questions and would later try to trap you with your answers as his questions became more complicated. Only after you had completed Isai's 'matrix of truth' would he be satisfied. But today Sam had no time for 'The Matrix'. He was just going to hit him with it.

'Isai, I know you like people who work with you to be honest. So here it is: I've come here to tell you that I know we owe you a lot of money. But the thing is, we can't repay it.' Isai's thick eyebrows shot up, resulting in severe frown lines on his forehead. 'Not yet, anyway,' Sam continued tentatively, as he sat on the edge of his chair. 'We have a short-term cashflow problem brought on by a number of factors.

But I have a proposal for you to consider which will see you get all of your money back in full.'

Reaching forward, Isai picked up a heavily buttered hot-cross bun and slowly took a bite out of it. His right eye squinted heavily as he looked at Sam. It was the type of look a disappointed father may give his son when they misbehave. 'Go on,' he finally said, his mouth still full of food. 'I'm listening.'

Taking a spreadsheet from his black leather suitcase, Sam handed it over. Removing a pair of square reading glasses from the top pocket of his white shirt, Isai perched them on the end of his nose and muttered to himself as he read through Sam's proposal.

'As you can see,' Sam said, 'not only can we repay you one hundred and fifty thousand dollars a week, but if you ramp processing levels up to three million dollars a day with us, we will process for free until the debt is fully repaid. If you agree to this then everything will be squared off within six months.'

This was a high-risk strategy. Despite telling Isai Intabill could not immediately repay the huge debt, Sam had effectively asked for an increase in business from PokerStars. Leaving Sam to squirm in silence, Isai continued to read before he placed the papers on the table in front of him. Resting back into his chair he took off his glasses and placed them back into his pocket. It seemed like an age had passed before he spoke again. The only sounds in the room were the rain hammering against the windows and the wind whistling through the trees outside. The British weather had once again not failed to disappoint.

'You are asking a lot for someone who owes my company a lot of money,' Isai finally said, his tone not giving much away.

Sam decided it was time Isai knew about the reservation processing solution. After all, if Sam was going to persuade him to ramp up the volume, he had to know they could process it all.

'I know we are asking a lot, Isai,' Sam said, looking him dead in the eye. 'And I know things have been tough lately, but we think we have come up with a solution that is going to make all of our futures bright and rosy.'

With that Sam launched into a description of how the reservation solution would work. Isai listened on, not interrupting. He looked to be working out a complex mathematical equation. As Sam finished speaking, PokerStars' head honcho put his hand up to his mouth as he went into a deep thought: 'That is very interesting, Sam. Very interesting. But I need to see a sign of good faith from you before I agree to this.'

Sam nodded his head. He understood that Isai was in the position to call the shots. They had to do whatever was necessary to keep him on side. 'I want two five-million-dollar payments made by the end of March,' Isai forcefully demanded. 'I don't care how you do it but that's what I want.'

This would be difficult. Sam knew that the only way they could raise that sort of cash immediately was by taking it out of the payday loan portfolio or by selling assets. Sam knew that this could significantly slow down the new processing solutions which were relying on that cash, and infrastructure, to get set up. In fact, it could scupper them altogether. And there was another thing: he didn't even know if he could get his hands on that sort of money in that timeframe.

'I know you like honesty,' Sam said leaning forwards. 'So I won't bullshit you. I don't know if that will be possible. I will try everything within my power to raise that money in that amount of time but I can't guarantee it.'

Again Isai squinted, showing his obvious displeasure. 'Those are my terms, Sam. I want ten million dollars by the end of March, as well as some sort of security. Just to give me some reassurance that you intend to carry out your obligations.'

Giving out any sort of personal guarantee was the last thing Sam wanted to do. However, he knew that it may well have come to this.

At the moment, he didn't really have that much choice. 'If that is what you want, Isai, then that is what we will do. I will put my balls on the line. I am a man of my word, as I know you are. But you have to agree to ramp up the processing volume with us. That is the only way we can sort out all of this as quickly as possible.'

'If you keep your word, then you have my word,' Isai replied. 'But if for any reason you renege on this deal, Sam, I will not hesitate to enforce the guarantee. Do you understand?'

Sam slowly nodded his head. He was still in the game but the pressure was continuing to increase.

With the meeting at an end, and an agreement in place, Sam got a taxi straight back to Heathrow and was on the next plane to Brisbane. While PokerStars were somewhat satisfied, he now had a meeting with Full Tilt Poker's representatives to prepare for the following day, followed by a conversation with Brent Beckley at Absolute Poker. In order to keep Intabill afloat, they needed all of the poker companies on board. Without them, it could very well be game over.

Unsurprisingly, Full Tilt was also determined to drive a hard bargain. Chief Ray Bitar had sent head of processing Nelson Burtnick and his associate David Quach to Brisbane to get to the bottom of things. Having met in the boardroom at Intabill negotiations were fraught. Burtnick in particular was hell bent on making things as difficult as possible. They were fed up of hearing excuses. They just wanted their money.

After a day of toing and froing, an agreement was finally put in place. Intabill would pay Full Tilt $250,000 a week, and would also process for free until the full debt was paid off. Unsurprisingly, Full Tilt also wanted personal guarantees. In exchange for all of this they had, however, thankfully agreed to ramp up the volume.

With Full Tilt and PokerStars on board, Sam also managed to negotiate a fee-free processing deal with Absolute Poker chief Brent

Beckley for the $4 million they owed him. It was time to celebrate. Not only was the company still alive, but if they could get through the next six months then they stood to make more money than ever before.

Sam was a nervous wreck. Over the course of the last four days he had barely slept. At least his efforts had not been in vain. As far as he was concerned, while it had been a nightmare, it had also been a vital learning experience. The company had grown enormously in the past year and as such it didn't have all of the necessary safeguards and procedures in place. From now on, he wanted to see the Trendsact books on the Intabill accounts. It was too much of a headache having the main cash cow hidden away, especially as it was out of his control.

Sat around their state-of-the-art, $50,000 boardroom table, Sam proceeded to pour Daniel, who had recently arrived back from Las Vegas, a large glass of champagne. Daniel still wasn't sure what all the fuss was about. Yes, they had owed a large sum of money, but they had more than enough in the pipeline to cover it. Why would the poker companies cut their nose off to spite their face? Intabill was the only company that could repay them their money and continue to process for them on such a large scale.

Taking a large sip from his glass, Sam picked up the phone. 'Let's call Curtis,' he said. 'Tell him the good news and sort out transferring some cash over so we can start making the repayments.'

'Sounds good,' Daniel replied, as Sam dialled Curtis Pope's number and put him on loudspeaker. After a few rings there was an answer.

'Curtis. It's Dan and Sam,' Sam shouted towards the phone. 'Good news. We've got all the boys on board. We need you to start sending through the money as we discussed.'

There was a long pause on the other end. 'Curtis? ... Curtis?'

'Yeah. That's good news guys,' Curtis murmured slowly. 'Did you meet with Isai and Ray?'

Sam was puzzled. How did Curtis know who Isai and Ray were?

He and Daniel had never let Curtis get too close to the source of their deals. He certainly shouldn't have known who they had been meeting with.

Putting his hand over the loudspeaker, so that Curtis couldn't hear, Sam whispered: 'Did you tell him about Isai and Ray?'

'No. Of course not,' Daniel whispered back, feeling equally as confused.

'We met with the poker guys, Curtis,' Sam said cautiously, as he took his hand off the speaker, 'and all is good so, like I said, we need the money. I know it's a pain in the short term, but the good news is that the poker companies are going to ramp up the volume, so soon we will have even more money to process via the reservation solution as well as to plough into loans.'

Again there was silence. Usually Curtis would be jabbering away. For some reason he didn't seem himself. 'Did you have to sign any guarantees?' he finally said.

'Yeah,' Daniel replied. 'We haven't signed them yet but that's what we are going to do.'

'Don't sign them,' Curtis blurted back. 'Whatever you do, don't sign them.'

'Why Curtis?' Sam shouted. 'Why shouldn't we sign them?'

This time there was no response. Curtis had hung up. Sam and Daniel both turned to look at each other with the same sinking feeling in their stomach. What the hell was going on?

24

Las Vegas, USA, April 2009

Civil war had erupted: Intabill v Trendsact. Intabill needed access to the loan portfolio to pay off the poker companies. Trendsact refused to release any funds for fear it would bring the whole pay-day loan operation down. The crux of the argument basically all came down to one thing: who actually owned the portfolio? Both parties thought they had a good case, as the emails below show.

From: Sam Sciacca
To: Mike Lane, Curtis Pope, John Scott Clark
Cc: Daniel Tzvetkoff; Michael Hui
Subject: Ownership

Hi Mike,

I sincerely appreciate the chat.
As spoke, we are the only owners of Hugo, which owns the portfolio and is the lender. Hugo, as you know, has the office leases, the agreements with the Selling Source, and licenses the software. You are our CEO.

*We are also the investor and we have invested funds obtained
from our merchants that we process on behalf of from the
processing reserves. Put simply: without the merchants and our
direction of those funds, none of this would be where we are today.
That was clear from the outset. When Curtis, John and Derek
visited us in Australia, it was made clear that this was the source
of funds for the investment.*

*I completely agree that we don't want to destroy this business and we
are not. We simply need to take out funds that can be taken from
not purchasing or funding new leads for a short period, to ensure
our longevity. I understand that it's not ideal, but again we don't
have a choice. I don't want to blow everything up. So in the overall
scheme of things, considering the outcomes of what will occur, this
should not be a problem for you, Curtis or anyone.*

*Moving forward, we would like to receive the daily wire. Please
have the discussion with Curtis as we spoke.*

Thanks, mate. This just has to be done.

Sam

From: Curtis Pope
To: Sam Sciacca; Daniel Tzvetkoff
Cc: Michael Hui; Mike Lane; John Scott Clark
Subject: Ownership

Daniel/Sam,

*I had a very long discussion with Mike regarding the disturbing
call last night with the both of you, Scott and myself.*
We have agreed on the following:
*The payday loan portfolio cannot sustain the change of direction
you are asking for, which is to stop funding new loans for 4-6*

*weeks. It will simply blow up the business model and
seriously damage our relationship with Selling Source/
London Bay Capital.*

*Your investment in the portfolio will be honoured by us. However,
you are an INVESTOR and nothing more. This has **always** been
the agreement, however, we have allowed you to cross the line in
the past in the interest of being cooperative. Given the
circumstances at hand, we now have to draw the line and set clear
boundaries. We will **not** allow Trendsact to be run into the ground
by irresponsible decisions and spending. This means, as with ANY
investor, you can visit our offices with prior notice for a day or two.
We will openly share with you the current state of the portfolio, but
will NOT allow you to make directorial decisions.*

*Over the last few months, we have had to pay a total of
$1,063,000 on expenditure for Daniel, which includes 200k
towards the Vegas nightclub venture, 91k towards his residence,
21k for televisions and computers, and 250k for the overly
extravagant, unwanted furniture fit-out on top of other things. We
only paid these things in the interest of being cooperative.*

*Regarding the above, there were multiple attempts by Mike and
myself to stop these magnificently irresponsible decisions. Mike
and I were **completely** against these expenditures now or at ANY
time!*

Curtis

Upon reading Curtis's response to his email, Sam felt his heart
tighten, his pulse race. Everything about the email offended him.
Everything. It had been clearly agreed who owned the portfolio.
Emails between Selling Source's John Hancock and Intabill had made
explicitly clear that Intabill could take money out whenever they
pleased. Draft contracts, which frustratingly had not been signed,
also said the same thing. Trendsact held the money on trust for

Hugo. Without Intabill there was nothing. If Intabill needed their money to keep the whole company alive then that was their right. What they needed the money for was of no concern to Curtis anyway. He was just their employee. Plain and simple.

Having looked at the numbers himself, Sam knew that Trendsact may have needed to slow down for a few weeks, but the amount they were looking to withdraw wouldn't bring the whole thing down. In any event, once they had got over this small speed bump, the new contracts with the poker companies were going to see them make more money than ever. Intabill would then be able to provide even more money for the loan portfolio. Why couldn't Curtis see this?

As for the expenditure allegations, Sam had concerns about that himself. He didn't need Curtis Pope to tell him that Daniel had been spending a lot of money, particularly on his Hedges Avenue mansion, but it was money that Sam thought was theirs to spend. The books showed it, Daniel confirmed it, and the accountants had signed off on it. In any event, Daniel was confident that even more money would soon be coming in. In spite of Sam asking him to calm down in the meantime, Daniel told him not to sweat it. Their business plan was foolproof. Nothing could stop them.

Daniel had also made a good point in his own defence: half of the payday loan profits were Intabill's! If he wanted to spend it, who was Curtis to dictate how and when he did? Curtis certainly didn't complain when Daniel had bought him a Ferrari or had treated him to nights out in Vegas. It was all a bit rich complaining now.

Just as things appeared to be getting out of hand, and Intabill was staring directly into the abyss, a conversation with Curtis saw things swing back around. Suddenly, it was all back on. Curtis had seen sense: he would forward them the money. This much was confirmed in emails the following day between Sam and Trendsact CEO Mike Lane.

From: Mike Lane
To: Sam Sciacca; Daniel Tzvetkoff
Cc: Curtis Pope; John Scott Clark
Subject: Moving Forward

Daniel, Sam,

*I've just spent an hour recapping the call that the both of you had
with Curtis last night. It's wonderful news!*
*It's a relief that we are now in a position to continue moving
forward as partners! It's been very uncomfortable the past few
weeks, and I am glad we are now over that.*
*In addition, I wanted to inform the both of you that I will be travelling
to South Dakota as the 'front man' for the tribal processing deal.*
In Curtis's words . . . he's too aggressive.
In Butch's and Scott's words . . . they are too bald.
*It's a good fit for me with my extensive background in opening
casinos (59 total) with a good portion of them being tribal.*
Thanks in advance. Onward and forward!
Mike

From: Sam Sciacca
To: Mike Lane
Cc: Daniel Tzvetkoff; Curtis Pope; John Scott Clark
Subject: Moving Forward!

Mike,

*That's fantastic mate. Thanks for all your help. Daniel and I are
ecstatic about the go forward. Sorry for any discomfort, but we
now have the best partnership around to make us an unbelievable
group and a money-making machine!*

*Daniel is out of the office til later, but I just called as soon as I
read your email and he is over the moon with this.
Thanks again, buddy!
Sam*

Everything now looked all set. The troops had been withdrawn
from the battlefield. The focus was now very much on settling debts
and realising Intabill's potential. The reservation processing deal
was imminent; HKB Bank was five or six weeks away from com-
pletion; Jason Galanis and others were set to invest over $100
million into the payday loan portfolio. Meanwhile, Trendsact continued to smash its targets, making over $1 million in profit most
weeks; Access Cash was one month from opening its doors in
Australia; and IB Global now had John Lilley and Andrew Pipolo
onboard. As well as that, Zuri nightclub was packed out, attracting
some of the world's biggest stars. And PokerStars, Full Tilt and
Absolute Poker had all ramped up their volume. Intabill was a
whisker away from absolutely smashing it out of the park. But for
all of this to kick off, they were relying on Curtis to come up with
the money, as he had promised.

However, as March came and went, and the deadline to start
making repayments to the poker companies had passed, Curtis still
failed to send through the wire. All he sent was excuse after excuse.
His favourite being: how could he trust Sam and Daniel to pay off the
poker companies? As far as they were concerned, that was none of his
business. Still they had to try to keep the fragile peace. Without the
money they were dead. Effectively they were already late making payment. If the money didn't arrive soon, then Sam knew full well that
PokerStars and Full Tilt would shut them down.

As Daniel sat across from Sam in their ground-floor office in
Brisbane, a cold sweat came across him as he looked at one of his
emails. Ashen-faced, he quickly scrolled down the screen. This

couldn't be happening. Feeling nauseous he turned to Sam and solemnly announced, 'We may have a problem.'

Looking up from a stack of papers, Sam tilted his head to the side: 'What do you mean, mate?'

'Come over here,' Daniel urged. 'Quickly.'

Sam had never seen Daniel look so worried. Usually everything was just a joke. Hurriedly walking across the room to see what was up, Daniel continued to talk. 'I've just had the Daily Payments Report sent over from Trendsact.'

'Right?' Sam said, not sure why this had caused his partner so much concern.

'Usually the report refers to Hugo, doesn't it?' Daniel said, pointing to the top of the page.

'Yeah,' Sam agreed, flashing his eyes to where Hugo was normally written, only to find it had been replaced by another entity. 'What the hell is Red Rivers?' Sam asked.

Swivelling around in his chair, Daniel looked up at Sam. 'That's it. I don't know. But if they've replaced Hugo with a new entity called Red Rivers, and have switched everything over to that, we may have just lost control of everything!'

'Oh my God!' Sam whispered. Stumbling backwards, he put one hand behind his head and paced around the office in distress. 'Shit, Dan! We are screwed without that money. Not only will Intabill collapse, but we have signed personal guarantees! We will lose everything.'

Daniel stared back at his partner, rubbing his palms on his knees, as a million thoughts raced through his head. Why was this happening? Despite short-term problems, the company was in great shape. All that needed to be done was for Curtis to release the money – *their money* – and all would be good.

'We need to get to Vegas,' Sam suggested, turning to face Daniel with fire in his eyes. 'Before it's too late.' Daniel nodded in full agreement. Vegas was their only hope now.

25

Las Vegas, USA, April 2009

Within a few hours, Daniel and Nicole, Sam and Michael Hui were all on the private jet on a mission to Vegas. Whatever happened, the jet needed to be returned there anyway. As of now the company could no longer afford to justify it, unless of course they could make Curtis see the light. Nicole had been adamant that she needed to go to Vegas to pick up all of her clothes from their house, as well as to arrange shipping their cars over to Australia. It was clear that after today it was extremely unlikely they would be returning to live in Vegas, whether they got their money back or not.

One of the many questions being asked on the jet was whether they should bring in the lawyers: get into Vegas, freeze the accounts, gain an injunction and cut Curtis and Scott Clark completely out of the picture. In a normal industry, that would have seemed the most sensible option. But payday loans, mixed with processing for online poker, was not exactly normal. Did they really want outside parties rooting through the carcass? It could be more trouble than it was worth. Intabill might collapse, and they might lose everything, but at least that would be the end of it.

Besides, there was no clear contract that had been signed by the parties outlining the relationship, not that Sam and Daniel thought one was necessary anyway, as they were the primary shareholders of the portfolio and therefore the party in control. But while this was the case, and there had been conversations, emails and draft agreements, which had made clear who was in charge, there was nothing absolutely set in stone. Without something more concrete, it could take time to convince a judge to freeze the accounts and to issue an injunction. Time was not a luxury they had right now. The repayment deadline with the poker companies had already passed. It was now or never.

While Michael and Nicole slept fully reclined in their seats, Daniel and Sam sat in silence, both consumed with their own thoughts. Just a few weeks previously, they had been on top of the world: everything was on track to turn Intabill into a global financial juggernaut. Daniel had estimated that within twelve months they would be able to float the company for as much as $1 billion. It was a figure even Sam couldn't disagree with. Even after Shelley had highlighted problems with the accounts, Daniel in particular had felt extremely confident that all would be well. But this was now serious: they may have had money tied up in assets, but the payday loan portfolio was currently their only liquid cash. Their only hope was to get hold of a big chunk of it, pass it on to the poker boys straight away, apologise profusely for the delay, and pray that they would continue with the relationship. If not then they were finished – it was as simple as that.

Daniel still held out hope that this was just Curtis trying to show them who was boss: a power-play that established him as the guy at the top of the food chain. Now he had made his point, there was a chance that he would stand down when they talked face to face. Surely his friend wouldn't do this to him?

Over the past year, Daniel had been closer to Curtis than anyone. Together they had played golf, gone to shows, raced cars and savoured the abundance of restaurants, clubs and bars that Vegas had to offer. Such was their relationship that they thought nothing of buying each other extravagant gifts: a Ferrari for Curtis, a top-of-the-range Rolex for Daniel. Their two families had also spent an enormous amount of time socialising, even spending Christmas together in Lake Tahoe. Curtis was almost like a second father to Hugo. The more Daniel thought about it, the more he thought he could win Curtis round. After all, Curtis was his mate, and mates don't feed each other to the wolves.

Yet across the other side of the plane Sam was rueing the day Andrew Thornhill had put them in touch with Curtis Pope. He should have trusted his gut. From the minute he had set eyes on the motormouth from Tampa, he had known he was no good. As far as he was concerned, if they could regain control of the portfolio, then he was cutting all ties with Curtis Pope.

After a refuelling stop in Hawaii, the plane eventually touched down at McCarran Airport at 11am Las Vegas time. Striding across the tarmac, with the hot sun already beating down high in the sky, the party made their way to the taxi rank. Finances dictated that limos were out of the question, for now anyway.

With no time to waste, Daniel, Sam and Michael hopped into a car to take them straight to Trendsact, while Nicole went to the house in Southern Highlands. It was time for an ambush. Curtis had already played enough games – now it was their turn. They were going to use the element of surprise to their advantage. Not only that, but they were going to march in and match fire with fire. Curtis usually did most of the talking, but not this time. They were going to take control, lay down the law and show him who was boss. At least, that was the plan.

However, upon jumping out of the taxi, and marching towards the Trendsact lobby like the cast from *Reservoir Dogs*, each of them dressed in dark suits and sunglasses, they were stopped in their tracks by a man mountain.

'Excuse me, gentlemen,' the Goliath greeted them in a thick New Jersey accent, looking like an extra from a Martin Scorsese film. 'What can I do for you?'

'We are here to see Curtis Pope,' Sam confidently announced, with Michael and Daniel flanked either side of him.

'Curtis Pope ain't seeing nobody today,' the goon growled, blocking the entrance.

'Listen, mate,' Sam shot back, his temperature rising, blood rushing to his head. 'These offices are ours. You can't stop us entering. Now move aside.'

Crossing his arms across his chest, the giant refused to budge.

'OK, mate. Have it your way. When I'm through with this shit, consider yourself on the unemployment line,' Sam threatened, as he took his phone from his pocket and called Curtis.

'Curtis!' Sam said, putting on his best don't-mess-with-me voice. 'It's Sam. We are outside and want to have a chat.'

Looking towards Curtis's office, they could see the blinds move and a pair of eyes peer through them.

'Sam,' Curtis hesitantly replied. 'Glad to see you've finally made it over here. Decided to finally get your hands dirty huh? Give me two seconds.'

While the goon now stood aside, having been given the go-ahead to let the party in, he continued to walk closely behind them as they entered the building. Daniel began to feel very uncomfortable. What were they walking into? After his conversation with Curtis about Chad Elie, he understood that his friend knew people who operated on the wrong side of the law. Were those people now involved in this?

Marching into Curtis's office without waiting to be invited, they saw that he was sat behind his desk, chatting on the phone. No matter. They were like wild dogs about to be let off the leash. They weren't going to be dicked around. This was their time to speak. And by God, Curtis Pope was going to listen.

'Just one second,' Curtis said to the person he was speaking to on the telephone. 'I'm just going to put you on loudspeaker so you and I can explain to the guys what's what.'

Who the hell was he speaking to, Daniel wondered? Probably John Scott Clark. No doubt the two of them had concocted some sort of bullshit story by now, but it wasn't going to wash. They weren't interested in anything but getting their money back.

'Boys,' Curtis said with a huge grin on his face. 'I want you to meet my new partner in the processing game, Isai Scheinberg.'

Sam, Daniel and Michael all looked at each other in horror. *Isai!*

'Curtis, what's going on?' Sam stuttered, completely deflated.

Flashing a smile, and putting his right index finger to his lips to silence Sam, it was clear that Curtis was relishing the moment. 'Isai,' he continued, 'As we have discussed, all of your money is tied up with me in Las Vegas in payday loans. Not only that, but as you now know this is where we do all of the processing. I'm just telling the boys that you don't trust Daniel to do the right thing any more so you've decided to be my partner. I can repay you all of the money and process for you, so you don't have to worry about a thing. It will all be perfect, my friend. Perfect.'

'Very good, Curtis,' the voice of Isai Scheinberg confirmed, cutting through the tense air. 'Very good.'

Daniel felt weak at the knees; he was close to throwing up. Curtis, on the other hand, continued to smile like he had just won the lottery. 'And as you now know,' Curtis continued, 'Ryan Lang and Andrew Thornhill have been out here, along with Ray Bitar and Nelson Burtnick of Full Tilt, to look over the tribal processing deal in South Dakota. It's a no-brainer, Isai. Ryan and Andrew will take real good care of that for you at my end.'

The hits just kept on coming. No wonder Curtis hadn't released the money to Intabill: he knew he was onto a winner if he could persuade the poker companies that he could repay them all of their money as well as handle all of their future processing needs. Curtis had used PokerStars to kill Intabill. And while Sam and Daniel had run themselves ragged trying to ensure they could meet the repayment deadline, Curtis had ensured that would be all but impossible as he tried to construct and broker his deal. As a result, Intabill had been forced to default on the written and verbal agreements with the poker companies, making Curtis the main beneficiary in the process. Curtis Pope had just got a full house on the river. And Intabill were drawing dead. In one swoop, they had just lost their payday loan portfolio as well as their biggest clients, PokerStars and Full Tilt.

Sam was stunned. Intabill was a legit company on the verge of global expansion. It had top lawyers, accountants, police officers and security staff working for it, yet Isai and Ray had decided to make a commercial decision and go with Curtis – a Las Vegas hot-head with a criminal record. But this was what it had come to: in their eyes, Curtis Pope was a safer bet than Intabill. And why not? The way it looked to them, Intabill was a company who owed them a heap of money and had repeatedly failed to meet set deadlines. Sam couldn't blame them. At the end of the day they just wanted their money back.

'One moment, Isai,' Curtis said, while the boys tried in vain to process the bombshell he had just dropped. 'I've got someone else on the line who I think you will want to speak to.'

What now?

'Chad!' Curtis shouted cheerfully. 'I've got our new partner Isai Scheinberg on the phone. I was just about to tell him how you've got his four million bucks for him.'

'No problem, Curtis,' the voice of Chad Elie confirmed. 'I've got it ready to go for Mr Scheinberg.'

Chad! How did Curtis suddenly know where he was? He had told Daniel that his efforts had hit a dead end and that Chad had disappeared with the money, which they were unlikely ever to see again.

'OK, Isai,' Curtis continued, as he wrapped up the conversation. 'Great speaking with you again. I'll see you in the Isle of Man!'

The click of the phone being placed onto the receiver signalled the end of the conversation, as well as the end of Intabill.

'Well, boys,' Curtis chirped smugly. 'That's the way the chips fall, I'm afraid.'

'But why, Curtis?' Daniel finally uttered, still reeling.

'Because I could,' Curtis smirked in return, suddenly darting his thick neck forward. 'Because you fucked this up for everyone and now I'm taking care of business.'

Who needs enemies when you have friends like these, Daniel thought to himself, knowing full-well the game was just about up. Or was it . . .

26

Las Vegas, USA, April 2009

Following Curtis Pope's revelations, it seemed the party was officially over. But Sam and Daniel realised that they might still have one solitary card left to play: Selling Source, the patron saint of all that was supposedly good and holy in the payday lending universe.

Trendsact was one of Selling Source's brightest stars, a multi-million dollar payday loan monster who was hungrily devouring all of their top leads. And Intabill were of course the primary money men behind Trendsact. So Sam and Daniel hoped that Selling Source would see that, without Intabill, Trendsact would suffer, and in turn they would suffer. It was a long shot but appealing to Selling Sources' wallet appeared to be their only hope.

Over the last few months, Daniel had become very close to Alton Irby, one of the top guys behind the money-making machine that was London Bay Capital, the private equity group who actually called the shots at Selling Source. Alton was a Texan billionaire in his mid-seventies who liked to shoot from the hip. He had made his money in banking and prided himself on knowing a good thing when he saw one. When he saw Daniel, he thought he was seeing a real good thing. He virtually treated him like a son. Many a time they had enjoyed a fine meal together in Las Vegas shooting the breeze, where Daniel would talk excitedly about his various new business ideas while Alton would try to give him some friendly advice, things he wished he had known when he was Daniel's age. There was no doubt that he held a soft spot for the whiz-kid from Brisbane. If Daniel was in trouble, then Sam could just envision Alton getting on his horse, packing his pistol into his holster and riding valiantly to the rescue.

What's more, for some reason, Curtis Pope was scared of him. He knew Alton was the big swinging dick of the payday loan empire. If Alton wanted to take you down then you might as well forget about it. Your career in that industry was as good as dead. It was a long shot, but if they could just get Alton to lay down some home truths to Curtis – that he was nothing but a butt-sniffing employee of Intabill, not the main man – then they may yet get out of this catastrophic mess.

Meeting at Alton's suite at the Four Seasons, one of Las Vegas's more sophisticated hotels, which was located on the top floor of the glittering gold monument that was the Mandalay Bay Tower, Sam and Daniel explained their position: Intabill was flourishing but had a short-term cashflow problem. If they could get over this speed bump, then the future fizzed with possibilities, with Selling Source being a prime beneficiary. But if Curtis was allowed to pull the plug on them, then Intabill couldn't survive and all the great things they had in the pipeline would be over. Effectively, Sam and Daniel were saying: who do you trust more to pump business your way, Curtis or us?

Listening intently, and nodding his head when required, Alton seemed particularly convinced that he could sort this whole mess out for them. He saw no reason why they couldn't work this out like gentlemen. Maybe some wires had got crossed somewhere along the way, but if they all sat down and talked it out then Selling Source, Intabill and Trendsact could all get along just fine.

Inviting Curtis to join them in the oversized suite, Daniel and Sam prayed that once he had been read the riot act they could salvage this situation. Alton would be the principal, Curtis the naughty school-boy. After six of the best from Alton's cane, then Curtis would be a quivering wreck. Yet far from acting contrite, Curtis refused to back down. Gesticulating wildly, and refusing to take a seat, he vented his spleen: 'No. No way. No fucking way,' he repeated. 'This is my company and it's my deal. If Sam and Dan can't pay their customers on time then that's their problem.'

He was sweating profusely, his eyes bulging as he ranted. Good, Sam thought. Let Alton see just what a crazy son of a bitch he is.

'Let me stop you there,' Sam interrupted, as Alton watched on, not yet wanting to take sides. 'Firstly, Trendsact isn't your company; it's ours. We set it up; we provided the capital. You were installed to run it for us. You are our employee.'

'Then why the hell isn't your name on any of the Trendsact company documents?' Curtis snapped, jutting his head forward aggressively. 'I work for no one but me. Curtis fucking Pope!'

'And the money isn't yours, either,' Sam ploughed on, not wanting Curtis's rants to break his stride. 'We had an agreement that we could withdraw it at any time. You knew this. That was the poker compa-nies' reserve money that we had an obligation to pay back.'

'Bullshit! Fucking bullshit. If you take that much money out, then you'll wreck the whole thing.'

Walking backwards and forwards with energy to burn, Curtis ruf-fled his hand through his hair. Large sweat patches began to emerge through his blue shirt as he continued to work himself into a frenzy. 'No. No. No. This is bullshit! Bullshit! You hear me!'

Daniel, who up to now had been sat in his chair quietly, still unable to comprehend what had happened, finally spoke up. 'No, Curtis, that's not true. I've looked at the projections. Taking the amount out that we want to withdraw would barely affect the portfolio in the long run. Once we have repaid our merchants we have an agreement to do more business with them than ever before. The portfolio would be in better shape than ever. Do the math!'

Curtis snarled in Daniel's direction. If they had been in a different setting, Daniel had little doubt he might have wanted to sock him on the jaw. What had happened to his good friend who used to enjoy reading stories to Hugo on his lap?

'You do the fucking math, Daniel!' Curtis spat out in disgust. 'You're the shithead who fucked up. Not me. I've been making coin!'

'Now listen here, fellas,' Alton said calmly. This is what Sam and Daniel had been waiting for: the riot act was coming for Curtis. 'There ain't no need for all this unpleasantness. And I don't want to be like some schoolteacher telling y'all off like naughty boys. Now what I suggest here is everyone is tired and tensions are running a little high. So why don't y'all get some sleep, think about things, and meet up again tomorrow.'

That was it! That was all Alton had to say on the matter? So much for setting Curtis straight. It was hardly drawing a line in the sand.

'I'll meet with Sam,' Curtis yelled, already walking towards the door. 'But not Daniel. I don't want to see Daniel.'

Fine with me, Daniel thought. He didn't fancy another day of listening to Curtis gabble on anyway. Sam was more than capable of sorting things out. This was what he was good at: cleaning up a mess. He had done it before, he could do it again. Besides, Daniel had several missed calls and text messages from Nicole. She was on the warpath. All of their belongings and cars at Southern Highlands were gone. Curtis had put them all in a lock-up and hadn't told them where it all was. If Sam sorted out Curtis, then at least that gave Daniel time to pacify Nicole and find all of their stuff. If he didn't, then the plane ride home was not going to be an enjoyable one.

With the meeting coming to an abrupt end, and the situation still no closer to being resolved, Sam, Daniel and Michael headed back to their hotel to regroup. But for once they didn't have their normal five-star luxury accommodation to return to. Shelley had pulled the plug on that. Tonight they had to slum it with the tourists at the Mirage.

As their taxi reached the north end of The Strip, and stopped at the hotel's entrance, Daniel looked across at the crowds who had gathered at the front of the gold monument of eighties excess, and were marvelling at the synthetic volcano spewing lava. As he looked up at it, a thought suddenly dawned on him: that volcano pretty much summed up Vegas – a fake, just like Curtis Pope. A fake that eventually exploded. A fake that was ultimately a disappointment. But if Sam couldn't pull them out of the shit tomorrow, then the hotel name was certainly going to be an appropriate summing-up of the last eighteen months: a mirage. It would be as if it had all never happened. Everything would be gone. He would be right back where he started. A nobody.

27

Las Vegas, USA, April 2009

Sam was getting used to this routine: Puff. Pace. Puff. Pace. Puff. Pace.

As had been arranged, he had arrived at Trendsact at 9am on the dot, but Curtis wouldn't see him yet. Apparently he had some stuff he urgently needed to take care of. So until the overlord was ready Sam could do nothing but get through a pack of cigarettes and walk back and forth outside. Thankfully, the sun was still only half-risen over the mountains in the distance, so it wasn't yet burning Sam's bald head. For once, there was actually quite a nice breeze in the air, a miracle in the desert. It certainly helped to calm Sam down, as did the peacefulness away from the madness of The Strip. There was no ringing from slot machines, hollering from drunks or propositions from hookers out here, just the sound of the traffic.

He had woken in the early hours desperately battling jet lag. A sleeping pill didn't help matters, so he tried the next best thing: the gym. For half an hour he had pounded the running machine, playing things over and over in his head. He wasn't going to go down like this, not to Curtis Pope. He and Daniel had built a great company, one that would soon have the infrastructure in place to make its mark on a global scale. A cheap hustler like Curtis Pope wasn't going to ruin it for them.

After a hearty stack of pancakes drowned in maple syrup, at Cravings, the Mirage's buffet extravaganza, Sam had arrived at Trendsact ready for action. But as the hours passed, the mixture of jet lag, sugar, nicotine and caffeine started to take its toll. Twice already he had jogged across the six-lane highway to grab some cigarettes, coffee and doughnuts from the convenience store to keep himself awake. And now the sun was out in all its glory, searing through the dry air, scorching Sam half to death. Despite this huge inconvenience, Sam would still rather be in his position right now than Daniel's, who was trying in vain to contain an enraged Nicole. Not only was her Bentley gone but also all of her jewellery, handbags, shoes and designer dresses. She was far from impressed.

Finally, just after 1pm, Curtis Pope decreed that it was time to see his supposed subject. Whether or not Curtis had planned it like this, it had certainly quashed some of the fire in Sam's belly. Having waited for over four hours, he was starting to flag. At the very least, Sam had hoped that they could talk things through. Obviously there were misunderstandings on both sides of the fence. If they could just have a civilised discussion, perhaps they could reach a mutually beneficial agreement. All that mattered right now was staying in the game. He could worry about repaying Curtis for all of this bullshit another time.

Upon striding into the boardroom Sam was greeted by Curtis and Mike Lane standing side by side. Both had shit-eating grins plastered across their faces. Sam couldn't believe it. After shamelessly trying to pull a fast one, they could still manage to smile at him like they were his best friends.

'Thanks for seeing me,' Sam said sarcastically, taking a seat before he was invited to do so. After all, this was his office; Hugo had signed the lease on it. Technically he should be able to do as he pleased.

Pushing a thick wad of paper across the table towards Sam, Curtis announced: 'You're going to sign.'

So much for negotiation. Picking up the document, Sam saw that it was titled 'Global Resolution Agreement'. No wonder Curtis had been taking his time. He had instructed his lawyers to prepare this while Sam had been forced to wait outside. Rummaging through the pages, Sam snorted at clause after clause. As if he was going to sign this: it was effectively signing everything over to Curtis – the portfolio, the profit, the company, the future.

'You must be joking,' Sam laughed, sliding the contract back across the table, getting out of his seat and walking out of the room. This was an ambush. He wasn't going to stand for any of this shit. Let them meet him on his ground, on his terms. Marching down the corridor he heard Curtis and Mike chasing after him, but he was beyond caring. He was through with this crap. All he wanted to do was to get a car back to the Mirage and get out of this place as soon as possible. They would have to re-group and think things through. It was clear that Curtis wasn't going to budge just yet.

Having quickly ordered a taxi in the parking lot, Sam heard Curtis and Mike's footsteps stride menacingly behind him.

'I thought you may react like that,' Curtis said, placing his left hand in his cream slacks pocket while he pointed at Sam with his right index finger. 'So let me make this real simple for you: without the loan money you can't repay Isai or Ray, and there is no way on God's earth you're getting that money. You hear me. No fricking way. You've already defaulted on your agreement with those guys and they are going to take you to the cleaners – your fancy cars, your fancy mansions, the fucking lot are going to be taken right from under your feet. There is only one way that stops all of that happening. You sign that fucking contract.'

Sam was reeling. He knew that without Curtis's cooperation it was going to be almost impossible to get his hands back on the money.

The legal option had already been discussed and shot down. Even if lawyers got involved it could take months, if not years, to untangle this mess.

Curtis pulled the crumpled contract out of his back pocket and thrust it into Sam's hands. 'Isai and Ray want you to sign it all over to me today. Today! Or they will start legals straightaway. This way it's all neat and tidy. I will ensure they get their money and keep processing for them, but you guys are out. You hear that. OUT!'

It was over. Sam knew the game was up. At least this way Isai and Ray would be repaid in full and kept off his back. While this was by no means the ending he had hoped for, he realised it could have been far worse. And he recognised that there was also a silver lining to all of this: it would be the last he would ever hear of Curtis Pope or of online poker.

'Once I sign this, then you guys are responsible for the PokerStars and Full Tilt debt,' Sam said angrily, as he flicked through the pages to ensure such a clause was present. 'I don't want to hear about this ever again. Once I sign this, me and Daniel are done.'

Pulling a black ballpoint pen out of his shirt pocket, Curtis nodded while Mike Lane said: 'It's better for all of us this way, Sam. I'm sorry, but this is the way it has to be.'

'Oh yeah, I bet you're real sorry,' Sam snapped, grabbing the pen from Curtis, who was looking on anxiously. He knew that once Sam put pen to paper he was the new king of the online poker payment processing world – and what a fitting coronation, in the parking lot of a Las Vegas payday loan company.

'Hey buddy, you call a taxi?' a Hispanic driver shouted through his window as a black Lincoln Town Car pulled up.

'Yeah, he did,' Curtis yelled. 'Give us two seconds.'

Finding the execution page, a fitting description for this situation, Sam placed the contract on the bonnet of the car and scribbled his name where indicated. Without waiting for the ink to dry, Curtis snapped it away from his grasp: it was done.

Opening the door and collapsing on the seat inside, Sam asked the driver to take him back to the Mirage. Waiting impatiently for him in his room were Daniel, Nicole and Michael. They were desperate to find out what had gone down. He wasn't sure how he was going to break the news. There was no way to break something like this softly.

When Sam opened the hotel room door, his demoralised demeanour told the whole story. Hunched over, with dark bags under his eyes, he virtually staggered into the room and sat on the end of the bed where Michael was laying. Looking over at Daniel and Nicole, who were laying side by side on the opposite bed watching some American sitcom, he tried to find the appropriate words.

'So?' Daniel asked in the forlorn hope that Super Sam had once again saved the day and the money-making machine could continue.

'Pack your bags,' Sam sighed. 'It's over.'

'What?' Daniel cried, as Michael slumped back down on the bed.

'Ray and Isai wanted me to sign an agreement signing everything over to Curtis, so I did.'

'Why the hell did you do that?' Daniel shouted, leaping off the bed, walking towards Sam.

'Because it wasn't our money, Dan. We had to pay them back. We were already behind on the repayments. If I didn't sign it, they were going to come after us and take the lot. It was the only decision to make. And it was the right one.'

Placing his hands behind his head, Daniel walked up to the window where he could see the Encore Hotel towering across the other side of The Strip. Taking deep breaths, he tried to calm himself but it was too late. Tears had already started to trickle down his cheeks.

'I'm sorry, mate, but at the end of the day you just spent too much money too quickly,' Sam said softly, feeling sympathy for Daniel, but at the same time realising that while some of the expenditure had been necessary some of it had not. Daniel's rampant purchase of cars, houses, clothes and nightclubs had put pressure on the company when it couldn't withstand it, even if the money was in the pipeline. In effect, he had driven Isai and Ray straight into Curtis's warm embrace.

'So what do we do now?' Michael asked.

'We ring HR and tell them that as of now all of our employees are officially unemployed,' Sam replied mournfully. 'Intabill is dead.'

28

Gold Coast, Australia, July 2009

The last few months had been nothing short of disastrous. Intabill was finished. The media were digging their teeth in. Assets were being sold. Liquidators were set to be appointed. And lawsuits were flying around left, right and centre. While Sam Sciacca was engaged in a fire sale of Intabill's assets, trying to ensure various creditors, and Intabill staff, got paid the money they were owed, Daniel holed up in his condo on the Gold Coast sticking his head firmly in the sand.

There, in paradise, he tried to hide away from it all. It seemed almost every day there was another media story revelling in his demise. The Tall Poppy Syndrome was in full effect. Once they had built up the young genius, now it was time to kick him when he was down. Even for a guy with his confidence, he struggled to remain immune from the barrage of criticism. Money and success had defined him: Daniel Tzvetkoff, internet tycoon, self-made multi-millionaire. Now he was a cautionary tale: too much too young; another Generation Y whiz-kid bites the dust. And that fall from grace stung. It got right under his skin and left him falling head first into a deep bout of depression.

Spending most days locked in his room, he barely spoke to

anyone. Lying on his king-sized bed, he watched DVDs in the darkness and gorged on junk food. Just a few months earlier he had been one of the richest people in Australia. How could it all now be gone? All he wanted to do was sleep and hope that when he woke up it had all been a nightmare. But now wasn't the time to hide away: lawsuits needed to be answered, debts needed to be repaid. The longer he took to sort them out the more his reputation was plummeting.

Unbelievably, Full Tilt's parent company, Kolyma, had launched a $52 million lawsuit against Intabill. It seemed they wanted two bites of the cherry. Under Isai Scheinberg and Ray Bitar's instructions, Sam had assigned all of Intabill's debts to the poker companies to Curtis and Trendsact. If the poker boys wanted to get their money then Curtis Pope was now their man. And if they couldn't get it from Curtis then that was hard luck.

What frustrated Sam most of all was that, if PokerStars and Full Tilt hadn't been persuaded to link up with Curtis, then Intabill wouldn't have defaulted in the first place. Curtis would have wired over the money and by now they would have been well on course to repay all of the debt within the agreed timeframe. In Sam's eyes it was Bitar's own damn fault if all hadn't gone to plan with Curtis. Furious at such treachery, Sam had launched an aggressive defence and counterclaim. Daniel, however, didn't even bother to respond to the complaint. He was done with it all.

Almost immune to the daily barrage of lawsuits, complaints about unpaid debts and negative publicity, one phone call did however startle him from his self-imposed hibernation. One Friday afternoon, as he lay wallowing in bed, he was surprised to see that Sam was calling him. Since Vegas the two had barely spoken. Everything was still too raw to go over.

'Sam,' Daniel answered, raising himself upright. 'What's up?'

An awkward silence followed. Sam coughed nervously, muttered something unintelligible, and then finally said: 'I'm just giving you a heads up, mate. There is a process server at your door. They are going to serve you with some legal papers.'

Not another lawsuit, Daniel thought. Just put it on the pile with all of the others.

'Who's it from this time?' Daniel asked, running his hand through his unkempt hair. 'PokerStars by the sound of your voice.'

Another pause, then with a sigh Sam broke the news: 'No Dan. It's not from PokerStars . . . It's from me.'

Daniel shot upright.

'I just wanted to let you know personally,' Sam continued. 'No hard feelings, mate, but I've got to do it. That's all.'

Scrambling off the bed, Daniel peeked through the window to see a large man walk up towards his door. The doorbell rang. Nicole answered.

'Daniel,' she shouted, speaking to him for the first time in days. 'There are some more court papers here for you.'

Racing out of the room, Daniel looked at the guy at the door, mumbled something, and slammed it behind him. Ripping open the white A4 envelope, he stared in shock at what lay inside, the heading read: SALVATORE SCIACCA v DANIEL TZVETKOFF.

'Why Sam?' Daniel spluttered, as Nicole tried to work out what was going on.

'Because when you were in Vegas, I trusted you. You were in control of the money out there and you blew it. I've seen the books and you spent money on stuff that was never approved by me or Shelley. Regardless of Isai, Ray and Curtis screwing us, if you hadn't have spent so much then Intabill may still be alive today. I'm sorry, I've got to go.'

Holding the phone still in shock, as the tone told him Sam had hung up, Daniel slumped onto the sofa and rifled through the lawsuit pages. He was stunned. Yes, he had spent a lot of money, but in his eyes the company had more than enough in the pipeline to cover it all. It wasn't his fault Curtis had cut them off.

'What's the matter?' Nicole asked, having failed to gather much sympathy for her fiancé the past few weeks.

Looking up, Daniel softly replied: 'I think Sam is suing me for a hundred million dollars.'

Yet that wasn't the worst of it. Just a few months later, under the weight of lawsuits and debt collectors, Daniel Tzvetkoff had no choice but to do the hardest thing in his life: he declared himself bankrupt. It was rock bottom. It seemed the only way to go was up, but a deeper, much darker, pit awaited him.

Various organisations he most certainly did not want to get on the wrong side of had started to take a keen interest in his activities. Since Intabill's collapse, a series of private investigators, apparently on the instruction of the poker companies, had descended on Brisbane and the Gold Coast. His family and friends had been harassed and Daniel was certain that not only was he being followed but that his home had been bugged. It seemed that these guys had been instructed to recover monies any way that they could.

While Daniel was well aware of the involvement of the investigators, he wasn't quite as clued up as to what was happening on the eighth floor of 1 St Andrews Plaza, New York. This was the location of the office of the new United States Attorney for the Southern District of New York, Preet Bharara. The son of Indian immigrants, Bharara was the first Asian-American ever to inhabit the role. With a stellar background in Washington, where he had worked as chief counsel and staff director of the US Senate Judiciary Committee's Subcommittee on Administrative Oversight and the Courts, he was regarded by many as the shining light of American justice.

Playing Bruce Springsteen's greatest hits on loop, Bharara tried to get a swift handle on what needed to be done: he was swamped with files, each apparently more urgent than the last. He was responsible for sifting through all of these files, which included cases involving domestic and international terrorism, narcotics, arms trafficking, white-collar crime, public corruption, gang violence, organised crime and civil rights violations, and working out where to allocate the resources of the 220 assistant US attorneys who were now under his command. It was a daunting task.

Among the files there was evidence pressing for the indictment of Raj Rajaratnam, a millionaire hedge-fund chief who was involved in insider trading. There was also Viktor Bout, a Russian, who was regarded as one of the most notorious arms traffickers in the world. Christopher Coke, the leader of the Jamaica-based international criminal organisation, the 'Shower Posse', who had flooded the US in recent years with drugs and illegal weapons, was also there.

Yet while Bharara would initially focus his attention on bringing down those who had partaken in insider-trading, earning him the nickname, the 'Sheriff of Wall Street', there was another file on his desk on which he would soon focus his attention. The name on the file was that of Daniel Tzvetkoff.

29

Las Vegas, USA, Present Day

Every sport has its legends. In the current day, soccer has Lionel Messi, basketball has LeBron James, golf has Tiger Woods, tennis has Roger Federer, and online poker has Isildur1. Between September and December 2009, the mysterious Isildur1 caused a sensation. Out of nowhere he rocked up to the No Limit Hold'em tables at Full Tilt and proceeded to take on all-comers. Within twenty-four hours of his arrival, he had taken one of the world's top players, Haseeb 'DogIsHead' Qureshi, for $500,000. It was a massacre. But this was just the start. The games that followed in the proceeding weeks were some of the biggest nose-bleed high-stakes games ever seen. It was truly the pinnacle of online poker.

Up against some of the world's top pros, such as Tom 'Durrrr' Dwan, Ilari 'Ziigmund' Sahamies, Phil Ivey, Patrik Antonius, Cole South and Brian Townsend, the unknown newcomer showed absolutely no fear. On one crazy day he even took on Ivey, Antonius and Durrrr, all at the same time, across eight tables, at the highest stakes possible, $500/$1,000. To put this into context, it was the equivalent of an unknown tennis player attempting to take on Federer,

Nadal and Djokovic all at once, for several hours. It seemed a suicide mission, but Isildur1 more than held his own.

During his marathon sessions against Tom Dwan, Isildur1 racked up over $5.3 million. Up until this stage, Dwan had been the young prodigy of the online world himself, who at just twenty-two years of age had made over $5 million in 2008 alone. Now, after a week of high-stakes action, he was left battered and bloodied, his stellar reputation called into question. Ziigmund was also hit for $1.6 million, while Townsend, Ivey and Antonius also all dropped seven figures. By November, Isildur1 was up over $6 million in total.

Pros who had thought they had been there and seen it all lined up to play tribute to the mystery man, who thus far had failed to reveal his true identity. Haseeb 'DogIsHead' Qureshi praised his opponent's 'grasp of hand-reading, levelling and bet-sizing', which he said were 'second to none'. Patrik Antonius seconded this when he stated that Isildur1 was changing the world of high-stakes online poker, with a fearlessness never before seen. Ilari Sahamies, however, felt that 'the guy must be missing a chromosome'.

However, in true rollercoaster fashion, the enigma's ultra-aggressive style also saw him suffer some sizeable losses, most notably to Phil Ivey, the man coined the 'Tiger Woods of Poker', who hammered him for a grand total of $3.2 million. Ziigmund, Townsend and Antonius also recouped their losses with seven-figure victories. Having been up over $6 million in early November, the mystery man's bankroll was down to just $897,000 by 1 December.

Incredibly, during this short space of time, he was also involved in eight of the biggest online pots in history, which all came between 16 and 21 November. The record was set on 21 November against Patrik Antonius, where the duo matched up on four tables of $500/$1,000 Pot-Limit Omaha, a game in which Isildur1 was decidedly average compared to his world-class standard as a No Limit Hold'em player. Over just one hand, Isildur1 managed to lose

$1.3 million to his rival. It was a hand that sent shockwaves through the game.

Never before had a player suffered such dramatic highs and lows in such a short space of time. The poker community was in raptures. Here was a guy who was playing how everyone wished they could: ultra-aggressive against the world's best, without regard for money or caution. Renowned poker forum Two Plus Two was suddenly jam-packed with threads written by delirious fan-boys. Fellow poker forum PocketFives was equally as enthusiastic, with one thread on Isildur1 reaching over sixty pages. Most posts speculated on who was actually the man, or woman, behind Isildur1. Names such as Phil Hellmuth, Todd Brunson or David 'Viffer' Peat were thrown into the mix, but still Isildur1's mysterious identity was not revealed. This only added to the hype. Who was this individual who had enough balls to take on all of the world's best, at the highest limits, often at the same time?

Despite participating in some of the most epic match-ups in history, the one that will forever be remembered occurred on 8 December 2009 when Isildur1 went head to head with twenty-one-year-old Cornell University student Brian Hastings. And it was Hastings who I had sought out when I attended the Main Event of the World Series of Poker at the Rio Hotel in Las Vegas.

Seeking out just one player among the three thousand or so who were playing during day two of the tournament would have been extremely difficult, but thankfully the media room had provided me with a list of where players of note would be sitting. From that list I could see that 2003 world champion Chris Moneymaker would be in the enormous Pavilion Room, *Seinfeld* actor Jason Alexander would be in the dark and intimate Amazon Room, along with UFC fighter Georges St Pierre, while in the Brasilia Room there was an array of big names, from soccer star Teddy Sheringham, cricket legend Shane Warne, who had his model girlfriend Liz Hurley looking over his shoulder, to one of the most successful poker players of all time, Phil Ivey. Among all these stars, I also managed to spot the man I had come to see, Brian Hastings.

While I walked between the tables, brushing shoulders with the players, who as they played either listened to their iPods, read books on their iPads, had back massages, engaged in banter or sat stony-faced, I finally spotted Brian sat at a table in the middle of the room. Dressed in nothing more flashy than a regular pair of jeans and a black T-shirt, he was relatively inconspicuous. Anyone who didn't know his story couldn't have guessed that the baby-faced man, now twenty-four, with short-cropped brown hair, who looked a lot leaner in the flesh than pictures I had seen, was responsible for a moment that had caused near hysteria in the online poker world.

When the first break in play came, I took the opportunity to introduce myself. After a brief chat about my interest in his story Brian said he would call me after the tournament had finished for the day so we could talk further. True to his word, later that evening Brian called me at my room at the Flamingo and suggested meeting him at PURE nightclub, which was situated just across The Strip in Caesars Palace, as he would be having a few drinks there that night with some old friends. Just a few hours later, having queued for what had seemed an eternity, alongside the Pussycat Dolls-themed poker tables at Caesars, I had forked out thirty dollars for the cover and was finally inside.

As arranged, Brian was already upstairs on the open-air veranda, which had spectacular views of the neon-lit Strip. To my left was the gold-mirrored glass of the Mirage, to my right the white-marbled roman statues of Caesars Palace, while straight ahead was my own hotel, the Flamingo, whose front sported a huge picture of their star act, Donny and Marie Osmond, who grinned out of the façade like two wholesome Cheshire cats.

After a few minutes of aimless wandering we finally managed to find a 'quiet' seat on the edge of the balcony, just a few metres away from the bar. Finding a quiet place anywhere in Las Vegas at 11pm was always a tough ask, and PURE was no different. Down below the incessant traffic of The Strip roared along while the earth-shaking beat of hip-hop music, bachelor parties and VIP wannabes erupted around us. That said, with a pitcher of beer on the table between us, this was certainly one of the more pleasurable interview spots we could have picked, despite the noise.

Giving off an air of calm, the softly spoken college graduate told me that he was born in State College in Pennsylvania, a small town where everything was focused on Penn State University. His upbringing was middle class and comfortable, and his conservative, Catholic parents stressed the importance of a good education while holding a dim view of anything connected to gambling.

'In that case how did you get involved with poker?' I asked, intrigued by this juxtaposition.

Straight-faced Brian replied: 'My secondary school math teacher! During the last two years of high school I was one of the best math students in my class. He told me that over the last year he had made a lot of money using his math skills playing online poker. I had been playing small-time home games with friends and had never taken it seriously up until that point. He inspired me to give it a go, so I put fifty dollars into an account on Ultimate Bet. By the end of high school, I had made over two hundred and fifty thousand dollars playing Pot Limit Omaha.'

It was almost impossible to imagine that an eighteen-year-old, doing nothing more than playing poker on a computer in his bedroom, could have reached such heights. 'So what did your parents make of it?' I probed.

'They were pretty wary to begin with,' he laughed, reaching forward to have a quick sip of his drink before continuing. 'But when I showed them how well I was doing – that it wasn't down to luck, that a lot of my success was down to using my math and logical thinking skills, having the ability to quickly calculate odds, put players on hand ranges, and stuff like that – they soon saw that there was something more to poker. It was more a game of skill. In the end, they were actually supportive of me playing.'

Brian's prowess at the poker table could have quite easily seen him devote himself full-time to the game, where he could have made a more than comfortable living. Instead, however, he opted to attend Cornell University, to major in economics. Despite being well intentioned, putting education before poker, his first two years saw his attention diverted by the lure of easy money at the tables. Indeed, he was doing so well playing poker at this time he was even recruited to be an instructor by leading poker-training website CardRunners, as well as signed up to be a pro by Full Tilt Poker.

'Didn't playing so much poker affect your grades?' I asked, remembering just how little I had attended lectures in my own university days, preferring to devote my time to marathon poker sessions with my flatmates.

'It did a bit,' he answered. 'My grades in my first two years weren't that awesome. But by my final year, I was playing just ten hours a week and my grades started to pick up.'

'Obviously that would have had an effect on how well you were doing on the poker tables, though?'

Shrugging his shoulders, Brian confirmed that while it did have some effect, by this stage he had already made enough to pay off his college tuition fees and had been able to buy a house, where he and his friends lived. While most college students had to wait tables or work at a bar to make ends meet, Brian never had to leave the sanctuary of his bedroom.

Yet while he tried to focus on his studies, the emergence of Isildur1 soon caught his attention. 'I first heard about Isildur1 at a Halloween party in California. A friend of mine was telling me he recently lost a bunch to him playing a few tables of Heads-Up Pot Limit Omaha. A few days later I was online and checked him out. He was battling against everyone. It was crazy. I watched his games against Tom Dwan and my friend from CardRunners, Brian Townsend. I couldn't believe it. It was insane. I didn't have any idea who he could be, but it was exciting.'

'So how did your own match-up with Isildur1 come about?' I asked, getting to the meat of the interview, one of the most talked-about online poker games of all time.

'We played on the eighth of December,' Brian revealed, his eyes widening at the memory. 'It was finals week so I was doing a bunch of studying in my room. I had my computer on, though, and I could see Isildur1 was playing some pretty heavy matches against Jungleman12, Brian Townsend and Cole South, who I also knew well from CardRunners.'

Despite his recent downturn in luck, Isildur1 now looked to be on a hot streak. He had already taken Daniel 'Jungleman12' Cates for $471,000 at No Limit Hold'em and $722,000 from Brian Townsend at Pot Limit Omaha. Cole South wasn't faring much better.

'I was itching to play him,' Brian continued. 'It looked fun. Better than studying anyway. Then out of nowhere Cole South sent me an instant message and said he was tired. Did I want to step in? Sure I did.'

Putting his books to one side, Brian asked in the chat box if Isildur1 fancied playing Pot Limit Omaha. This was a game that was Brian's specialty and Isildur1's supposed Achilles' heel, yet Isildur1 rarely turned down any challengers, especially those with deep pockets. Besides, he was on a streak. He had already won close to $1 million that day playing Omaha. His skills were improving, although he still had some way to go to match his No Limit Hold'em expertise. Nevertheless he agreed and thus began an epic five-hour duel, consisting of over 3,000 hands, initially across six tables of $500/$1,000 Pot Limit Omaha.

While Isildur1 was a frightening prospect, Brian was confident. 'I had played a few sessions with him previously and had a decent feel for his game. I had also exchanged a few emails about him with Brian Townsend. He had purchased some hand history of Isildur1's to analyse so he was getting an idea of his general tendencies and strategies. We didn't really go into specifics, though, just general stuff.'

If Townsend's research was correct, and Brian played to his potential, then he was sure he could give Isildur1 a run for his money. If, however, Isildur1 continued his streak, and Brian was below par, then there was the very real chance he could lose his entire bankroll. The stakes were that high.

By the end of the first hour of play, Brian was over $1 million down. It seemed Isildur1 was going to be too strong for him on this occasion. Many players would have been 'put on tilt' by such a blow, but incredibly it barely registered on Brian. 'To be honest it wasn't something I realised' he told me. 'I never remember thinking I was a lot of money down. Things are so intense and happening so quickly, you just focus on the games and not the money so much.'

So far the game seemed to be just like any other that Isildur1 took part in: big swings, aggressive, fast-paced. And just like most of these games Isildur1 was up, and up big. But then the tide started to turn after the three-hour mark.

'You know, I don't remember a specific hand or anything like that, but I just started to get into the groove,' Brian said, a glimmer of satisfaction emerging on his face at the fond memory. 'After around three hours of play, I knew I was doing well. I wasn't sure how well as I was locked in, but I felt things were going my way. I also noticed he was starting to tilt. He became overly aggressive: three-betting and bluffing too much, trying to win every pot. It played into my hands. I started to take advantage of it.'

Incredibly, after being $1 million down Brian was now over $3 million up. This news rocketed across the poker forums as players flocked to Full Tilt to watch the match-up in action. The hero of the poker world was taking a battering. With every hand he grew more and more erratic. It was almost like watching the previously invincible Russian, Ivan Drago, in *Rocky IV*, getting hit time and time again by Rocky. He was on the ropes; all Brian needed to do was to deliver a knockout blow, but he was getting tired.

'After around four hours I was feeling it,' Brian told me. 'I just couldn't make decisions any more. It had taken a lot out of me concentrating so hard, and I knew I had to get back to study, so I told him I was almost done.'

When Brian wrote in the chat box that he may be finished for the day the following exchange unfolded, which revealed Isildur1's intense frustration.

Isildur1: ??
Dealer: Brian Hastings has 5 seconds left to act
Brian Hastings: getting very tired . . .
Dealer: Hand #16648979788 has been cancelled
Brian Hastings: i feel bad quitting tho
Brian Hastings: would be cool w/ playing someone else?
Isildur1: just f off
Isildur1: u know how lucky u are ?
Brian Hastings: yes i know
Isildur1: i can promise this is the worst
Brian Hastings: will give you 30 more min if you want
Isildur1: luck anyone had
Brian Hastings: but im rly tired
Isildur1: k 30 mins more
Isildur1: take my last $$
Isildur1: i dont want it
Isildur1: ::S:S

Agreeing to play for a little bit longer may have been a risk when Brian was so tired, but soon afterwards he won the biggest pot of the match: $500,000. Suddenly, Isildur1, who had always insisted on playing multi-tables, was now down to just one. Those watching knew they could be witnessing something special. Isildur1 looked to be on the verge of losing his whole bankroll. The legend was about to be knocked clean out.

Shortly afterwards, the knockout blow arrived: Isildur1 was on the canvas, his account down to zero. Brian Hastings had taken him for everything he had. The student had won $4.2 million in just under five hours of play. It was an online record that still stands.

'How did you feel?' I asked, trying to imagine how I would have felt if I had won such a vast amount of money during my final year in university, knowing full well I would have spent the next week partying, not giving a second thought to my exams.

'I was in a state of euphoria,' Brian reminisced. 'It finally hit me what had happened and how much I had won. I went downstairs and told my friends. None of them knew I had been in my room playing for millions of dollars. They couldn't believe it. I tried to get them to go out and celebrate, but they all had exams the next day so I ended up drinking a few beers by myself while my friends went back to studying.'

Just as incredible as the win itself was how Brian dealt with it. Not only was he now a huge name in the poker community, but he was also a millionaire by the age of twenty-one. Many in his position would have let it go to their heads, but Brian didn't. He paid for his parents to go on a trip to Italy and invested some into Kiva, a non-profit charity that facilitates global micro-financing loans. He even sat his exam two days later and passed with flying colours.

He said of this amazing level-headedness: 'I didn't really want to do anything flash. There are certain things I value spending my money on. I'm not the type of guy to just blow it. I wanted to be smart.'

However, things soon took a turn for the worse when Brian gave an interview to well-respected ESPN poker journalist Gary Wise shortly afterwards. In that interview he innocently said about Isildur1: 'We've done quite a bit of studying of his habits. Honestly, I give most of the credit to Brian Townsend here. I mean, Brian is honestly the hardest worker I know in poker. He analysed a database of heads-up hands that Isildur1 had played and constructed ranges of what Isildur1 was doing in certain spots. In a way, I feel bad that it wasn't Brian who got this win instead of me. Obviously I'm happy and I'll take it, but Brian did a ton of work. The three of us discussed a ton of hands and the reports that Brian made, so I'm very thankful to him and to Cole as well.'

This seemed innocent enough. Brian Townsend had acquired a total of 30,000 hands that Isildur1 had previously played, on top of the 20,000 hands he had played against him himself. He had then analysed that data and had passed on some general observations to Brian Hastings. Yet what Brian Townsend didn't realise was that by purchasing hands that Isildur1 had played against other players, he was breaking the rules of Full Tilt Poker's terms of service. As a result, Brian Townsend had his Full Tilt Poker Red Pro status suspended for one month.

After this revelation there was outrage. Disciples of Isildur1 rushed to condemn his conqueror, branding him a cheater, despite the fact that this sort of analysis was pretty common, as well as the fact that Full Tilt had never before enforced this obscure rule. While Brian Hastings, who was also a Full Tilt Poker pro, was not punished, he told me that he still found the outcry hard to deal with. 'I didn't expect there to be any issues. I was surprised at the attention it got. I didn't see any of the actual data, so I didn't break any rules, but it was still frustrating. It went from being one of the happiest moments in my life to me now being portrayed as the bad guy. Any time the word "cheater" is thrown around with your name, it's tough to deal with. My integrity is something I value very highly. Thankfully, most people I spoke to were supportive and knew I hadn't done anything wrong.'

Skulking into the shadows, Isildur1 left the tables behind and made vague threats about trying to reclaim the money that Brian had won from him. However, in late February 2010 he returned. Refreshed from his break he looked to be back on top. In just three days he wiped out some of the world's best, making $806,685, with $567,000 coming from top pro Justin 'ZeeJustin' Bonomo alone.

Having reclaimed his throne at the top of the poker world, everyone was waiting to see if a re-match with Brian Hastings would emerge. And on 15 March 2010 the moment everyone was waiting for arrived – Isildur1 v Brian Hastings – on six-tables of $500/$1,000 Pot Limit Omaha.

'It wasn't planned,' Brian revealed. 'I saw he was at a table and decided to go for it.'

'Did you have something to prove to people?' I asked.

'No,' he answered emphatically. 'I treated it just like any other poker match. I just tried to play my best.'

Once again Brian's best was good enough. Proving to any doubters that the first time around wasn't a fluke, he won $1.5 million, busting Isildur1 again for all of his bankroll. Retreating once again, Isildur1 kept a low profile for most of 2010, with his identity still unknown. But on 8 January 2011 PokerStars made an announcement that had everyone waiting with bated breath. Not only had they signed Isildur1 to their stable of pros, but they would also be revealing his/her identity. As speculation became feverish, it was finally revealed that the enigma was none other than Viktor Blom, a twenty-one-year-old from Sweden who, with his pale complexion and messy, long blond hair, looked like he belonged in a *Twilight* vampire movie rather than being one of the world's great poker players.

Since those halcyon days, Blom and Brian have continued to

prosper, in both online and live games. Blom not only won the $100,000 Super High Roller event at the PokerStars Caribbean Adventure 2012 for $1,254,400, but he followed that up by improbably winning two back-to-back tournaments at the Spring Championship of Online Poker. Indeed, Brian has fared just as well. He has notched two victories in live poker tournaments, winning a World Poker Tour Summer Splash Event in 2011, which saw him net $213,877 and then won his first World Series gold bracelet in 2012 when he won the $10,000 Heads-Up No Limit Hold'em event for $371,498.

When I ask Brian if he's happy with the way things have gone, he characteristically downplays his achievements. 'I guess,' he says. 'You know I love poker and if I'm doing well then I'm happy, but I try to ensure that's not the only thing going on in my life. I like to have variety.'

That certainly seems to be the key to his success. Right now he is heavily involved with a new project, www.draftday.com, a daily fantasy sports website where competitors can play against each other for real money. While Brian has already made a name for himself in the poker world, I wouldn't bet against him also doing so in the world of business. But, in spite of this, he still looks forward to resuming old rivalries with Isildur1 soon: 'It would be a lot of fun. It would be awesome if we could do it again some time.' It is a sentiment that is shared by everyone who plays and loves poker.

Yet while the poker world revelled in this titanic clash, it was a poisoned chalice for the main beneficiary. Ordinarily, Full Tilt Poker would have been thrilled to see that their traffic had surged by up to twenty-five per cent, thanks to fans flocking to watch Isildur1 in action. However, with more and more action on the site, Full Tilt was now struggling to process it all. Rumours had even popped up on some forums accusing Full Tilt of crediting players' accounts without actually debiting their bank account. Some were concerned that this was a sign that all was not well. And they would be right to feel this way, because by this stage Full Tilt Poker was in a world of shit.

However, while this was a serious issue, Full Tilt also had another equally serious problem to contain, the roots of which began in 2007. Back then poker player Jimmy 'gobboboy' Fricke had sent an email to Full Tilt enquiring as to whether they would be interested in sponsoring him for the forthcoming Aussie Millions tournament. In response he received a standard email turning down his request. Yet there was also something else in the email. The sender, Jason Newitt, a Full Tilt employee, had neglected to delete a chain of emails between him and one of his superiors, namely, Howard Lederer. Not only did Lederer describe gobboboy in the email as a 'freak' and a 'weird dude', but he also CC'ed two other Full Tilt board members into the exchange, Ray Bitar and Robert H. Wolf. To date Full Tilt had been extremely careful not to reveal who actually ran the company. Now it was clear just who the key decision-makers were.

Unsurprisingly, after this exchange was made public, Full Tilt fired Jason Newitt. Feeling aggrieved, Newitt decided to file suit against the company in September 2009, where he threatened to shine a very bright light on the secretive workings of Full Tilt Poker, something the board members were keen to avoid at all cost. But while these revelations may have been inconvenient, what no one could have realised was that another party was also following these proceedings with great interest.

The Department of Justice had been looking for a way to infiltrate the mysterious workings of Full Tilt for some time. This case finally gave them the opportunity they had been waiting for. And they would take it. Just over a year later, Jason Newitt was subpoenaed by the US Attorney's Office for the Southern District of New York. It appeared as if the genie was about to escape from the bottle.

30

Las Vegas, USA, April 2010

Daniel Tzvetkoff was back: back in Las Vegas, back in action, back at the top. Well, sort of. That's what he wanted everyone to think anyway.

Since the collapse of Intabill, several businessmen had expressed an interest in purchasing the company's intellectual property from the liquidators. They could see it was a good business; it had just grown too quickly and had a bad slice of luck, that was all. In the right hands it could be a gold mine. That's certainly what Gold Coast-based billionaire Bruce Mathieson was thinking when he took the plunge.

With all of the key software and databases at his disposal, Mathieson began to focus on putting his new company, Payovation, together. In an ideal world, he wanted to bring the old Intabill team back on board, but there were problems. From an early stage Sam Sciacca was out. Knocking back Mathieson's lucrative offer, he had declared that he would never work again with Daniel. In any event, he had decided to return to law. It was time to put his family first and knuckle down for a bit. He owed this to his ever-supportive wife, Jo-Anne, who had been a rock throughout the whole ordeal.

Preferably Mathieson would have hired Daniel to run the show, but he knew that would be impossible as by now his name was mud. He was the brash young kid who had been sued for over $150 million by his customers and his business partner. No matter that he claimed most of the charges were bullshit, if people saw that Daniel was officially connected to Payovation then the company wouldn't stand a chance.

However, after arranging to meet Daniel on the Gold Coast, Mathieson liked what he saw. The kid was hungry, bright, switched on and eager to prove people wrong – just the type of guy he liked. So, even though he couldn't officially hire him, he agreed to pay Daniel $10,000 a month to work as a consultant. Better yet, if he hit his targets then Mathieson would be willing, eventually, to give up a twenty-five per cent slice of equity to him.

This was just the sort of opportunity Daniel had been waiting for. He had stopped feeling sorry for himself and was now ready to ram the critics' words down their throats. Having learned from his mistakes, and with a successful, experienced billionaire backing him, he knew that he was on to a good thing. Plus the salary, while much less than he was used to, would certainly stop him from starving in the meantime.

With Daniel working in the background, Mathieson decided to ask Michael Hui to head up the company. Michael was sensible, bright, hardworking and knew the game inside out, on top of which people trusted him. He was the perfect, clean-cut, public face for Payovation. In spite of Mathieson's generous offer, Michael would only accept on two conditions: they wouldn't touch poker, and he, not Daniel, would actually be calling the shots. Mathieson readily agreed.

Now, after a few months in business, Payovation was preparing to announce its arrival on the world stage at the Electronic Transactions Association (ETA) Tradeshow at the Mandalay Bay, Las Vegas. This was a big deal. Anyone who was anyone in the payment-processing world would be at the show, including an array of merchants looking for processors. With this in mind Michael, chairman Tony Tripoli and sales manager Damien Gollani were all set to descend on Vegas looking for business. Michael was also planning on taking his new girlfriend, Caroline, a pretty, slim, brunette lawyer, with him for company. However, Daniel was not invited. In this embryonic stage it was just too risky for him to be seen to be connected with Payovation. The Intabill stigma still stuck.

Regardless of this, Daniel had decided he was going to go anyway. Damn the stigma. He was the one who had been screwed over, and he had nothing to hide. This was his moment. If the top dogs of the payment-processing world were going to be there, then he was going too. He was going to walk the floor and let everyone know the big man was back in town. They couldn't get rid of him that easily. Anyway, what better place to announce his comeback than Las Vegas, where just a year earlier his whole empire had come crashing down.

And there was another reason for a trip to Vegas: Nicole was pregnant. A baby girl would soon be added to their family. This would be Daniel's last hurrah before knuckling down. So joining Daniel in Las Vegas was his close friend Michael Kollosche, who was a sucker for the charms of The Strip. Together they would mingle with the great and mighty at the ETA before swanning off into the night to hit Las Vegas head on.

It was fair to say that Nicole was decidedly unamused when Daniel had announced he was going to Vegas. With a baby on the way, and with everything that had happened there just a year earlier, she thought it was a risk he should avoid at all costs. She had told him as much quite forcibly, but Daniel couldn't be persuaded to change his mind. This was his moment: the comeback. Nothing was going to stop him being there – not even his fiancée.

Having flown in on a separate flight, Michael Hui did all that he could to avoid seeing Daniel in Vegas. This included ensuring that he stayed at the opposite end of The Strip to him. Michael was staying at the southern end, in the Hotel, next to Mandalay Bay, while Daniel and Kollosche were at the northern end, at Steve Wynn's luxurious Encore. Ideally, Michael would have preferred an ocean between them, but if they were going to be in Vegas together then at least they weren't in the same hotel.

Although Michael had also begged Daniel not to go to the ETA, it had been to no avail. But thankfully, while Daniel had walked the floor, making it known to all and sundry he was back in town, he had not associated himself with the Payovation stand. This was a small mercy. As was the fact that he and Kollosche had both jumped ship early on to hit the bars on The Strip. All in all, Payovation had enjoyed a good night: some new merchants had signed up, and no one was any the wiser that the pariah, Daniel Tzvetkoff, was connected to them.

Michael's spiel had been so successful that he actually had a number of breakfast meetings lined up with merchants for the following morning. As Tony and Damien partied the night away, Michael retired to his bed, with his new girlfriend, Caroline, for company.

At 7am Michael's alarm woke him from his slumber. Still jet lagged he slowly opened his eyes and remembered where he was: Las Vegas, the Hotel, ETA Trade Show, breakfast meeting lined up at 8am with a merchant. That's right.

Peeling off the white cotton bedcovers, he kissed Caroline's forehead as she continued to sleep soundly. Hopefully he could get the meeting done by 9am so that he could take her shopping at Caesars Palace before they had to catch their flight home later that day. She had been as good as gold so far. Helping out with the stand when necessary and then leaving him be when he needed space to deal with clients. There was no doubt in Michael's eyes, she was a keeper.

Crunching his toes together on the carpet, Michael stretched his arms towards the ceiling. Through the gap in the curtain he could see the early morning sun casting its light over The Strip. The green neon lights of the MGM across the road were out, traffic was minimal and the pavements were virtually empty. It was the calm before the storm.

As he walked towards the bathroom, Michael picked up his phone from the bedside table. He had decided to turn it off as he slept as he knew that Tony, Damien, Daniel or Kollosche would be bombarding him with drunken phone calls telling him to stop being boring and get out of bed and have a drink. The usual stuff. Clicking the phone on, Michael ran the faucet in the bathroom so that he could brush his teeth. As the phone kicked into life, a message immediately popped up onto the screen. The number wasn't one he recognised. Without his glasses Michael squinted at the screen to see what it said. Holding it close to his face, he almost dropped it into the sink when he finally deciphered the message. What the hell! Surely someone was playing a prank. The message from the unknown number merely read: 'Daniel's been taken by a group of guys. They asked after you.'

As his heart-rate quickened, Michael sat on the edge of the bath and wondered what to do. Kollosche! He had been with Daniel last night. Surely he would know if this was true. Hurriedly scrolling through his phone, he found Kollosche's Australian number. After what seemed like an age, the real estate agent finally answered.

'Michael! Thank fuck! I've been trying to get hold of you.'

Whispering so that he wouldn't wake Caroline, Michael replied, 'Was that you who messaged me saying Daniel had been taken?'

'Yes, mate,' Kollosche replied. 'We were in XS nightclub together. He left before me, but I followed him out. By the time I got to the lobby I saw this group of guys bundle him out of the door. They were asking after you, mate. I heard them ask where you were.'

Holy shit! Michael's hand firmly gripped the side of the bath as he shut his eyes tight. What the hell was going on?

'Who took him?' Michael asked. 'Do you know?'

'No idea,' Kollosche's hoarse voice replied, a victim of a night of excess and drama. 'I just saw a group drag him away. I've spoken to Nicole and the embassy are doing all they can to find out more, but if I were you I wouldn't hang about. You can be sure that whoever they are they will be after you as well.'

In a panic Michael hung up and raced into the bedroom. Throwing on a pair of crumpled jeans, a creased white T-shirt, and finding his glasses next to the bed, he shook Caroline awake.

'Michael. What are you doing?' she mumbled, still half asleep.

'I've got to get out of here for a bit,' Michael said, kneeling down to look her in the eyes, trying his best not to worry her. 'Someone has taken Daniel and they were looking for me. I'm going to try and work out what is going on. It's probably nothing to worry about, but keep your phone on you. I'll call you when I know more.'

Without another word being spoken, Michael shoved his wallet and passport into his jeans pocket and rushed out of the room. Looking both ways down the endless corridor, he checked no one was lying in wait for him. Satisfied that he was alone, he raced towards the lift at the far end of the hall. Tony and Damien had a suite at the Mandalay Bay, just across from the Hotel. He would go straight to see them. Hopefully they could put his mind at rest, and maybe they would have a plan of action. But when he arrived at their suite less than five minutes later, with his T-shirt already sticking to him through perspiration, no one answered. Had they been taken as well, Michael wondered? Banging relentlessly on the door, not caring that he was waking up half the corridor, he finally heard some noise from inside.

'All right, all right,' the comforting voice of Damien Gollani shouted. 'Jesus fucking Christ. I've got the hangover from hell here.'

As soon as the door swung open, Michael barged into the room. Standing in nothing but a baggy pair of boxer shorts, the unshaven Damien Gollani stared at him in disgust. 'What the hell, Mike? It's seven fucking thirty. I've only been in bed for two hours. I'm still fucking wasted.'

'Where's Tony?' Michael asked, ignoring Damien's hangover.

'He's in bed, mate,' Damien yawned, already walking back towards his double bedroom. 'Where I should be.'

'Daniel's been taken,' Michael shouted. 'We don't know who by yet. Could be the FBI or gangsters.'

Blinking his eyes quickly together, Damien looked as though he was trying to think of something clever to say but eventually just shook his head. 'Fuck that. I'm going back to bed.'

Damien was clearly still drunk. He wasn't going to be of much use, and Tony Tripoli was no better. He was so wasted he wouldn't wake up, even when Michael poured a glass of water over his head. Realising that any room linked to Payovation wasn't going to provide him with much protection, Michael did the only thing he could think of: he ran straight to the lift, down to the lobby, out to the front entrance and into a cab.

'Where do you wanna go?' the taxi driver asked.

'The Palazzo at the Venetian,' Michael answered, his head on a swivel looking this way and that for any suspicious characters. If he could get to the large shopping centre at the Venetian, it could hopefully buy him some time. He could blend in with the thousands of tourists, grab a coffee and get his head together while he thought this thing out.

At this time of the morning The Strip was dead, so in less than five minutes they had passed New York New York, the Monte Carlo, Paris, Planet Hollywood, Caesars Palace and the Flamingo and were soon pulling up outside the Venetian. Thrusting a crumpled heap of notes into the taxi driver's hand, Michael jumped out into the cool Vegas morning air. Briskly walking past the man-made lake at the front, where later on in the day gondolas would provide rides to tourists, Michael tried his best to remain incognito as he entered the shopping centre.

Upon seeing an Italian coffee shop, Café Presse, Michael dived inside, ordered an Espresso and found a quiet booth in the corner where he could gather his thoughts. Gulping down the Espresso to give himself a much-needed jolt of caffeine, Michael selfishly realised one thing: he hoped it had been gangsters who had taken Daniel. At least that way he could leave the country. If, however, it was the FBI then not only could he be trapped, but he could also be facing jail. Stewing over everything, unable to relax, he finally made a decision: he needed to flee. The longer he stayed in the USA he was a target, whether it was the FBI or the mob that were looking for him. He called Caroline immediately. It had been their first trip abroad together. She sure wasn't going to forget about it in a hurry.

'Michael. Where are you?' she answered, clearly worried sick.

Turning to face the coffee shop's wall, so that no one could hear him, Michael tried his best to sound calm and collected. 'Everything is OK. Don't worry. Just pack our bags and meet me at the airport in ten minutes. We need to get back home.'

'But our flight doesn't leave for another five hours.'

It was a good point. Even if he checked in now, it would give whoever was looking for him ample time to track him down while he waited to board.

'We may have to get on another plane. Any one will do, as long as it's out of the country. We can get a flight to Brisbane once we are out of here.'

Michael was conscious of the fact that he must be scaring Caroline half to death. It was almost like they had woken to be plunged straight into a Hollywood thriller. To her credit, she was coping admirably. There were no hysterics or irrelevant questions, just straight to the point. Sometimes it was good to date a fellow lawyer.

'OK,' she replied. 'I'll see you in ten minutes.'

Wasting little time, Michael knocked back the rest of his Espresso and was soon back at the front of the hotel hailing a cab. Ten minutes later, as he stood waiting at the Qantas desk in McCarran Airport, he saw Caroline arrive, wheeling two bags behind her.

'I've looked at the flights,' she said, with hair or make-up barely out of place. She looked as if she had been to a beauty spa rather than having spent the morning worrying how she was going to help her boyfriend go on the run. 'We have two options. One plane goes to Mexico in forty-five minutes. Or there is a plane to London in just over an hour.'

By now Michael was already starting to think of the future. What country would be more likely to have an extradition treaty with the USA: the UK or Mexico? Both probably he realised. As he pondered this, his phone vibrated in his pocket. Scrambling around he hurriedly pulled it out to see that it was Nicole.

'Nicole!' he answered. 'Have you heard anything? What's going on?'

'The embassy has just called me,' she said, sounding remarkably calm in the circumstances. 'It's the FBI. They've arrested Daniel.'

Michael's heart sank. If it was the FBI then he was going to find it very difficult to get out of the country. Even if he did, the likelihood was that he would be sent straight back. 'Shit!' he replied, his mind already wondering what options he now had. 'Is that all we know? Did they say anything about me?'

'That's all we know. We are trying to get Daniel a lawyer right now. I'll call you if I know more.'

Putting the phone back into his pocket, thoughts raced through his mind. Go on the run? Hire a car and hide out for a few days? Give himself up?

'I think you should speak to a lawyer before you do anything else,' Caroline interjected, the voice of reason.

It was good advice. Michael had no doubt that both he and Intabill had a defensible position, but he realised that it would be prudent to speak to a local lawyer to see what was going on. So, within half an hour he was in the office of the first criminal lawyer he could get hold of, John Spinelli, a brash, in-your-face, fast-talking, loud-suit-wearing Vegas lawyer.

Dripping in gold jewellery, Spinelli wore a cream suit with wide lapels, a garish red patterned tie and sported an impressive slicked-back pompadour. Holding court behind his desk, Spinelli told Michael not to sweat it. He had been in these situations many times before. The worst thing that Michael could do was go on the run. The best thing he could do was surrender, but not in Vegas, in New York. That's where he understood the Department of Justice would be looking to press charges in this matter.

'How can I surrender in New York?' Michael asked, holding Caroline's hand as they sat in front of Spinelli.

'Well, you sure as hell don't wanna fly there,' Spinelli advised. 'That's making it too easy for them to pick you up. So you'll have to hire a car and drive. Gun it straight up there; should take two days or so if you put your foot down. But there's one thing you really don't want to happen?'

'What's that?' Michael asked.

'Get picked up here and have to ride the prison bus there. You'll be on that thing for days, stopping off at a different prison every night, with all sorts of assholes. We need to avoid that at all costs.'

Caroline squeezed Michael's hand harder. She could see he was starting to panic.

Spinelli's phone suddenly jumped into life. 'Oh good,' he answered to his secretary, flashing Michael a smile as he whispered. 'It's the Department of Justice returning my call. This should see where we stand.'

Over the course of the next few minutes all Michael could hear of the conversation was Spinelli nod his head and grunt in satisfaction. It was hard to tell whether it was good or bad news. Finally, he put the phone down, leant back and brushed his hands through his thick hair. 'You're OK, kid,' he laughed. 'They just want to frickin subpoena you. Whole lot of worry for nuthin.'

Michael sighed in relief: thank God – no jail, no charges, just a few questions.

'You need to get your ass on a plane to New York today, though,' Spinelli continued, his tone more serious. 'I'll sort out a lawyer who will meet you at the other end. You'll both meet with Assistant District Attorney Arlo Devlin-Brown and then you will face questioning by a Grand Jury. Piece of cake. All being well, you'll be back home for shrimp on the barbie in a few days. That's what you boys from Oz like, isn't it?'

'We like anything that sees us avoid doing time,' Michael laughed for the first time that day. What a relief! Maybe this wasn't going to be so bad after all.

Later that day, Michael and Caroline flew to New York where they then met with Dermot Whyte, a slick criminal attorney, in his early sixties, who carried an element of class and experience about him. Whyte had already been hard at work. In exchange for Michael surrendering himself, the DoJ would provide him with a certificate of immunity. He was now untouchable. However, Whyte was clear about one thing: 'Don't answer one single question. Not one. You're in America now. The Fifth Amendment was made for situations like this.'

The very next day, in front of twenty jurors, Michael faced the Grand Jury. Arlo Devlin-Brown, a podgy, balding, bearded beacon of justice, sat at one end of a long table, while Michael sat at the other. In between them was the chairman of the Grand Jury who opened by saying to Michael: 'I understand that you have been advised by your lawyer to respond to our questions in a certain manner today?'

'That is correct,' Michael replied, quoting Whyte verbatim. 'I've been advised not to answer any questions on the basis of my Fifth Amendment rights not to incriminate myself.'

Amazingly, that was that. Michael was free to return to Brisbane, the nightmare apparently over. If they required his services again, the Department of Justice would be in touch. God bless the American justice system!

However, for Daniel Tzvetkoff the worries were only just beginning. He was holed up at North Las Vegas Detention Center, sharing a tiny cell with a man charged with murder. Worst of all, his attorney had advised him that if found guilty of the charges, which included breaches of the UIGEA, Illegal Gambling Business Act, New York Penal Code, as well as being charged with conspiracy, bank and wire fraud and money laundering, he was facing seventy-five years in jail. It was all certainly a far cry from his heyday as the playboy prince of the Gold Coast.

31

Las Vegas, USA, April 2010

Shackled, bedraggled and sporting a khaki prison-issue jump-suit, Daniel staggered into the packed US District Court in Las Vegas feeling the weight of the world on his shoulders. Having spent the weekend in jail, he was praying he wouldn't have to spend much more time behind bars. He wasn't made for such insalubrious surroundings.

Taking a seat next to his lawyer, Robert Goldstein, who had flown in to represent him from Boston, Daniel stared vacantly ahead. This was a bail hearing. If Goldstein worked his magic, he could fight the charges from the outside. If not, then he faced at least the next few months in the slammer, not to mention the cross-country prison bus trip to New York, something which didn't bear thinking about.

Opposite them sat Assistant US Attorney Nicholas Dickinson. He had already let it be known to Goldstein that the State of Nevada would be fiercely opposing any bail application. So as Judge Peggy Leen entered the room, and took her seat at the front of the court, Daniel prepared himself for the worst. Up against money laundering, gambling conspiracy and bank-fraud conspiracy charges, all connected with processing online poker money, Daniel slumped in his chair as Goldstein opened the hearing. As far as he could see, he was fighting a losing battle. In order to get bail, he needed to put up a large chunk of cash as surety, money which he claimed he no longer had.

'Your honour,' Goldstein opened, standing up and speaking in a measured tone. 'My client is a good young man of good character. He is a devoted father to a three-year-old son and committed partner to his heavily pregnant fiancée, Nicole Crisp. If Mr Tzvetkoff is granted bail, Miss Crisp has confirmed to me that she would relocate to New York to help her fiancée fight the charges against him. This would of course also allow him to help raise his young family.'

This was news to Daniel. Since he had been arrested, he hadn't been able to speak directly with Nicole. Indeed, now he was bankrupt, and facing the prospect of the rest of his life in jail, he wasn't exactly a catch any more. He couldn't have blamed her if she had washed her hands of him, especially after the way things had been going between them lately. Taking a sip of water from the glass in front of him, Goldstein continued to paint the court a picture of a wronged man.

'Mr Tzvetkoff is not a drug dealer or a mobster. In fact, up until this arrest he has never been involved in any criminal proceedings. The money he is accused of laundering is connected to online poker. This is not drug money. It is money connected with a pursuit which, under US federal law, has never been officially declared illegal. This is of course an argument for another day, but I am emphasising that this money was not stolen or used for immoral purposes.'

Goldstein was doing a grand job. That was why he was paid the big bucks. But even Daniel knew that if he couldn't offer any security then obtaining bail was going to be close to impossible. However, Daniel's ear's pricked up when he heard Goldstein say to Judge Leen, 'Your honour, the defendant's father, Kim Tzvetkoff, has travelled from Australia to be with us today.'

Looking behind him, Daniel could see his father sat in the gallery.

He couldn't believe it. They had barely spoken since the V8 Racing in Adelaide, but now he was here. Daniel smiled widely as his father nodded at him. 'Mr Tzvetkoff is willing to put his Australian home up as surety,' Goldstein continued, 'and he has also volunteered to drive his son to New York where he will then formally face the charges levelled against him.'

Taking a note, the judge looked out at the gallery. 'Mr Tzvetkoff will you make yourself known to the court please, sir?' she asked, to which Kim stood, looking dapper in a grey suit, white shirt and black tie. It was a far cry from the casual attire he usually wore when at work in the marketplaces of Brisbane. 'Sir, if I were to grant this bail application, you do understand you could lose your home if your son fails to appear?'

'Yes, your honour,' Kim replied. Daniel couldn't believe it. After all that had happened his father was still standing by his side.

Yet the fight was not yet over. Dickinson was determined to have his say. As far as the State of Nevada, as well as the State of New York, was concerned, Daniel Tzvetkoff was a significant flight risk. 'The defendant is an Australian national with no ties to the US,' Dickinson informed the judge as he stood up. 'And what's more, there is reason to believe the defendant has hundreds of millions of dollars hidden in offshore bank accounts. Those funds are out there and could quite easily be used to aid any flight from justice.'

Judge Leen shook her head. Was this good or bad?

'Mr Dickinson,' she began, 'if Mr Tzvetkoff was a US citizen this would be a no-brainer. And with the surety provided by his father, I therefore see no reason why bail should be withheld.'

Turning her attention towards Daniel, Judge Leen asked him to stand: 'Mr Tzvetkoff I am going to grant you bail. However, you must surrender your passport to the court and your father must drive you to New York to face charges. Failure to do so will see him lose his house. Is this understood?'

'Yes, your honour,' Daniel answered, struggling to stop himself from breaking out into a huge grin.

'You must understand that you are still subject to a detainer by US Immigration,' Judge Leen continued, ending Daniel's shortlived joy. 'It will take several days before this can be lifted. In the meantime, you are to remain at North Las Vegas Detention Center.'

Daniel nodded his head. Goldstein had warned him that if they were lucky enough to get bail then this would probably be the case. It was far from perfect, but he could last a few more days, particularly if he knew he wasn't going to have to spend the next few months behind bars while the case rumbled on. Smiling at his father, as he was escorted by guards from the courtroom, Kim gave him the thumbs up. Daniel could have kissed him.

Later that day, as Daniel sat in his cell at the North Las Vegas Detention Center, a guard shouted through the bars: 'Tzvetkoff. You got a visitor!'

With the cell door opened, Daniel was led down a long corridor, before entering a grey room where prisoners and their visitors were separated by a wall of glass. Led by a guard towards a seat Daniel looked up to see who was sitting on the other side. His heart skipped a beat: it was Nicole. She looked beautiful, more beautiful than ever. Picking up the phone to speak, neither initially said a word. The enormity of the moment was too much. Finally, Daniel softly stuttered the only words that seemed appropriate: 'I'm sorry.' Nicole nodded her head, as a tear trickled down her cheek.

'Thanks for being here,' Daniel continued, never taking his eyes off his heavily pregnant fiancée for one second. 'I wasn't sure if you were going to come.'

'Why would you think that?' Nicole replied tearfully, putting a tissue to her face, dabbing away at her running make-up.

'Because I've been a jerk.'

Nicole smiled. 'You're still a jerk. But I love you.'

The sound of those sweet words caused a lump to emerge in Daniel's throat. Over the last few years, he had lost count of the amount of people who had claimed Nicole was only with him for his money. This was proof that she was not. He was bankrupt and facing life in jail, yet she was here, standing by his side. He promised never to take her for granted ever again.

'I love you too,' Daniel managed to mutter back, his voice shaking with emotion.

'I don't have much time, but we think we have an idea of how the FBI knew about you,' Nicole started.

'Full Tilt Poker?' Daniel answered, suddenly snapping back into reality, knowing full well that Ray Bitar had effectively issued a fatwa against him.

Nicole shook her head. 'No. We don't think it was Full Tilt.'

'Then who?' Daniel prodded, clearly confused.

'We've done some research,' she continued. 'Did you know John Scott Clark, Andrew Thornhill and Curtis Pope were all arrested by the FBI last year and charged by the Department of Justice?'

Suddenly Daniel felt sick. This was news to him. He had cut all ties with that crew since last year. But if the FBI had arrested those three guys then maybe they now had access to the servers which contained emails, documents and wire transfers. They would know everything. What's more, what was stopping one of them telling the FBI everything they wanted to know in order to cut a deal? They had already proven there was no loyalty in this game. While Daniel tried to process that information, over the next few days more bad news was still to come. In the interim, the US Assistant Attorney for New York Arlo Devlin-Brown, under the instructions of his boss Preet Bharara, was hard at work appealing the Las Vegas court's decision to grant bail.

In front of Judge Lewis Kaplan in the New York Southern District Court in downtown Manhattan, Devlin-Brown persuaded the court that there was a possibility that Daniel Tzvetkoff had hidden millions of dollars in offshore bank accounts throughout the world. In spite of defence lawyer Martin Weinberg pointing out that there was no concrete evidence for this assumption, and that even notorious Ponzi scheme con-man Bernie Madoff was released on house arrest, it was to no avail. Bail was overturned.

Daniel now faced a cross-country trip across America on the prison bus, as well as spending at least the next few months in jail. In the meantime, Curtis Pope, John Scott Clark and Andrew Thornhill were all enjoying the benefits bail provided . . .

32

New York, USA, June 2010

One blanket, one pillow case, two washcloths, two sheets, two towels – this was the sum total of Daniel Tzvetkoff's possessions at the Metropolitan Detention Center (MDC), Brooklyn, the home for pre-trial inmates, the newly arrested or recently indicted, of which Daniel was now one. He had arrived just a few weeks earlier, following a tortuous cross-country road trip from Las Vegas. For three straight days he had sat at the back of a hot and stuffy bus, alongside murderers, rapists and drug dealers. Nervous, tired and above all scared, he tried to blank the nightmare out. In his mind he pretended he was on a tour of America, taking in all of its famous sights. Sadly, the bus spent most of the time driving in the wilderness, down long, straight roads that seemed to go on forever.

Most of his fellow travellers had done time before. This was no biggie for them. In fact, some spoke of MDC as if it were a holiday camp. Word was that this would be a cushy little number. Daniel prayed the rumours were true. So far, his experience of prison life had been bleak. Each night of the trip he had been subjected to another prison, Oklahoma being the worst. That night he had to bunk up with a man accused of murder, something he took great pride in. 'Yeah man. I slashed them fools up. They been talking shit. You talk shit to me, I put yo ass in a bodybag,' he had bragged. Daniel made a mental note: don't talk shit to the crazy man on the bunk below.

Upon arrival at MDC, a nine-storey jail situated between 2nd and 3rd Avenue on 29th Street, he had undergone a humiliating strip search before swapping his khaki jumpsuit for a brown T-shirt, brown boxers, white tube socks, blue shoes and orange overalls. Following this he was assigned to his living quarters, which would be home for the foreseeable future.

MDC consisted of two buildings. One was an old converted postal centre, a dilapidated relic, where prisoners were housed on bunk beds in big open dorms. The other was a modern, purpose-built facility that provided forty two-man cells. Neither was exactly the Bellagio, but Daniel thanked his lucky stars when he was shown to a two-man cell, especially when he found that, for now, he would have it to himself. And what's more he even had a view, although it was only of a grey-slated factory roof.

In this new world, Daniel was fresh fish, a newbie, a corn-ass muthaphucka, as some had taken to calling him. In short, he was a newly incarcerated inmate who had to watch his every step. Soon, he became accustomed to his new routine and knew what to do to avoid trouble: keep your head down and keep quiet.

Most days prisoners were given the run of the block, free to come and go as they pleased. However, it wasn't as if there was anything that tempting to do outside of the cells. One of the main things to do was to sit in the common-room area and chat to fellow inmates, where conversations tended to go one of two ways: 'I ain't tellin' them jack shit' or 'I ain't doing life for no bitch'. In this world you were either a rat or a soldier, there was no middle ground.

If the conversation didn't relate to your case, then it focused on the female guards, who were usually big, hoochie mamas. The inmates just couldn't get enough. Out in the real world they wouldn't have looked twice, but in here these guards were the answer to all of their fantasies. Some even spoke of them as if they were their girlfriends: 'Hey girl. You better back that ass up. You looking mighty fine today.' The guards seemed to lap it up, revelling in being the centre of attention.

If Daniel wasn't tempted by the scintillating conversation, and just wanted to watch some TV, then he was in luck, as the common room had three of them. Sadly, they were small, had no sound, and he had no say in what was being shown. With so many Spanish prisoners on the block, most wanted to watch Latino TV shows. It was hardly stimulating viewing, but God help anyone if they tried to change the channel. They were literally risking their lives. Whenever he was allowed, Daniel took every opportunity to leave the sanctuary of his room to get some fresh air. He couldn't be cooped up all day in his 12 x 12 cell without going crazy. But the outside area was nothing to write home about. It was small, offered no facilities, other than a basketball board with no rim, and the tall walls meant you could hear the hustle and bustle of life outside but not see it. Not that there was anything in Brooklyn that would have re-invigorated the mind in any event.

With the outside areas providing little in the way of respite, Daniel found other ways to occupy himself, other than wallow in self-pity. In between the set prison schedule, he concocted his own to help preserve his sanity.

7am: Rise and shine. The cell doors are unlocked and inmates stagger out of their rooms yawning and stretching. Most barely say a word. It's the quietest time of the day. A headcount is taken before the day can officially get underway.

7.30am: Breakfast. Usually something like cornflakes and a banana washed down with a cup of water or milk. The room is broken up into cliques: the gangs, Latinos, blacks, Asians, punks – and corn-ass muthaphuckas. Daniel initially sat alone. However, he soon became one of the head honchos of the last group, the white-collar gang of inmates who were predominantly computer hackers or hedge-fund managers.

8.30am: Shower. Having heard plenty of notorious prison rape stories over the years, Daniel initially watched his back. Thankfully, MDC didn't appear to have that sort of environment, although the eight showers that were provided were ice cold and so filthy that you daren't go in there without shower shoes – if you were lucky to own a pair, and white collar prisoners like him would certainly not have them for long.

9.30am: Lockdown. Everyone returns to their cells. During this time Daniel kept to a strict regime of push-ups and sit-ups. If he was going to be fed meagre portions, and be kept inside, then he was determined something positive would come out of the situation, so his goal became to drop the weight he had gained after two years of gastronomic indulgence.

10am: Head count. All prisoners again had to report to the front of their cells while the guards ticked them off one by one.

10.30am: Free time. Having given up on ever watching anything decent on the television, Daniel had the next best thing: a radio. Sat on his bottom bunk, he would spend the next few hours flicking though Howard Stern, Dan Patrick and any station that played decent hip-hop. If he was lucky, he would nod off and get some sleep, something which always made the days go faster.

12.30pm: Lunch. More time sat with the white-collar guys trying in vain to enjoy overcooked chicken and rock-hard mashed potato. However, they got served less than most. The orderlies had a racket going on: proper portions went to those who carried muscle, and if anyone else wanted something extra then they had to pay for the privilege. The guards knew what was going on but turned a blind eye. And with a cash limit of just $320 per month, for once Daniel Tzvetkoff couldn't buy himself much.

1.30pm: Free time. With the radio on in the background, Daniel tried his best to digest the newspapers or a good book. He still wanted to be in the loop on all of the latest business developments, so he avidly scoured the *Wall Street Journal*. Sometimes a new idea would even pop into his head, which would lead him to frantically scribble down some notes. One book he just couldn't get enough of was *The Wolf of Wall Street*, the true story of a young stock-market millionaire who blew his fortune and ended up in jail. The parallels were obvious.

3pm: Phone. Just being able to make a phone call was extremely stressful. Not only did calls cost 23 cents per minute for local calls, and 99 cents for international calls, but you were also limited to just 300 minutes of call time a month. Once you had hit that threshold that was it. You had no option but to wait for the next month to come around. This was especially frustrating for Daniel, with Hugo and a heavily pregnant Nicole now in New York. If he could have, he would have spoken to them every hour of every day.

5.30pm: Dinner. Same drill as lunch, more time spent eating dried meat, covered in apple sauce to make it edible.

6.30pm: Free time. More of the same: radio, book, phone calls, push-ups, sleep.

8pm: Lock down and final head count. The day is over, but another day just like it awaits tomorrow. And the day after. And the day after.

Just as Daniel had settled into his routine, he was disturbed by the addition of a cell-mate. After his experience in Oklahoma, he prayed that he wouldn't have to share a room with another crazy. Spending even a few minutes in some of these guys' company was hard work, let alone spending hour after hour, day after day with them. However, when he was introduced to his new cell-mate, a quietly spoken, clean shaven, glasses-wearing Miami-born-and-bred Cuban by the name of Albert, he relaxed immediately. Albert was no trouble at all. He liked to read, especially history books, he enjoyed listening to the radio and, best of all, he was a computer genius. Before long, Daniel not only tolerated Albert, but actually counted him as a good friend.

Slowly but surely the two cell-mates began to tease their stories from each other. Daniel told Albert everything, right from the beginning: porn, Sam, UIGEA, Ryan Lang, PokerStars, Full Tilt, Curtis Pope, Payovation, and then his dramatic Las Vegas arrest. Albert lay on his bunk and sympathised. He also had a story to tell, although he admitted he was guilty as hell. As Albert proceeded to spill his guts, Daniel couldn't believe what he was hearing. It turned out that his cell-mate was responsible for the biggest credit-card fraud in history.

'Back in 2003 I had a good thing going down,' Albert explained from the top bunk. 'Me and a group of hacker guys I met online had a racket going on which let us get hold of people's credit-card information. Once we had that, we programmed a load of blank debit cards with the information and began cashing out.'

'Cashing out?' Daniel asked, unsure of the lingo.

'Putting the cards into ATMs and clearing the accounts,' Albert shamelessly explained.

'So I'm doing this, making myself a fortune, when I get picked up by the police. Soon they raid my flat and find all my shit. I'm done for. I'm facing twenty years in jail. There's only one way out of this shit!'

'What's that?' Daniel asked, getting more intrigued by the minute.

'I flip. Tell the Feds everything they want to know about how me and my crew did it all. I mean I was twenty-two years old back then. No way am I doing twenty years in jail.'

Stepping off his bunk, Albert walked towards the wall, leant against it and smiled. 'I had the Feds eating out of my hand' he laughed. 'They loved me. Not only did I avoid doing time, but the Secret Service even asked me to work for them. They paid me seventy-five thousand dollars a year. I went round the country giving conferences on fraud and even met the head of the Secret Service. I couldn't believe it.'

Daniel couldn't work this out. If Albert had been working for the Secret Service what was he doing back in jail?

'But I couldn't help myself,' Albert ruefully explained. 'And soon I was back in the game. Now I'm back where I started. Facing twenty years in jail.'

Daniel was astonished: Albert had been doing something that was obviously illegal, which he fully admitted. Yet for the biggest credit-card fraud in history, he was facing twenty years in jail. Daniel, on the other hand, had operated in a grey area of the law, merely helping people to play online poker, and he was facing seventy-five years in jail. It just didn't add up.

'Listen, Dan,' Albert continued. 'If they're offering you a deal, take it man. Get on with your life and don't look back. And certainly don't make the same mistake I did, take the deal and then get done again. That's just plain stupid.'

Daniel nodded his head. This was something that he had been mulling over for the last few weeks. The DoJ already knew a lot. Not only had the FBI been monitoring Trendsact for quite some time, but they also had Curtis, John Scott Clark and Andrew Thornhill in custody, as well as another major poker payment processor by the name of Douglas Rennick. Furthermore, they even had the Intabill servers, which contained a host of information. In short, they had almost everything they needed. But it would take time for them to work it all out. It wasn't easy piecing it all together. However, there was no doubt that they would get there in the end.

Despite this, Daniel's lawyer had made it clear to him that it was in his interest to help them out and tell them what they wanted to know. If he did, he might be able to work out some sort of deal – bail, a shorter sentence, witness protection – basically anything that would see Daniel avoid rotting in jail for the next seventy-five years. It was tempting, and it was certainly something Daniel was considering. Although he still had half a mind to fight the charges head on. Go to court and prove that poker was a game of skill, hence a legal gambling activity. But if he took this path his lawyer told him he would have to fight the charges from behind bars and that could take years to sort out, even if he was eventually cleared. And the longer this whole thing took, the more expensive it would all be.

Just as Daniel was contemplating all of this, an oversized guard approached the cell. 'Tzvetkoff,' she barked. 'Just got word. Congratulations: your wife just gave birth to a baby girl.'

Leaping off the bunk in excitement, Daniel approached the bars, desperate to get out. 'Can I call her?' he asked.

'You got five minutes,' the guard answered, as the bars opened leaving Daniel to run towards the bank of telephones down the corridor.

Sat at one of the booths, Daniel hurriedly dialled Nicole's approved cell-phone number and waited impatiently as it rang. Running his hands through his hair, he felt a mix of exhilaration and nausea. He was delighted to be a father again, but he couldn't believe he had missed the birth. 'Nicole,' he exclaimed as the phone was finally answered. 'How are you? Is everything OK?'

'It's a baby girl, Daddy,' the voice on the other end said. It was Hugo, his voice nearly bringing Daniel to tears. He should have been there with them.

'How are you champ?' he asked, his voice breaking. 'What's her name going to be?'

'Sofia,' Hugo replied. Sofia! Daniel liked that name. It was his favourite on their list. 'Let me speak to your mum, mate. I'll be back on again in five minutes.'

'Hi, babe. I'm OK,' a breathless Nicole greeted him. 'She's absolutely beautiful. Say hello to your father, Sofia.'

Right on cue, Sofia let out a wail which Daniel heard down the phone. Tears started to well in his sodden eyes. 'I love you,' he spluttered. But there was no response. 'I love you,' he repeated, but once again nothing. And then it hit him: his 300 minutes for the month was up. The phone had been cut off. Leaving the phone to hang by its cord, Daniel looked up at the grey, peeling ceiling and bit his lip. He had to get out of here. Now. Whatever it took. He didn't have time to waste. He needed to be back home with his family. They were all that mattered now.

33

New York, USA, April 2011

It was a cramped two-bedroom apartment in Harlem. The heating barely worked, there was no double-glazing and the furniture looked like it had come from a flea market. But for Daniel Tzvetkoff, Nicole and their two children, it was now home. And it certainly beat jail, that was for sure. By now, Daniel had been out of MDC for just over eight months. A deal had been cut. In exchange for Daniel becoming an informant, he would be placed in witness protection. However, it certainly wasn't like the witness protection schemes you see in the movies, where agents trail your every move and watch your back. In this case, Daniel had been left pretty much to his own devices. As long as he checked in when called upon, and he stayed in the city, then he could come and go as he pleased.

This had the bonus that Daniel felt like a free man: the small cell in MDC had been replaced with the freedom of one of the greatest cities in the world. But at other times he felt exposed. The memory of the cold gun being placed to his head in Las Vegas continued to haunt him. However, as Nicole repeatedly pointed out, the vast majority of people had never heard of Daniel Tzvetkoff, and his location was a closely guarded secret anyway. It would be very difficult for anyone to track him down to New York. And even if they knew he was in the city, it would be like looking for a needle in a haystack.

In any event, New York was quite the place to be ensconced. Daniel and Nicole both loved it, as did their friends and family who came to visit them on a regular basis. It certainly beat some of the places where they could have been holed up. Despite the circumstances, they had actually enjoyed some of their nicest moments together there. In the past it had been non-stop work, but now they could spend some quality time in each other's company.

Walking through Central Park in the autumn, with Daniel holding Hugo's hand, while Nicole pushed Sofia in a buggy, had been one of their favourite memories. The leaves had been turning different shades of brown, green and red while the air was crisp and refreshing. Around them they could hear the sounds of the city, the incessant beeping of horns, the racing of the traffic, the shouts of hotdog vendors, but in the park it felt as though they were in another world, away from it all, together.

Being stuck in New York for Christmas was no bad thing, either. As snow fell, and the famous New York lights were switched on, they tried to make the festive period one to remember. Together they visited the Christmas tree in the Rockefeller Center, where Daniel took Hugo to ice skate for the first time, as well as marvelled at the displays on Fifth Avenue, where department stores had extravagantly decorated windows.

In a past life, Daniel could have bought whatever took his fiancée's fancy for Christmas, but this year that wouldn't be an option. They were just surviving on whatever money their families sent them. However, Nicole didn't mind. She was more than happy to shop for bargains in Target and K-Mart. She actually found the challenge of looking for bargains more exhilarating than being able to buy whatever she wished. These days, they just took great pleasure in the simple things.

Amazingly, when Daniel thought about it, he couldn't remember them ever being happier together. The mansions had been swapped for a decrepit apartment. He now rode the subway instead of a Lamborghini. The nearest he got to a boat was taking the ferry to Staten Island. And the nightclubs and booze had been traded in for cups of coffee on the sofa watching TV. He had long since realised that being together as a family was more important to him. As long as they were together then that was all that mattered.

So did he feel guilty at enjoying his newfound freedom? Not a chance. His family needed him, and he needed them. And the people he had informed on had it coming. That was his view anyway. In his mind, many people in the poker world had screwed him over, so if it meant giving some of them up to avoid seventy-five years in jail then it was a no-brainer. Let them rot. They had showed no loyalty to him, so why should he give it back to them?

Working with the Department of Justice, Daniel helped them sift through the mountain of information they possessed. Over 90,000 emails, documents and statements were already at their disposal, but once Daniel got to grips with it all he helpfully explained the processing game to them. He showed how some banks were happy to process the money, knowing full well it came from online poker. However, with others you had to dress it up a little by setting up shell payday loan companies and the like. He even reverse-engineered some transactions to show the trail of money. Placing deposits into the poker companies' websites he proceeded to track the money around the globe until finally it ended up in the up-to-now secret offshore main poker bank accounts, before he then traced the money all the way back to his original account.

However, the DoJ knew a lot of this already. After all, they had been keeping close tabs on Trendsact since hearing Curtis Pope's conversation with E-Z Bill in 2008. It was also quite clear that many others had flipped before Daniel. No names were given, but the number of 'cooperating witnesses' already in the DoJ's possession was frightening. Evidence taken months before Daniel had even been arrested showed another witness already helping the FBI to keep track of the trail of money.

One cooperating witness had deposited funds into both PokerStars and Full Tilt Poker accounts. Descriptors www.net-bill.com and www.echeck365.com subsequently appeared on the witness's bank statement debiting the deposited funds. The originating bank for each of these transactions was Four Oaks Bank and Trust. When the witness then requested for the funds to be credited back into his bank account, he received a cheque from the Bank of America account of Arrow Checks, a company with an address in Calgary, Canada. An investigation into Arrow Checks, and of the account, led the FBI to one name, the godfather of poker processing middlemen: Ryan Lang.

Daniel saw no harm in merely confirming information that the DoJ had already. In most cases they hadn't even needed his confirmation; it was all tied up tight. However, not only had Daniel agreed to act as a cooperating witness, but should any of these cases ever go to court he had crucially confirmed that he would be happy to testify on behalf of the state. This was something he was actually looking forward to. These people had cost him his home, fortune and freedom. As far as he was concerned, if they had stuck by him, then it was unlikely any of this would have ever happened. You reap what you sow.

But even Daniel Tzvetkoff was shocked at the events that transpired on the afternoon of 15 April 2011. Having woken up just after 10am, he had followed his regular routine: shower, breakfast, walk, coffee. It was a routine he had come to know and love, far removed from his monotonous schedule at MDC. On this particular day, upon arriving back at the apartment around 2.30pm, Daniel went to the kitchen to grab a snack while Nicole, Hugo and Sofia crashed on the sofa.

Opening the refrigerator, and peering deep inside for something to take his fancy, Daniel heard Nicole shriek from the other room. 'Shit, Daniel! Come in here quickly. Hurry! Quick!' Probably just some lunatic on an American chat show, Daniel thought, as he closed the refrigerator door, and poked his head around the corner. 'What is it?' he asked, to be greeted by Nicole telling him to 'Shhhhhh!', pointing at the TV as she frantically switched the volume up.

Wondering what all the fuss was about, Daniel stood in the door-way and focused on the television. 'Breaking news at this hour,' the news presenter announced, 'online poker players received a nasty surprise today when they found that their accounts were no more. More on this breaking story after the break.'

'What's that all about?' Daniel said, looking at Nicole who had Sofia in her arms, while Hugo played with his toy soldiers at her feet. 'Look!' she yelled, nodding her head towards the taper at the bottom of the screen. Edging closer to the TV, Daniel was stunned when he made out what it said: 'Feds shut down Online Poker.'

'Did you know anything about this?' Nicole asked.

'No,' he spluttered, speaking in a hushed tone, unable to process the information. 'I didn't know a thing.'

Quickly moving to the small wooden table in the corner of the room, he sat down at a chair and switched on his laptop. Impatiently waiting for it to load, he wondered what the hell was going on. As he thought this Nicole stood up and peered over his shoulder, also des-perate to get to the bottom of things. With his wireless connection kicking in, Daniel hurriedly tried to access the Full Tilt website only to be greeted by an unfamiliar sight. This couldn't be happening! Clicking on to PokerStars, Absolute Poker and then Ultimate Bet he found all of the top online poker sites were showing the same thing. Under the Department of Justice's official seal there was a message on all of the poker homepages that read:

'This domain name has been seized by the FBI pursuant to an arrest warrant in Rem obtained by the United States Attorney's Office for the Southern District of New York and issued by the United States District Court for the Southern District of New York.

'Conducting, financing, managing, supervising, directing or owning all or part of an illegal gambling business is a federal crime (18 U.S.C. & 1955)

'For persons engaged in the business of betting or wagering, it is also a federal crime to knowingly accept, in connection with the participation of another person in unlawful internet gambling, credit, electronic fund transfers, or checks (31 U.S.C. & & 5363 & 5366)

'Violations of these laws carry criminal penalties of up to five years' imprisonment and a fine of up to $250,000.

'Properties, including domain names, used in violation of the provisions of 18 U.S.C. & 1955 or involved in money laundering transactions are subject to forfeiture to the United States. (18 U.S.C. & &981 & 1955 (d)).'

'Well what does that mean?' Nicole asked after a moment of silence.

Unable to take his eyes off the screen, reading the message over and over again, Daniel finally turned around to face her. His mouth wide open in shock, he said falteringly: 'I think they've shut down online poker in America. It's gone.'

'What?' Nicole exclaimed, putting her hand to her mouth while Daniel brought up all of the poker news websites and forums to see what was being said. Headlines screamed out of the screen at him: 'The Shit Hits the Fan', 'Poker Panic', 'Players Lose Everything', 'DoJ Shuts Down Online Poker'. There seemed to be one phrase in particular that every media outlet was using to describe it all, 'Black Friday'.

Scouring through article after article, Daniel slowly pieced the whole story together. It appeared that the Justice Department had charged the founders of PokerStars, Full Tilt Poker and Absolute

Poker with criminal offences, specifically involving conspiracy, bank fraud, money laundering and offences under the UIGEA and Illegal Gambling Business Act. Furthermore, seventy-five bank accounts had also been seized in addition to the Justice Department announcing that they were seeking to claim over $3 billion in civil penalties. For now, online poker was dead. All of the players' accounts were frozen. No one knew if they would see their money again. For online poker it was Armageddon.

Not only were key employees – such as Isai Scheinberg and Paul Tate of PokerStars, Ray Bitar and Nelson Burtnick of Full Tilt Poker, and Scott Tom and Brent Beckley of Absolute Poker, named in the indictments, but so too were a number of payment processors. Some processors, such as Ira Rubin and Bradley Franzen, Daniel had never heard of before, but two names jumped out of the page: Ryan Lang and Chad Elie. Reading through the US v Scheinberg et al indictment, which was now posted all over the internet, Daniel suddenly felt sick to his stomach.

'I don't believe it,' he muttered, placing his finger to the top right of the screen.

'What's the matter?' Nicole asked, noticing that her fiancé's shoulders had slumped and his face was white.

Continuing to point to the front page of the indictment, Daniel highlighted the words, 'Superseding Indictment'.

'So what does that mean?' Nicole responded, confused as to why this was such a big deal.

'Look at the case number as well,' Daniel replied.

Peering closer Nicole saw that it read S3 10 Cr. 376. (LAK). 'So what?' she said.

Turning to face his confused fiancée, Daniel struggled to get the words out: 'That case number is the same as mine,' he said. 'This is a Superseding Indictment to my case.'

Suddenly Nicole realised the implication: this provided a clear link between Daniel and the complete collapse of online poker in America. 'No one is going to link you with all of this,' she said unconvincingly, placing her hand on Daniel's shoulder as he looked up at her. 'I wouldn't worry, babe.'

But Daniel wasn't just worried – he was terrified. How long was it going to take for people to put this information together? And then how long would it be before Daniel Tzvetkoff was primarily blamed for the collapse of online poker? He was a dead man walking. He would probably have been safer in MDC with murderers, rapists and terrorists. So much for witness protection.

34

Las Vegas, USA, Present Day

Groggily awaking from a deep sleep, twenty-three-year-old online grinder Greg Merson, a skinny, shaven-headed University of Maryland dropout, lay perfectly still, staring at the ceiling. He was man down. Having got through a ton of Adderall (synthetic cocaine) the night before, in order to perk himself up during a private cash game with friends, he had needed to smoke some weed to wind down. Finally, at 8am he had crashed, but while he had enjoyed ten hours' sleep he was still wiped out. The weed was still in his system.

Propping himself up, he looked across to his bedside table to see some Adderall capsules already crushed. Just what he needed: a quick snort to kick-start his day. Rolling up a dollar bill, he hoovered the fat line into his nostrils. The rush was instant: a pulsating, throbbing orgasm rocketed through his veins and slammed into his eyeballs. Now he was ready to start his working day.

This was a routine that Greg had gradually been sticking to since early February. Until then he had enjoyed almost three years' completely clean, since he had first checked into rehab at his parents' request on 8 August 2007. During high school he had been a straight-A student, but by the time he was finishing his freshman year at the

University of Maryland his grade point average had slumped to just 1.1. He had looked like crap as well, having lost over thirty pounds during a five-month cocaine binge.

When he had emerged from rehab, his conservative parents had hoped that the worst was behind their wayward son. Now he could concentrate on his studies, which would allow him to get a dependable, professional job in the future. So when Greg told them that he was quitting university to play online poker full time, they were horrified, not only because they held a dim view of online gambling but also because since 2003, when Greg started to play online, having been inspired by Chris Moneymaker's World Series win, he had enjoyed only moderate success. How could he hope to support himself? And what about his future?

Just a few weeks later, their prophecy of doom appeared to be fulfilled. Greg had blown most of his bankroll. At this point even he doubted whether he had what it took to play professionally. Heeding his parents' advice, he enrolled in community college to try to kickstart his education. But again, just a few months later, Greg had quit: it wasn't for him. He needed to follow his dreams and play online poker.

Having crashed and burned so miserably before, Greg appeared to have learnt his lesson as he spent the next three years grinding out over $200,000 in online winnings, including $40,000 which he pocketed as a result of finishing second in the PokerStars Sunday Second Chance tournament. While it was a healthy income, it was nothing spectacular, certainly not when you compared it to the hauls of the big beasts of the online domain, such as Viktor Blom, Brian Hastings and Phil Ivey. Yet Greg was supporting himself, he was clean, and he was happy, even if he was just a regular grinder. Gradually, even his parents came to respect his career choice.

However, in February 2011 a drunken night out with friends led to a major relapse. Soon Greg was burning his way through his bankroll to keep up with his drug habit. Thankfully, he had a job where he could make some easy money doing nothing more than just sitting in his sweatpants playing online poker in his bedroom. Yet on 15 April, when Greg had finally got out of bed and sat down in front of his computer, he had found that his bankroll, as well as his source of income, were gone. Having logged on to Facebook, Greg had seen his friends talking about the Feds shutting down online poker. Quickly logging on to his PokerStars account, then his Full Tilt account, and then finally his Ultimate Bet account, he found it was true: they were all down. He had almost all of his money, $125,000, tied up in them. And it didn't look as if there was any way to cash out.

As panic overwhelmed Greg, as well as the poker community, good news was soon at hand. On 20 April the Department of Justice announced that the poker companies could re-open their domains with the sole purpose of reimbursing their players. The result was akin to the aftermath of the 1929 Wall Street Crash, as players flooded the sites desperately trying to withdraw their money.

Within a matter of days, Greg was relieved to find that the $30,000 he had tied up in PokerStars was back in his bank account but, despite promises to the contrary, Full Tilt and Ultimate Bet still hadn't paid up. His Ultimate Bet account had just $5,000 in it, but his Full Tilt account held most of his bankroll: $90,000. He had planned to use that money to fund a summer in Vegas, playing cash games at the Bellagio, as well as entering some World Series tournaments. A fair chunk of it was also needed to keep up with his drug habit. With no access to it, he was screwed.

While Full Tilt continued to release statements claiming that players would soon be reimbursed in full, and that their money was safe, Greg and thousands of other players who relied on that money to survive didn't receive a penny. Some decided to wait it out, hopeful that Full Tilt would deliver on their promise, but Greg told me, when he agreed to be interviewed for this book, that he just couldn't wait a moment longer. 'I sold my Full Tilt Poker money at eighty cents on the dollar in May as we were just three weeks away from the World Series starting and I wanted to be as liquid as possible for the big games over the summer. I also looked at it as time/value of money and how long I may have to wait to get paid, if in fact I did ever get paid, so it was an offer I jumped at.'

It was a wise choice. As the summer dragged on, Full Tilt Poker continued to promise full reimbursement without actually paying back a dime. Players besieged the company demanding to know if their funds had been segregated from the operations account. The company confirmed, as they had done in the past, that the funds had been kept separate. Indeed, Full Tilt remained open for business outside of the US, so technically funds were still being deposited. It was, they said, only a matter of time before they managed to process all players' reimbursement requests. Players just needed to be patient.

When Greg arrived in Vegas to play at the World Series in late May 2011, he saw first-hand just what damage Black Friday had inflicted on the poker world. Player numbers were down significantly, owing to most of their bankrolls being tied up in Full Tilt, while one of the biggest names in poker, Phil Ivey, had decided to boycott the event altogether. Instead, he concentrated his efforts on suing Full Tilt Poker (a company in which he reportedly held a five per cent share) for $150 million. However, he would soon drop the lawsuit after many accused him of using his status to try to leap-frog other players who were also waiting to receive their money.

Although some players who were sponsored by Full Tilt, such as Tom Dwan, fronted up at the tournament, and took a considerable amount of abuse, the main guys in charge – Howard Lederer, Chris Ferguson, and Ray Bitar – were conspicuous by their absence. Since Black Friday they had all been lying low, much to the consternation of the players who were owed a considerable amount of money.

The World Series ultimately turned into a disaster for Greg.

Steadily increasing his dependence on Adderall, as well as introducing Roxy (synthetic heroin) into the mix, his decision-making at the tables became erratic. As he told me: 'Black Friday had taken my relapse into a new level of depression. I lost between fifty and sixty per cent of my net worth during a ten-month binge.'

On the ropes, both personally and professionally, Greg knew he had to get out of Vegas and find somewhere to continue to play online. He desperately needed the money, and tournaments weren't his thing; grinding online was his speciality. It was a path many other online players also had to consider, now that their profession had effectively been outlawed overnight by the Department of Justice. Some players managed to stay in the States, and continued to play online, although this wasn't easy and was very risky. As the European poker sites didn't allow anyone with an American IP address to play on their sites, some players got around this by paying for a Virtual Private Network ('VPN'). This would route their connection to an overseas location, such as London, and change their IP address so it would appear that the computer was in England. However, some poker companies, such as PokerStars, soon cottoned on and not only banned the offending player but also seized all of the money they had in their account.

Many players decided that the best option was to emigrate. Companies such as Poker Refugees had started to spring up, where for a fee they would help set up online players abroad. In this way, the company helped many players relocate to places such as Mexico, Costa Rica, England, South Korea and Canada. Many had to leave their families behind, often feeling that they had no choice, as online poker was all they had known. They were effectively unemployable, especially in a recession, and they desperately needed to keep playing to support themselves, as well as their loved ones.

Weighing everything up, Greg decided to move to Toronto. He hoped it would be a fresh start, but as he fell deeper into his addiction, worrying news started to emerge from Full Tilt. In late June, the Alderney Gambling Control Commission suspended Full Tilt's licence, which led to the site shutting down worldwide. However, the true bombshell emerged in September when the Department of Justice amended its civil complaint.

Adding the names of Chris Ferguson, Howard Lederer and Rafe Furst (a Full Tilt pro and minority owner) to the complaint, it was alleged that as of 31 March 2011, Full Tilt had just $59,579,412 in its bank account yet owed its players a grand total of $390,695,788. While there was a huge shortfall, shareholders had continued to be paid tens of millions of dollars in distributions immediately prior to Black Friday. Ray Bitar was said to have received $41 million, Howard Lederer $42 million, Chris Ferguson $85 million and Rafe Furst $11 million. The other nineteen shareholders, such as Phil Ivey, were also said to have received the remainder of the $443,860,530 that had been distributed since the company had been incorporated.

Perhaps most damagingly, US Attorney Preet Bharara labelled Full Tilt Poker 'a global Ponzi scheme'. In a statement, he claimed that the company had 'cheated and abused its own players to the tune of hundreds of millions of dollars ... insiders lined their own pockets with funds picked from the pockets of their most loyal customers while blithely lying to both players and the public alike about the safety and security of the money deposited with the company.' It seemed that after Black Friday, Full Tilt, knowing full well it had a significant shortfall, had tried to raise the funds to repay its US players by acquiring deposits from players outside of the US. By way of default, it had to all intents and purposes become a Ponzi scheme.

Unsurprisingly, shortly after this announcement, the Alderney Gambling Control Commission opted to officially revoke Full Tilt's licence. From that moment, Full Tilt was finished, and it appeared that the players weren't going to get their money back after all.

While mayhem broke out, with thousands of players who had lost everything baying for blood, Greg continued his slump into oblivion. Spending his time playing online in Toronto, or playing cash games in Atlantic City or Vegas, he was strung out on drugs and playing worse than ever. The nadir would come on Greg's twenty-fourth birthday, 8 December 2011, which he spent in Vegas, gunning his way through an arsenal of drugs. He told me, 'I have no idea what I did. I was as high as a kite, and that's about as far as I can remember. I was on about a hundred and fifty milligrams of Roxy per day and had lost about forty thousand dollars in less than a week in the Bellagio.'

Thankfully, two good friends and fellow poker professionals, Anthony Gregg and Christian Harder, had joined Greg on the trip to Vegas. By this stage they had become concerned at the state of their friend. He had lost a lot of weight, his bankroll was rapidly diminishing and his habit was steadily growing: something needed to be done. 'Christian just called me out on it after seeing me snort some Roxy,' Greg remembers. 'For some reason something just clicked when he bitched me out.'

Vowing to clean up his act, and with the help of Christian and Anthony, on 10 December Greg holed himself up in a room at the Aria Hotel in Vegas for four straight days. Vomiting and shaking, as he went through withdrawal symptoms, he told me that the experience 'was the worst four days of my life'. Clean once again, Greg returned to Toronto where he continued with his recovery, attending Narcotics Anonymous meetings, and gradually getting back into the groove on the poker tables. 'My goal was to regain my focus at the table,' Greg recalled, 'and fix my tilt/emotional issues I had been having due to my relapse. I had never worked so hard or been that focused on poker since I had turned pro.'

Starting to crush No Limit Hold'em games online, Greg set off for Vegas in June 2012 hoping to make some money at cash games at the Bellagio, and also cash in at some of the World Series tournaments.

However, this was very much a long shot. Greg had never before had much success in live tournaments. For instance, his best finish to date in the World Series Main Event had been 639th in 2009. Indeed, he hadn't fared much better in any other tournaments. But with a new-found focus and determination, Greg shocked even himself when on 11 June he cashed in for $16,850 playing in the $3,000 Six-handed No Limit Hold'em event. Things went even better just a few days later when a fifth-place finish in the $2,500 Four-handed No Limit Hold'em tournament saw him pocket $70,000.

Riding the crest of a wave, and playing the best poker of his life, Greg entered the $10,000 Six-handed No Limit Hold'em World Championship on 3 July in high spirits. Rampaging through a field of 472 players, Greg sat down four days later to take on his opponent, Jim Lehr, in the final. Having faced off against each other the day before, without a winner emerging, the finalists sat back down again on day four of the tournament, with Greg having 9.5 million chips to Lehr's 5 million.

On the first hand Greg was dealt King Nine. He opened with a 280,000 chip bet. Lehr re-raised to 915,000. Greg went over the top, hoping to bully Lehr out of the pot, but instead his opponent upped the ante. He went all-in; it was only the first hand of the day. Calling Lehr, Greg was stunned when his opponent showed his hand to reveal he held Ace Queen. Greg had just a forty per cent chance of winning the pot. But when the flop came, 10-9-10 Greg hit his 9. He was now ahead. The odds had shifted to seventy-five per cent in his favour. Yet the fourth card looked to have dealt a fatal blow: Lehr had hit a Queen. Greg's odds now slumped to just twenty per cent. With his family keeping up to date with the proceedings on the internet back home in Laurel, they knew Greg needed a miracle on the river. And he got it: a Jack. Greg had pulled an inside straight. Not only had he just won his first World Series of Poker bracelet, he had also just added $1,136,197 to his bankroll!

While Greg quietly celebrated his extraordinary win, shunning all alcohol and drugs, it seemed that players who looked to have lost money in Full Tilt would also soon be rejoicing. Rumours had begun to circulate that PokerStars was in negotiation with the Department of Justice to buy its rival, Full Tilt Poker. On 31 July the rumours were confirmed as true. PokerStars had agreed to pay the US government $547 million over the next three years for the site, a sum which would be used in part to reimburse former US customers of Full Tilt Poker, while PokerStars itself had directly agreed to reimburse non-US Full Tilt customers to the tune of $184 million. But this was all dependent on one condition: the government insisted that Isai Scheinberg, who remained in the Isle of Man, having refused to travel to the US to face the charges against him, would have to step down from the management of PokerStars.

In the circumstances, with so much at stake, there was only one possible outcome: Scheinberg duly fell on his sword. He had already ensured his own players had been repaid in full, now by stepping down he had also ensured that one his biggest rival's players would also in time have a chance of getting their money back.

When the World Series of Poker Main Event kicked off on 7 July, Greg was well and truly in the zone: his confidence had never been higher, his bankroll never so fat. Yet while he had performed well in the other tournaments to date, the Main Event was a different animal altogether. He would be up against 6,598 players, including some of the legends of poker, so if he was going to improve on his previous best he would have to be at the top of his game.

However, on day five of the tournament it looked as though Greg's valiant effort would end in failure. Down to his last 50,000 chips, he had just enough left for three blinds. But proving true the old poker adage, 'all you need is a chip and a chair to win', he soon doubled up, and then he doubled up again. From staring elimination in the face, he finished the day on 950,000 chips. And by 14 July he had once again smashed the odds and made the cut: he was down to the final nine players who would contest the final table in October. At the very least he had just made another $754,798.

Returning to Laurel to prepare for the final, Greg tried not to think too hard about what awaited him. 'I really didn't do anything different other than play a little more live poker instead of mostly online. I just needed a little tune-up before the big day. I did everything I was doing that got me there, which was staying clean and keeping my focus on poker at a peak without getting burnt out.'

However, two individuals who did help Greg prepare were his friend, Olympic swimming champion Michael Phelps, and Phil Ivey, who signed Greg up to his new free poker training site, www.iveypoker.com. While Greg tried to keep a low profile in the build-up, Howard Lederer of Full Tilt Poker was doing anything but. With the Department of Justice once again amending its civil complaint to introduce new forfeiture charges, which alleged that Lederer and Bitar had used 'illegal proceeds' to purchase an array of properties and cars, he came out all guns blazing. Having completely disappeared from the public view since Black Friday, he bizarrely decided to give a recorded interview with Mathew Parvis of PokerNews, an interview that would become known as 'The Lederer Files'.

Although Lederer spent most of the interview conveniently forgetting key events, he did reveal that the company knew there was a significant backlog prior to Black Friday. He also stated that many of the board were at loggerheads with Ray Bitar due to his abysmal handling of the situation. Bitar had apparently been aware that players' funds had not been segregated from the Full Tilt operational account, but he had not seen that as a problem. Indeed, the only thing that truly became clear during the interview was that the Full Tilt board, led by Ray Bitar, had been completely out of their depth. While they may not have intentionally engaged in criminal activity, the negligent way they ran the company had led to it imploding, as well as exacerbating an already volatile situation. Lederer had hoped that his interview would calm things down, but judging by the response he received he seemed only to fan the flames. Having agreed to do a host of other interviews, Lederer suddenly pulled out and retreated, fearing that he was not only doing his reputation further harm but he could also be doing irreparable damage to his defence in the civil suit.

As Lederer disappeared from public view, Greg Merson was preparing to be in the full glare of it. The final table was due to kick off on 29 October, at the Penn & Teller Theater in the Rio. There, in front of thousands of fans, and millions of viewers on ESPN, he would contest the greatest prize in all of poker. Up for grabs was not only a gold bracelet, and $8.5 million to the winner, but also a shot at immortality. It was a once-in-a-lifetime chance to join the pantheon of the greats that included Doyle Brunson, Stu Ungar and Phil Hellmuth.

Starting the day with the third highest number of chips, Greg entered the cheering theatre, wearing his lucky black Baltimore Orioles jersey, in confident mood. Taking a seat around the green felt table under the bright ESPN camera lights, Greg lapped up the applause from the crowd, who numbered his friends and family from back home, his new sponsor Phil Ivey, as well as his saviours Anthony Gregg and Christian Harder. He told me that it was 'a dream to perform on such a stage where all the practice from all the hours/hands/online/live playing are paying off. It was the biggest moment of my career, but I was never afraid of the moment. I was there to play poker and put on a show.'

The game that followed would turn into one of the most dramatic final tables ever witnessed at the World Series. Over the course of the next three days and nights, Greg rode a rollercoaster of emotions. Driven on by copious amounts of Red Bull, and the support of his friends and family, he battled through to the final three, after knocking out Andras Koroknai to become overall chip leader. Yet while

Greg had now shot into the lead, his two remaining opponents, Jesse Sylvia and Jacob Balsiger, did not give him an easy ride. During eleven hours of play they refused to budge until Greg outmanoeuvred Balsiger to knock him out of the tournament. From 6,598 players in July, two were now remaining: Greg Merson and Jesse Sylvia.

If it had taken over eleven hours to whittle the field down to two, it took just seventeen hands before one player was left standing. Greg, holding a King and 5 of diamonds, put Sylvia in for all of his chips. Sylvia, with Queen and Jack of Spades, called. As both players flipped over their cards, a wave of emotion erupted from the crowd. Screaming, cheering and hollering, they knew this was it: who was going to be the champion of the world?

The flop came down 6 of clubs, 3 of hearts and 9 of diamonds. Neither player had hit a card, but Greg was still ahead with just a King high while Sylvia's slim flush hopes were now gone. The turn produced a 6 of spades. Greg was now a strong favourite, but if Jesse hit a Queen or a Jack on the river then he would snatch away the world title in the cruellest fashion. However, if he didn't hit on the river then Greg would be world champion.

When the river came there was a hushed silence in the theatre. This was it! The hundreds of hours of play all came down to this: the final card. As it left the dealer's grasp and landed on the green velvet, the cameras zoomed in, the players held their breath, and the audience fell deathly quiet. Then there was a roar: 7 of clubs. Greg Merson was the World Series of Poker Main Event champion!

As his friends and family swarmed over the rails to rush to him, Greg calmly brushed them aside so that he could shake Sylvia's hand. Only then, after he had spoken to Sylvia, did he celebrate. On the table was a mountain of money, numbering $8.5 million. His prize. He was also awarded with the gold bracelet, which itself was worth $150,000. Sat at the table, posing for pictures, it all suddenly dawned on him: just a year earlier he had been a dropout, hopelessly addicted to drugs, close to blowing his whole bankroll; now he was a multi-millionaire and world champion. The very thought brought him to tears.

'A lot of emotion was running through me at the time,' he told me, thinking of the moment. 'I think the tears stem from all the stuff I've been through in my life. Also, to reach the pinnacle of my profession so quickly after having the worst year of my life on and off the table was such a surreal experience. Plus I get my emotional genes from my mom!'

And his advice for those who have been in a situation like his? 'Understand what works for you. For some people it's one-on-one counselling, for others it's group meetings. The ability to be honest as a drug addict is important, too. Understanding what makes you upset or stressed out is the key to staying sober. The environment and people you surround yourself with will also make all the difference in staying on the right path. If you want something bad enough, no matter what it is in life, if you put the time and effort into it, then your dreams will come true.'

While Greg Merson achieved the ultimate happy ending, not all online players have been so lucky. Many have not only lost money they were depending on, but have also lost their only profession. Although PokerStars' acquisition of Full Tilt was meant to see US players reimbursed in full, at the time of writing this has still not transpired, even though Full Tilt once again opened its doors for business, outside of the US, in November 2012.

As players watched on helplessly, there was one man many blamed for all of this: a twenty-eight-year-old Australian by the name of Daniel Tzvetkoff. The young whiz-kid, who had apparently sunk online poker, was now viewed by many as public enemy number one. He just had to hope he could stay under the radar in New York. Otherwise, according to the threats issued online, his life could very well be in danger.

35

New York, USA, April 2012

Rat, snitch, grass, dead man walking – all terms that over the last twelve months had been used to describe Daniel Tzvetkoff, the prodigy who many blamed for the complete collapse of online poker in America. After the events of Black Friday, it had taken less than forty-eight hours for his name to be connected with the indictments. What at first began as a few rumblings on forums rapidly turned into a full-blown media exposé. Major TV stations and newspapers throughout the world began to run the story, all ramping up the hate campaign. Headlines such as 'Poker's Liar' certainly helped to depict Daniel as the bad guy. He was described as being a scam artist who had stolen money from poker sites before turning rat. Names such as Curtis Pope and John Scott Clark disappeared under the radar; it was as if they had no part to play in this at all.

While Daniel shouldered the blame, it appeared that others were equally as culpable, and had also taken deals. Processors such as Ahmad Khawaja, Michael Schuett, Douglas Rennick as well as Daniel's old friend and employee Andrew Thornhill had all been arrested by the FBI before he had, and before Black Friday. Despite initially being threatened with long sentences, Thornhill received just three months in jail, Khawaja merely paid a civil penalty and avoided criminal prosecution altogether, Schuett paid a $3.2 million fine and spent eighty days in jail, while Rennick, whose processing company had also processed hundreds of millions of dollars, happily took six months under house arrest. No matter: in the eyes of the world, this whole thing rested squarely on Daniel Tzvetkoff.

A quick search of court documents could have provided anyone who was interested with the full story. They could have clearly seen how Intabill had been taken from right under Daniel's feet by Curtis Pope, but as Kim Tzvetkoff repeatedly told his son: why let facts get in the way of a good story. Night after night, day after day, Daniel scoured poker forums and Twitter to see what people were saying about him. It was far from complimentary; it seemed everyone wanted their pound of flesh. Often Nicole would have to resort to switching off the computer so that Daniel would stop looking at it. 'It's no good,' she would urge. 'Right now you can't do anything about it.'

She was right of course. Daniel had been desperate to give a public statement, or even get on TV and do a full-blown interview to clear his name. He wanted to tell everyone what had really happened, but it was impossible: the court had him under a gagging order, and any deviation from that would see him back behind bars. So while the poker world and beyond burned him at the stake, he had no option but to bite his tongue.

Before all of this, it had been quite easy for him to slip under the radar: no one in the wider poker community really knew who he was, or what he looked like, so being out and about wasn't a big issue. Now, however, his picture was all over the place, and for some he was public enemy number one.

No one had liked reading about how this cocky young Aussie had blown a load of dough while they lost all of theirs. The rumours that Daniel had squirrelled away hundreds of millions of dollars into offshore bank accounts throughout the world only made things worse. Feelings were running high.

For the first few months, Daniel had been very wary about being out in public and Nicole virtually had to push him out of the house to get some fresh air. He was convinced that poker vigilantes would be waiting for him around every corner. But what initially began as quick trips to the store across the street, looking this way and that, soon built up to going to watch a movie.

However, Daniel made certain that he always wore some kind of disguise and tried to keep away from large tourist areas. His rapid weight loss, coupled with his newly grown beard, meant that to those who didn't know him before, he was virtually unrecognisable. In all the time he was in New York, he was never stopped. As time went by, his confidence began to grow, and slowly but surely he began to get more adventurous. The poker community hate campaign against him had now moved on to the principals of Full Tilt Poker: Ray Bitar, Howard Lederer and Chris Ferguson. Hopefully, now he was out of the limelight, his life could return to some level of normality.

Delighted to see that her fiancé was beginning to loosen up, Nicole begged him to shave off his beard, which she had never liked. She also had a suggestion: 'Why don't we take the kids to Chinatown? Hugo will love it.' Daniel wasn't so sure. Up until now, he had avoided busy areas like Canal Street. It was too risky. But Nicole was persistent. It was a perfect spring day, and the kids wanted to spend some time with their father. She suggested that her reluctant fiancé should put on some nice clothes and they could enjoy acting like a normal family for once. Daniel hadn't felt normal since he had worked in Pizza Hut six years previously. Maybe it would be nice to try it. To hell with feeling terrified. Maybe it was time to put on his best clothes and face the world.

Dressing in his favourite dark blue jeans, black T-shirt and black blazer, all of which were now slightly too big for him, a fresh-faced

Daniel emerged from the bathroom after finally shaving, grandly pirouetted, and said, 'How do I look?'

Nicole laughed: 'You look like a recently released hostage.'

'Well, I'm a hostage no more,' he smiled, putting his arm around Nicole, and patting Hugo on the head. 'Let's get out of here.'

As Nicole cradled Sofia in her arms, Daniel carried her buggy down the stairs, before hailing a cab on the street. Crammed into the back of one of New York's famous yellow cabs, they instructed the driver to take them to Chinatown. Whisking through the streets, along Central Park, down Fifth Avenue, and then Broadway, the driver criss-crossed lanes and liberally beeped his horn, keeping faithfully to the manic New York cab driver's code.

'What do you want to see in Chinatown then, mate?' Daniel asked his excited son who sat on his lap.

'The fighting fish!' Hugo smiled, having heard that they were on display in shop windows.

'The fighting fish it is then.'

Pulling up on the corner of Broadway and Canal Street, Daniel thrust some money through the window at the driver, jumped out of the cab, and took in his surroundings. Chinatown was gritty, the faded shopfronts were covered in grime, smoke wafted out from between grills in the pavement and rubbish lined the street. Walking side by side with his family, Daniel completely forgot that he was meant to be a man in hiding as he took it all in. It didn't feel like America at all. It felt like another world altogether. And while New York was always busy, the number of people crammed on the pavement was overwhelming: Nigerian and Asian traders lined the side of the street, whispering to passers-by: 'Louis Vuitton. Coco Chanel. Armani.' Meanwhile, shop owners tried to drag unsuspecting tourists inside to inspect their wares. You couldn't walk a second without someone approaching you.

'The fighting fish! The fighting fish!' Hugo suddenly cried, racing towards a shop window.

Taking out her phone, Nicole desperately tried to capture the moment on camera. Her young son had talked about nothing else all day. Now they were in front of him, he pressed his face against the window in awe. Watching on, Daniel smiled. It had been a long time since they had been out as a family. He felt re-energised and refreshed. Perhaps, in time, he would be able to settle down into a normal life after all. But then he was snapped back into harsh reality.

'Daniel?' an Australian voice suddenly asked.

Swivelling around, Daniel came face to face with a skinny, dark-haired guy. He recognised him, though from where he wasn't quite sure.

'Daniel Tzvetkoff?' the guy asked again, walking closer.

Who was he? Was he one of the poker guys? A processor? An employee at Intabill? Either way, Daniel knew he had to play dumb.

'No, mate,' Daniel answered, trying to get Nicole's attention without causing a scene. He needed to get out of here. 'That's not me.'

'I know it's you, Daniel,' the guy said, now just a metre away, inspecting Daniel as if he were a rare artefact. 'I just want to ask you a few questions.'

Shit! Now Daniel remembered. It was a young reporter from the *Brisbane Courier Mail*. Alex Dickinson! He had written articles about Daniel in the past. What the hell was he doing here? Had he been following him or tracing his phone calls and emails? Surely that was the only explanation? It was just too much of a coincidence otherwise.

'Look, mate. I don't know what you're talking about,' Daniel said firmly, starting to panic, his hair standing up on the back of his neck, anxiety rippling through his tight chest. Suddenly the reporter took out his phone and snapped a picture. Daniel couldn't believe it. This was not good: he needed to get him away. Now.

'Listen,' Daniel cursed, walking aggressively towards the reporter. 'You're going to get in a lot of trouble. There are people with me who won't like what you are doing!'

Of course, no FBI agents or bodyguards were present, it was just

Nicole, Sofia and Hugo. That was the reality of the situation: Daniel was alone. Looking around the reporter smiled: 'I know there's no one with you, Daniel. Look. I just want to ask you some questions. That's all.'

'If you don't leave me alone you're going to get in a lot of trouble with me,' Daniel threatened through gritted teeth, at which the reporter finally backed away.

Scurrying into the road, Daniel held his arm aloft hoping to get a cab. The sooner he got out of there the better. Within seconds a cab pulled up at the curb. Daniel shouted to Nicole: 'Babe, get the kids, we need to go.'

'What?' Nicole answered, not having seen what had gone on.

'Now!' Daniel shouted, making it clear this was no time to argue.

Jumping into the cab, Daniel held the door open so his family could join him.

'Where to?' the driver asked, as a confused Nicole and the kids jumped in.

'Just drive,' Daniel ordered.

'Gee! What's got into you?' Nicole questioned, as the cab weaved through the traffic.

'I've just been photographed by a reporter from the *Courier Mail*. That picture is going to be all over the news. People are going to know that I am definitely in New York.'

Nicole let this thought linger in her mind. 'How did they know where you would be?' she asked. 'No one knew we were going to Chinatown but us.'

It was that very thought that frightened Daniel. Someone had to be listening, watching or both. People were on to him, that much was now very clear.

As the taxi hit gridlock on Fifth Avenue, Daniel knew what they had to do. 'We need to get out of here,' he said softly, as the thought played through his mind for the first time. 'We need to disappear.'

Nicole nodded her head in agreement as Sofia wailed in her arms. It was time to get the hell out of Dodge.

36

Las Vegas, USA, Present Day

Stepping out into the humid night air and looking up at my des-tination for the evening, the neon blue Binion's Hotel & Casino in Old Vegas, something struck me. By complete accident I had stumbled upon the perfect venue. I had come to do an interview on the future of poker at the very place where much of its history had been made.

To many who love the game of poker, Binion's is ground zero. Without Binion's, the poker world would be a very different place today. Earlier in my trip I had admired the statue of its founder, Benny Binion, which is now situated at the South Point Hotel and Casino, on the southern end of The Strip, having been relocated from Old Vegas in 2008. Immortalised in his favourite cowboy attire, while sitting triumphantly on a horse, the statue is a fitting tribute to the godfather of the poker world, of whom former World Series cham-pion 'Amarillo Slim' said on his passing in 1989: 'He was either the gentlest bad guy or the baddest good guy you'd ever seen.'

Born in Texas at the turn of the last century, Binion's earlier years were littered with trouble. Moonshining, theft and even murder were just a few of the things he was convicted of. After serving time in jail the self-styled cowboy eventually got a hold of illegal gambling in Dallas before moving on to Vegas in 1951, where he bought the Eldorado Club and the Apache Hotel, swiftly turning them into Binion's Horseshoe Casino.

'Good food, good whiskey, good gamble' became Binion's mantra. And he went out of his way to ensure his customers got a healthy dose of all three. He arranged for limousines to transport customers to and from the casino, offered free drinks to all players, not just the high rollers, and his two-dollar steak special became the stuff of legend. Furthermore, Binion's was also the first major casino to offer 100-times-odds at craps. If tourists wanted gaudy showgirls, then Binion's wasn't where they came. Binion's was a place strictly for those who liked to gamble, and gamble hard. That's the way it was and that's the way it has always been.

As I eagerly walked through the entrance, into a welcome blast of ice-cold air, I braced myself for a hit of old school Vegas. Sadly, having been out of the Binion family's hands for a number of years, the casino looked to have lost most of its unique charm. The floor was mostly full of tourists playing slot machines, the blackjack and poker tables were surprisingly hidden away, and the décor could have been from any other casino on The Strip. My first impression was that the place had lost its soul.

Feeling slightly disappointed at the new sanitised Binion's, I thankfully soon saw small nods to its founder's vision. One of the novelties Binion's was famous for over the years was a transparent horseshoe out front that had $1 million encased within it. While the horseshoe is no more, the new owners now have the $1 million display on the casino floor. Better yet, when I found the new poker room, which had opened in 2008, I was delighted to find the gallery of champions within it, where emblazoned on the red wall were pictures of each of the World Series of Poker Main Event winners.

Since Binion's first opened in the early fifties, it had become synonymous with poker, initially due to a five-month titanic tussle on the tables between Johnny Moss and Nick 'the Greek' Dandalos. By the end of this heads-up duel, Nick the Greek had lost $2 million. Wiped out after months of little sleep and relentless high-stakes action, he uttered one of the most famous poker quotes of all time to his opponent: 'Mr Moss, I have to let you go.'

However, it wouldn't be until 1970 when Binion would have his moment of inspiration that would forever change the world of poker. Wanting to settle once and for all who was the top poker player in America, he invited the very best players – Johnny Moss, 'Amarillo Slim' Preston, Sailor Roberts, Doyle Brunson, Puggy Pearson, Crandell Addington and Carl Cannon – to his casino to contest a tournament, which would in time become universally known as the World Series of Poker.

From those humble beginnings, where just seven players entered, and the winner, Johnny Moss, was decided by vote, the tournament has grown into an international extravaganza. As we have seen, 6,598 players of all nationalities each stumped up $10,000 to enter the Main Event in 2012. And while the tournament may have moved to the more spacious Rio Hotel and Casino in 2005, Binion's will always be regarded as its spiritual home.

Yet I wasn't at Binion's to learn about the history of poker, I was there to speak to John Pappas, executive director of the Poker Players' Alliance (PPA), who I had arranged to meet on the twenty-fourth floor, at Binion's Ranch Steakhouse. On entering the restaurant, I felt as if I had been transported back to the Rat Pack era. Binion's may have been modernised in recent years, but the restaurant remained very much in the Old Vegas tradition – so much so that I half expected to see Sammy, Dean and Frank misbehaving in one of the circular red leather booths.

Spotting John at a window table, which had a view overlooking the sparkling lights of Vegas, I introduced myself and took a seat.

Tanned, broad, clean shaven, with short black hair and sporting a well-fitted suit, John looked every inch the perfect candidate to be leading the charge to legalise online gambling in America. Not only did he look the part, but his easy-going manner and warmth were immediately apparent. These attributes would no doubt be vital in getting his voice heard in the corridors of power in Washington, where the PPA are based.

Over a glass of wine John explained the role of the PPA: 'It is a grassroots organisation with more than a million members nation-wide. Our mission is to work with policy makers to establish laws that give Americans freedom to play poker in a licensed and regu-lated environment.'

Despite the organisation being established following the intro-duction of the UIGEA, it was not until the events of Black Friday, 15 April 2011, that the poker community really started to rally around the organisation. 'You know,' John said, in his relaxed native Phoenix voice, 'It's taken six years for everyone to really get behind us. The online community, major US casinos, US tech companies, the players, politicians, even those who had previously been opposed to legalising online poker but now see that prohibition is not the answer.'

John and the PPA were as shocked as anyone at what had tran-spired on Black Friday. In particular, John was very surprised at the list of charges. While they included alleged offences under the UIGEA, Illegal Gambling Business Act (IGBA) and the New York Penal Code, as well as those relating to bank and wire fraud, con-spiracy and money laundering, there was no mention of the Wire Act, the main statute that the government had used in the past to prosecute those involved in online poker.

'It was curious,' John said, when considering this point. 'But the PPA had taken part in many good conversations with the govern-ment prior to this. We had presented a white paper and other materials to them as well which explicitly explained why the Wire Act and other federal laws shouldn't apply to online poker. I think they knew they would be facing a losing battle.'

Having considered the Wire Act, which had been passed in 1961 to deal with organised crime, it seemed that it only applied to sports betting over telephones. This was a view that had also been shared by the courts in 2002, in a case involving MasterCard, where the presiding judge had said: 'Because the Wire Act does not prohibit non-sports internet gambling, any debts incurred in connection with such gambling are not illegal.'

Despite this verdict it hadn't stopped the Department of Justice, prior to Black Friday, continuing to use the Wire Act to try and outlaw online poker. This was most notably seen in 2008 when Party Poker founder Anurag Dikshit faced charges under the act and was fined $300 million.

Although the Black Friday indictments didn't deal with the Wire Act, instead choosing primarily to focus on laws that were concerned with misleading banks, it was still a tremendous boost to the poker community when on 23 December 2011 the Department of Justice made a startling admission in a policy paper. Finally, they admitted that the act applied only to sports betting. In a swoop the government's interpretation of the only federal law that had been seen to specifically prohibit online poker was gone.

'We were surprised that they put it in writing,' John told me, the joy in his voice evident. 'But we had always thought that if this were ever to go to court that would be the opinion of the judge as well.'

This admission not only had a knock-on effect in regard to legislation such as the UIGEA, which had relied on the Wire Act's previous interpretation prohibiting online poker, but it also meant that pro-gambling states could now start to offer the game within their own borders. As such Nevada, Delaware, and eventually New Jersey, seized this unexpected opportunity and quickly passed bills to legalise online poker, while many others started to assess the pros and cons.

Although this was an encouraging development there were still many drawbacks, not least the fact that in some pro-poker states players would only be able to play against those who were based in the same state as them, hence dramatically cutting down on the player pool. Another major issue was that legalising poker on a state by state basis, instead of across the board, meant that the game would be operating under a patchwork of different laws and taxes. Not only could this make things incredibly confusing, it would also make it very difficult to achieve the ultimate goal, which is to formally legalise online poker via a federal bill.

A federal bill is seen as being vital to many as it will contain universal ground rules for all poker sites and states to abide by. This would therefore make the legal framework much clearer and should also provide a level playing field. However, if online poker continues to be enacted on a state by state basis then many feel that a federal poker bill will be all but impossible. As such it needs to happen sooner rather than later.

Thankfully, in the summer of 2012 a further legal development looked to have pushed the door further ajar for this dream to become a reality, following the verdict in the DiCristina case, which finally dealt with the age old question in court: was poker a game of chance or skill?

The government's position had always been that poker was a game of chance and thus should be outlawed. Yet during the trial an expert on behalf of the defence, Dr Randal D. Heeb, a renowned economist, had presented hard evidence to the court that backed up the assertion that poker, both live and online, was predominantly a game of skill.

Having analysed 415 million hands of poker played on PokerStars, Heeb had concluded that a player's level of skill had a statistically significant effect on the amount of money won or lost in a particular hand of poker. He said of this, 'When players are dealt the same hand, the more skilful player plays it much better and achieves a better result [and that] the lowest skill players according to the predicted skill index in fact achieve much worse results. Average players still don't do very well. Very good players are winning players.'

Based on these assertions, as well as evidence put forth by the PPA, Judge Weinstein accepted Dr Heeb's evidence. In his eyes poker was indeed a game of skill. This was a big blow to the Department of Justice, especially coming so soon after the reappraisal of the Wire Act. It is no wonder that at the time of writing the DoJ is frantically appealing the decision.

'When the judge's opinion came out we were thrilled,' John explained when discussing the verdict with me. 'It wasn't on the back of a cocktail napkin; it was a one-hundred-and-twenty-page document on why poker is a game of skill. The government's position certainly seems weakened by this. But the appeal process may not be resolved for quite some time so there is still a long way to go.'

While the DiCristina case rumbles on the fight to officially legalise online poker federally has continued in earnest. Indeed, one of the bills that has already been proposed, but sadly not yet passed, is the Internet Gambling Prohibition, Poker Consumer Protection and Strengthening UIGEA Act of 2012.

Drafted by Senator Jon Kyl and Senate Majority Leader Harry Reid, the bill proposed to legalise online poker, while outlawing most other forms of online gambling. However, certain restrictions would have applied. For instance, all poker operators would have had to be approved by a new regulator, the Office of Online Poker Oversight, who would have also required that banks could only process for those operators who had been granted an appropriate licence.

Another question the bill tackled was taxation, which would be a major issue in any talk regarding legalising online poker. It suggested that a tax rate of sixteen per cent would be levied on all online poker companies' income, two per cent of which would go to the federal government, ten per cent to the state of the player and four per cent to the state of the operator. Such an approach could raise billions of dollars in revenue.

While this bill has not yet been passed the proposals contained within it certainly seem the way most players in the US would like to see online poker go after the troubles involving rogue processors, cheating scandals and unsegregated player accounts. Such a bill would, of course, also allow US players to once again compete with players across America, as well as across the globe.

However, while John thinks a bill like this would be a positive step forward, he still has concerns. For example, many of the proposed federal bills, and even some of the state bills, have 'bad actor' clauses, which prevent any operator who continued to offer online poker in the US after 2006 from entering the US market for a period of five years. This would of course prevent established and trusted operators such as PokerStars from offering online poker in the US during that time and would therefore give a huge advantage to those Las Vegas/New Jersey casinos who wish to commence offering it themselves.

The most successful online poker sites, such as Full Tilt, PartyPoker and PokerStars, did not of course have any links to the big US casinos. As a result, the US casinos were left behind when online poker started to boom. Subsequently, they have been desperately playing catch-up ever since. Some conspiracy theorists believe that Black Friday may even have been at the behest of some of these casino groups. By effectively wiping out the industry, this would have provided those casinos with a clean slate once regulations had been approved by Congress. They could then enter the market at ground zero, with no competition from established online operators, thus having the opportunity to build up their client base and establish their brand before the likes of PokerStars were allowed to return. Unsurprisingly, many feel that this is not only grossly unfair but also 'unconstitutional'.

And there is also another issue to consider. While many are feeling more confident about the future of online poker in the US, one fact still remains: even if a federal bill does eventually legalise it, the spread of the game will ultimately come down to which states decide to allow it within their borders. If only a few states opt to offer online poker under federal regulations then not much progress will have been made if the rest of America decides against it.

In any event, it is still far too early to say if and when a federal bill legalising online poker may come to fruition, as at the time of writing no such bill has gathered the required support. As John commented: 'There are so many pressing issues facing Congress with the economy right now, I'm not so sure where internet poker stands on their priority list. But we are talking about untapped revenue here in an industry that could provide billions of dollars in tax.' It would certainly appear that legalised online poker, in its new, regulated form, could go some way in helping to alleviate the US budget deficits.

Having talked gaming law for the best part of an hour, John and I eventually decided to venture downstairs to fulfil a lifelong dream of mine: to play poker at Binion's. After finding a cash game where we could get involved, we sat down to play Texas Hold'em, my favourite game. I was feeling lucky and eager to show off the raw skills I had acquired at marathon poker sessions during my university years. My poker face was on, my reading antenna up and my bluffing honed to a fine art. However, within forty-five minutes of sitting down I had blown my bankroll. John, on the other hand, was still going strong. Folding my arms in disgust, cursing the bad beats, I suddenly remembered a phrase from the movie *Rounders*: 'If you can't spot the sucker in the first half-hour at the table, then you are the sucker.' It appeared that I was the sucker. And as my opponents continued to rack up more and more chips, it dawned on me that if ever there was an advert for poker being a game of skill, I am it. Up against the old guard and hot-shot kids I didn't stand a chance, even if at times I may have held the better hand. I'll either have to dig out Doyle Brunson's landmark book, *Super System*, to improve or stick to cursing bad beats.

37

Semara Uluwatu Cliff Edge Villas, Bali, November 2012

Lean, tanned and toned, the young holidaymaker slept soundly by the private infinity pool, which overlooked the crystal-clear ocean, with his white Panama hat pulled over his face. Snoring softly, and lying perfectly still, he looked peaceful, as though he didn't have a care in the world. The only sounds were the light breeze ruffling the palm trees' leaves, the trickling of water going over the edge of the pool, and the squawking of the birds circling overhead. But as the holidaymaker rested, a shadow suddenly blotted out the blazing sun. Jumping awake, the holidaymaker scrambled up the sun-lounger, sending his hat flying from his head as he did so. Who was it? What did they want?

'It's only me,' the voice reassured him. 'Relax.'

But Daniel couldn't relax, not in public. Never again.

'Hey. Don't worry. It's only me,' the soothing voice said again.

Taking deep breaths, Daniel's blurred vision slowly came around. Scrunching his eyes together he looked up at Nicole. Sitting down by his side, she proceeded to run her hands through his hair as he leant over to pick up his hat. After putting the hat back on his head, he reached across to the table next to him and picked up his glass of rum. He needed to take the edge off. And fast.

'Bad dream?' Nicole softly asked, as Daniel took a large gulp, which burnt the back of his throat.

'No,' Daniel winced, as the alcohol hit him. 'Just in a deep sleep.'

'I wanted to see if you fancied a walk on the beach?'

'Sure,' Daniel replied, groggily getting to his feet, still not quite with it.

This was meant to be a relaxing getaway. Finally, after all of the trials and tribulations, his time in the US was at an end, for now anyway. If the DoJ needed his services for anything else then they knew where to find him. Until then, Daniel was to get on with his life, pick up the pieces and start again. But before he could even consider that prospect, he needed to go somewhere remote and unwind. Somewhere where he could stop worrying about the past and just chill. And what better place to do so than in a luxurious private villa at the Semara Uluwatu Resort.

The resort was on the southernmost tip of the island of Bali, perched high above the Indian Ocean on the white limestone cliffs of Uluwatu. Not only was it a lavish tropical hideaway, but it was also very private. Daniel could completely disappear in a place like this. He had his own villa, his own pool and an almost deserted beach. It was perfect. But no matter how private the place was, he still found it hard to forget about everything that had happened. There was a dark blot in his memory bank that continued to give him nightmares.

Walking down the steps onto the almost undisturbed, white sand, Daniel and Nicole walked hand in hand towards Finns, the resort's Polynesian-style beach club, situated right on the beach. Ordering two glasses of champagne, the couple, wearing matching panama hats, proceeded to stroll along the shore, with the green, forested cliffs towering behind them.

'Are you OK?' Nicole asked, gripping her fiancé's hand firmly, noticing that he was being unusually quiet.

Daniel turned to look at her and smiled. 'Just thinking.'

Squinting his eyes he looked out at the inviting turquoise ocean in front of him. 'Let's have a dip,' he said to Nicole, as he took her by the hand and led her out into the calm, warm water until it was up to their waists.

'So what are you thinking?' Nicole probed, trying to keep her champagne glass out of the surf as she wrapped her arms around his neck. Daniel's silence, and the lines across his forehead, worried her.

'Just stuff.'

'What sort of stuff?'

Slowly breaking into a smile, Daniel looked into Nicole's wide almond eyes. She stared back at him. For a moment they rested their foreheads against each other as the waves slowly lapped against them. 'Now all of this looks to be over,' Daniel began, pulling away slightly, 'I was thinking . . . how do you feel about finally getting married?'

For a moment Nicole stopped breathing. It was a question Daniel had asked her before, a lifetime ago now, but then things had got out of hand. Was all of that stuff finally behind them?

'I know I messed up before,' Daniel continued, holding Nicole's hand in his. 'But I really think that now we are stronger than ever. We've gone through the worst kind of shit yet here we still are.'

Nicole nodded. It was true: their relationship had been tested to the limit. Life had thrown everything it could at them: jealousy, money, bankruptcy, public disgrace, arrest, scandal and danger. Despite it all, they were still madly in love with each other. Sure, things had got rocky, but they had stood side by side throughout it all. Many had mocked their relationship, claiming that Daniel had just seen her as another one of his trophies and that she was just in it for the money. Those sentiments couldn't have been further from the truth. True love had prevailed.

'Do you think you're ready to get married now?' Nicole asked, struggling to stop the smile that was curling up at the corner of her lips.

'To you? Definitely!'

Embracing each other in the lukewarm water, the two tenderly kissed before clinking their glasses. Putting their arms around each other, they looked out towards the ocean stretching far before them. It was a new dawn. While they had already lived enough for one lifetime, they were still only in their late twenties. There was more than enough time to start over. And as long as they were together then they both knew that they stood a fighting chance of making a go of it.

However, as Daniel and Nicole looked to have sailed off into the sunset there still remained a few unanswered questions, such as: was their stay at a resort where rooms were priced between $990 and $7,090 a night evidence that he had managed to stash away a large sum of money? And what about the rest of the missing poker millions? As ever, the truth was stranger than fiction.

38

Present Day

Mountains and lakes in Utah where crates of gold coins and cash are hidden, multi-million dollar Ponzi schemes, offshore bank accounts crammed with missing millions, and even more lawsuits. Since Black Friday, it seems that the stories surrounding some of the key players have created only more mystery and intrigue.

Chad Elie, the one-time GM of Hugo who was accused of stealing $4.2 million from PokerStars, has perhaps been involved in one of the juicer tales. While he has claimed that he was owed the money he removed from the National Bank of California, other sources remain adamant that in fact he was owed only $150,000. In any event, despite promising to repay Isai Scheinberg the disputed money, it appears that things initially didn't go quite to plan.

After arranging to meet Elie to discuss repayment of the money, PokerStars' lawyer, Jeff Ifrah has claimed that Elie stood him up. To Ifrah, and PokerStars, it seemed that Elie had no intention of paying it back. Fed up of chasing him, PokerStars issued a lawsuit against Elie in May 2009. However, it was arranged for the suit to be issued in the name of Intabill in order to avoid the embarrassment of it becoming public knowledge that an employee of one of their processors had misappropriated their customers' money. In any event, with the case now before the courts it looked as though time had finally run out for Elie. Surely, the game of cat and mouse would now come to an end?

However, with seemingly nowhere left to go, Elie played his last role of the dice. It is alleged that rather than defend himself in court, he threatened to reveal that it was in fact PokerStars who was behind the lawsuit, and not Intabill. Following this turn of events, PokerStars dropped the lawsuit to head off a messy public row.

In order to reach an out-of-court agreement, it appears that Elie agreed to repay PokerStars some of the money, as well as promised to help find them new processing solutions. While this agreement may seem unusual, desperate times called for desperate measures. By the autumn of 2009, the poker companies were near to collapse. Processing had all but dried up and new solutions were hard to come by. It appears that the arrests of John Scott Clark and Curtis Pope had put a swift stop to the planned tribal processing deal, which the poker companies had pinned their hopes on. Indeed, it also seems that the solution may not have even been legal, as Pope and Scott Clark had so confidently told everyone. While they may have been legally able to process from an Indian Reservation, they would have firstly required the tribe's explicit approval, something which they had failed to get. Subsequently, with the Indian Reservation processing failing to deliver, new processing schemes were highly sought after. If someone had a solution then the poker companies were all ears, regardless of prior disagreements. And Elie thought he had the perfect solution.

With Andrew Thornhill working alongside him, Elie and his associate Jeremy Johnson, who was CEO of telemarketing company I-Works, formed a new processing company called Elite Debit. Able to perform all standard processing services the company's trump card was, however, Johnson's close links with Utah's SunFirst Bank. Having the inside track Johnson knew that the bank was struggling and would be very interested in any increase in business, no matter where it came from. And he was proved right. After showing them legal opinions that claimed that online poker was in fact legal, SunFirst couldn't process the cash for Elite Debit quick enough, especially after Johnson also promised SunFirst vice-chairman John Campos a $10 million investment. As a result, Elie and Johnson were soon filtering hundreds of millions of dollars through Utah. No longer having to create a network of phoney companies, or lie about the source of the money, there seemed to be nothing that could stop them.

With things going well Elie has revealed that he travelled to Utah in late 2009 in order to pay his partner a visit. At his home Johnson allegedly showed Elie the considerable spoils of their venture, which he was looking after on their behalf. In a safe, hidden in an out-house, Elie has stated that he saw thousands of gold coins as well as boxes of cash, full of bandied bundles of $10,000. Business was obviously good.

However, while Elie may have been pleased with the company's progress things soon took a turn for the worse. With money continuing to pour into the company's account, Johnson is alleged to have siphoned off huge chunks of it to fund other ventures and purchases, including buying thousands of gold and silver coins, four aircraft, seven helicopters, luxury cars, mansions across America, as well as investing millions of dollars into a TD Ameritrade trading account. Apparently he also played for high stakes on Full Tilt under the screen name 'ginette22'.

Worried about Johnson's rampant spending, and not able to access any of the company's funds himself, Elie paid Johnson another visit in order to gain his share of the profits. But there was a snag. Upon arrival Johnson showed Elie a complaint he had received from the Federal Trade Commission (FTC). It alleged that his telemarketing company, I-Works, had defrauded consumers out of $275 million.

The complaint subsequently ordered Johnson to preserve all of his assets. Johnson therefore claimed that at this time he was unable to pay Elie a dime.

Yet rather than preserve his assets Elie claims that Johnson did nothing of the sort. He has alleged that Johnson buried millions of dollars' worth of gold coins in the mountains surrounding St George, Utah, as well as hid millions of dollars of cash in nearby lakes. While these assets were being hidden from the FTC, they were also out of the reach of Elie, who claimed that half of these assets were in fact his share of the profits from Elite Debit.

With no money forthcoming, Elie brought his own legal action against Johnson for failing to pay him his share, yet his lawsuit was stopped by the FTC, as they believed that Elie was 'engaged in a secretive race to the courthouse in an effort to grab money held by the defendants'. In other words, the FTC believed that Elie was trying to claim money from Johnson and/or I-Works before any of those who had been stung in the alleged I-Works telemarketing scam had had a chance to do so.

While the FTC concentrated its efforts on Johnson's I-Works, law enforcement officials may have also noted what Elie had to say in his complaint about Elite Debits. Although Elie's complaint didn't discuss online poker specifically, it did outline that the company was processing around $2.5 million a month for a client and that the money was being held in SunFirst Bank. Suspecting that Johnson's company, I-Works, was already engaged in illegal activity, it is easy to imagine that authorities also began to look a little closer at his other company, Elite Debit, and its relationship with SunFirst Bank. When Elie was subsequently charged on Black Friday, he probably only had himself to blame for alerting the authorities to where and how he had processed for online poker. However, he was no doubt somewhat consoled when the day after his arrest he married his fiancée Destiny Davis, a *Playboy* playmate!

Although Johnson avoided being charged under the Black Friday indictments, at the behest of the FTC, his case is still on-going, as are his troubles. In June 2011 he was arrested and jailed having been found trying to board a plane to Costa Rica with a one-way ticket and $26,000 in cash. Shortly after this incident, he was charged with mail fraud by the Internal Revenue Service, to which he pleaded not guilty. He was, however, eventually released from jail in September 2011 after friends and family put up security. While Johnson is still awaiting trial in regard to the FTC civil charges, as well as the mail-fraud charges, it was confirmed in January 2012 that he was also under another criminal investigation. He maintains his innocence on all charges.

On the other hand, Elie decided to plead guilty to a single count of conspiracy in March 2012 after hearing that the DoJ's star witness in the Black Friday trials, Daniel Tzvetkoff, would be testifying against him in court in regard to his time working at Trendsact. Following this, Elie was handed a five-month prison sentence, while John Campos, vice-president of SunFirst Bank, subsequently received a three-month sentence for his part in the scheme.

With millions of dollars of online poker players' money allegedly remaining hidden in the mountains and lakes of Utah, there have also been questions asked regarding the whereabouts of the Trendsact payday loan money. To date there is no evidence that the money was repaid to the poker companies as had been agreed. I have asked Curtis Pope about the whereabouts of this money, and while he initially agreed to answer my questions he eventually chose not to respond, as is his right.

While much of the payday loan money apparently remains unaccounted for, it appears that Pope was also involved in a dispute with his former employers, Selling Source. Court documents have shown that in the summer of 2009 Selling Source accused Pope of stealing some of their top payday loan leads. When Derek LaFavor confronted Curtis Pope and Mike Lane about this, Pope is alleged to have

admitted that he 'fucked up'. Though LaFavor claims that Pope promised to make amends, he instead cleared out the Trendsact offices and
disappeared. When the Trendsact staff subsequently reported for
work the next day they found their belongings in boxes and that they
were all out of a job.

After pleading guilty to crimes involving bank fraud, gambling
and money-laundering conspiracies, Curtis Pope received a twenty-
one-month prison sentence in June 2011. Despite cooperating with
the Department of Justice, he received a harsher sentence than others
guilty of similar crimes due to his prior criminal conduct.

A spell behind bars also appears to await Pope's business partner,
John Scott Clark, who has also pleaded guilty for his part in processing
for online poker. However, while Scott Clark is waiting to be sentenced,
he is currently in the process of defending himself against separate
charges that have been made against him by the US Securities and
Exchange Commission (SEC). On 28 March 2011, the Commission
released a statement that accused Scott Clark of masterminding
a Ponzi scheme. It was claimed that he had raised more than $47
million from 120 investors with the apparent purpose of funding a
payday loan portfolio. Scott Clark had promised these investors an
eighty per cent return on their investment.

With promises such as this, he managed to attract a wide range
of backers, including a Wall Street hedge fund who forwarded him
$15 million. However, rather than use the invested funds for fund-
ing payday loans, it is alleged that instead he opted to use them to
fund other business ventures, as well as to maintain his lavish
lifestyle. The complaint accused Scott Clark of subsequently using
new investor funds to pay promised profits to earlier investors.
Thomas Melton of the SEC has said of him: 'He's what we would call
"shiny". He looks like a salesman. You might buy a snowmobile
from him.'

While the Trendsact payday loan portfolio may still be unaccounted for, rumours persist that Daniel Tzvetkoff may have managed to hide away some of the money he earned. Indeed, his holiday in a luxurious Bali resort certainly seems suspicious for a man who declared himself bankrupt three years ago and had been in witness protection for much of that time since.

Despite these rumours, neither the Intabill liquidator (who was funded by the poker companies) nor the Department of Justice have found any evidence of the alleged missing millions. The many sources I have spoken to are also not convinced that this hidden haul exists. To them, Daniel was a guy who lived for the moment and spent every penny he had, thinking that his success would last forever. Knowing Daniel's incredible entrepreneurial knack for thinking up countless new business ideas, no one put it past him to already be hard at work building his second fortune. Although his first business ultimately ended in failure, most are in little doubt that the former boy wonder has it within him to come good again, having now learnt some valuable lessons.

So what happened to the other parties who were embroiled in this story?

After being cleared of any wrongdoing by all authorities who have investigated this matter, Sam Sciacca has returned to the law and now runs a successful private practice in Brisbane. These days he is happy to spend his time watching his four rugby-mad sons in action alongside his childhood sweetheart, Jo-Anne, who he remains happily married to and credits for keeping him sane through these trials and tribulations. Intabill legal counsel Michael Hui has also left the world of payment processing behind and has subsequently returned to private practice. He married Caroline in 2010 and both now live happily together in Brisbane.

Online poker processing fixer Ryan Lang pleaded guilty to the conspiracy charges against him in February 2012. At the time of writing he is still awaiting sentencing.

After serving three months in prison, fellow processor Andrew Thornhill is now a free man. His current whereabouts are unknown, as is his current employment, although some have suggested to me that he has now returned to payment processing.

PokerStars founder Isai Scheinberg remains offshore on the Isle of Man, out of the American justice system's reach. However, as already stated, he has now stepped down from running PokerStars, one of the conditions of the company purchasing Full Tilt. Despite the charges against him, Scheinberg is viewed as a hero by many in the poker world due to PokerStars swiftly paying back all of its customers, as well as putting in motion plans to reimburse all Full Tilt players following the takeover. Whatever happens, there is certainly a lot of goodwill towards Scheinberg in the poker community, something that can't be said about anyone connected to the running of Full Tilt Poker.

Former Full Tilt board member, Howard Lederer and founder, Chris Ferguson, settled the civil cases against them in late 2012/early 2013, with both agreeing to forfeit bank accounts, properties and cars, with no admission of guilt being made. On the other hand, after learning that he needed an urgent heart transplant, Ray Bitar pleaded guilty to all of the charges against him in April 2013 and as such was ordered to forfeit nearly everything of value that he owned. For Bitar it was as good a sentence as he could have hoped for, considering it was thought he would have faced a long spell in jail were in not for his health problems.

While the Full Tilt cases may now be over, all three men remain hate figures to many in the poker world. Such is the level of animosity towards Lederer that when he turned up at the Bellagio to play poker in late 2012, death threats were even made against him. Indeed, a petition was also made by the players at the Aria Hotel to try to ban him from the poker rooms. In regard to Bitar, when news broke that he required a heart transplant the reaction in the poker community was far from sympathetic. It seems that a return to the online poker world for anyone connected to the running of Full Tilt will be impossible. Many in the poker community are unwilling to forgive and forget when so many lost thousands of dollars thanks to the reckless way the company was run.

Others to have suffered a similar fall from grace include the founders of Absolute Poker. Brent Beckley is currently serving a fourteen-month prison sentence after pleading guilty to the charges made against him, while Scott Tom is said to be in hiding somewhere in the Caribbean, with no intention of returning to the United States any time soon to defend himself. In the wake of Black Friday, Absolute Poker, and its sister site Ultimate Bet, crashed. To date, none of their players have been reimbursed.

While Daniel and others will have to try to rebuild their lives, the future for online poker also remains uncertain. It should, however, be clear that outright prohibition is not the answer. The United States has of course already gone down this path when it outlawed alcohol between 1920 and 1933. The result was a disaster.

Although the intention then was to cut down on the problem drinking that was apparently plaguing American society, it instead opened the door to gangsters, such as Al Capone, to supply the American people with a product they craved. With so much money at stake, this led to gang warfare, most notably seen with the St Valentine's Day Massacre, where seven mob associates were murdered during fighting between two powerful criminal gangs in Chicago: the South Side Italian gang led by Al Capone and the North Side Irish gang led by Bugs Moran.

As J D Rockefeller said of the failure of Prohibition in 1932, one year before it was repealed: 'Drinking has generally increased; the speakeasy has replaced the saloon; a vast army of lawbreakers has appeared; many of our best citizens have openly ignored Prohibition; respect for the law has greatly lessened; and crime has increased to a level never seen before.'

While the effect of outlawing online poker has not produced quite the same criminal underworld and lawlessness that Rockefeller described, it has still created a seedy underbelly that has cost the United States, and its citizens, dearly. As shown throughout this book, there is a vast appetite for online poker in America, with the American Gaming Industry reporting that as many as one in five Americans played some form of poker in 2005 alone. When there is such a call for a product, then even if it is criminalised, many will continue to look for ways to circumvent the law, especially when the same prohibitions do not apply in other countries. And if the demand is there, those who are happy to operate outside of the law will look to supply it.

The UIGEA and Black Friday have seen online poker companies flee the US, to offshore locations beyond the reach of American regulation, law and justice. Some of these companies, as seen in the case of Ultimate Bet and Absolute Poker, have played their part in cheating US players out of tens of millions of dollars. Others, such as Full Tilt Poker, illegally used customers' money to fund its owners' luxury lifestyles. Indeed, the UIGEA also created a network of payment processors who were completely unregulated. Some of these payment processors, and even some banks, ripped off US online poker players by stealing millions of dollars. They knew that the poker companies would not risk reporting them to the authorities. As such they could do as they wished. They were untouchable.

Although it is now much harder for Americans to play poker online, I have spoken to countless individuals who continue to do so, either by paying for a Virtual Private Network which routes their IP connection to an overseas location or via the few remaining poker sites that somehow remain operational in the US. Just like Prohibition, this is almost impossible for law enforcement officials to monitor properly. And so millions of American online poker players continue to be at the mercy of unscrupulous providers and fly by night payment processors.

So, what is the answer?

For me, it seems that the first step forward must be legalising online poker at a federal level so that all states who decide to offer it do so under the same set of laws. This way everyone knows exactly where they stand. However, it is imperative that certain restrictions are strictly enforced if online poker is to become a respected and legitimate pursuit. A regulatory body overseeing online poker operators, as suggested in the Reid/Kyl bill, is much needed. With the regulatory body overseeing a strict licensing regime, this should mean that only the very best operators are admitted into the US market. This would significantly reduce the risk of companies partaking in cheating scandals or embezzling players' funds. Such an approach would also allow legitimate banks to process transactions on behalf of those licensed operators who have been strictly vetted. Rogue payment processors, as well as unscrupulous financial institutions, would subsequently be cut out of the equation, hence making it far more likely that players, and poker companies, would receive their money.

Yet while a regulatory body could oversee the poker operators, there also needs to be procedures put in place to monitor the players. There can be no denying that problem gambling must be addressed if online poker is to be accepted by those who remain sceptical and/or hostile towards it. With online poker providing 24/7 access to players, who can play significantly more hands per hour than in a land-based casino, those who are predisposed to a gambling addiction can very easily suffer, and this must be prevented, as far as is possible.

The good news is that, unlike problem drinking or problem gambling in land-based casinos, there is technology that could be utilised online which could play a significant role in combatting such issues. Such technology can monitor a player, allowing a poker operator to recognise certain red flags. When one of those red flags goes off, then the operator should have a legal duty to intervene. Such information should also be shared by the poker companies to ensure that problem gamblers are properly monitored across all sites and subsequently given the help and advice that they need. Doing this may reduce the level of profits the operators make, but by showing such responsibility they will be more readily accepted.

Other simpler ways that have been suggested to combat online gambling include requiring operators to allow concerned players to self-exclude themselves, players setting themselves a strictly enforced betting limit per day, having more information on problem gambling easily available on the websites, and even having a self-diagnostic registration page, for when players sign up for an account, which could help identify anyone who may be a problem gambler.

For some even this level of monitoring may not be enough. The ability to play 24/7 on multiple tables is for many unacceptable and a major deal-breaker. In light of this, it may be that a middle ground may have to be found, such as limiting poker sites to being open only for a set number of hours per day, or to cap the number of hands or tables a player can play. It may not be the ideal solution most want, but if it could get poker back online across America then, for now, it may be a price worth paying.

With so much money at stake, and at a time when the American economy continues to falter, the financial implications of legalising online poker can also not be ignored. Many experts have predicted that legalisation could raise billions of dollars for the federal government as well as for the states. Accountancy firm PricewaterhouseCoopers has estimated that taxing online gambling could bring in as much as $2.61 billion a year for the federal government. Bloomberg has gone even further. It estimates that a tax could raise as much as $41.8 billion over a ten-year period. It would seem foolish to ignore such an opportunity when the government desperately needs funds to reduce its borrowing and to fund its expenditure.

There is overwhelming evidence that poker is a game of skill, can raise billions of dollars in taxes, and that technology exists that can combat problem gambling. If a middle ground can be found then one of America's favourite pastimes, which has been enjoyed by many former presidents, as well as its current commander in chief, could flourish. If, however, the current situation is allowed to continue, a criminal underworld will thrive which will leave Americans at risk, and will see huge sums of money leave the United States instead of going into its government's coffers.

Online gambling can be dangerous, but what is more dangerous is allowing the current status quo to prosper. If it is allowed to do so then I fear that the current tales of scandal and woe will be just the tip of the iceberg.

And, to think, before all of this, many thought that online poker was just a game of cards . . .